Vitalized
PHYSICS
in Graphicolor

By

ROBERT H. CARLETON

Head of Department of Science,
Summit High School,
Summit, New Jersey

Edited by

MICHAEL N. IDELSON

Head of the Department of Physical Sciences,
Abraham Lincoln High School, Brooklyn, New York;
Formerly, Assistant Professor,
U. S. Naval Academy, Annapolis

STAFF EDITORS

BERTRAM COREN   A. V. GENTILINI

COLLEGE ENTRANCE BOOK COMPANY
New York

CONTENTS

PRINTED IN THE UNITED STATES OF AMERICA
IN FULL COMPLIANCE WITH WARTIME REGULATIONS

PREFACE

The study of Physics today has achieved a position of such vital importance that the publication of a new text meeting modern needs is most opportune. *Vitalized Physics* is a concise text in which the most up-to-date subject matter, fully accommodated to wartime teaching requirements, has been supplemented by the very latest devices for vitalizing the text.

GRAPHICOLOR PRESENTATION

The Two-Color Technique. By the use of the second color, the publishers have carried over to the printed page the dramatic effectiveness applied by the teacher when using colored chalk on the classroom blackboard. The second color accomplishes two objectives which cannot be achieved with ordinary black-on-white printing.

1. *To make the diagrams virtually self-teaching.* The underlying physical principles in each diagram are highlighted by means of color. The electrical diagrams at the latter part of the book, in particular, are excellent examples of the effective use of the second color.

2. *To "spotlight" important ideas.* Important formulas and equations are made to stand out by the contrast in colors. In many of the type problems, the use of the second color enables the student to follow readily the important steps.

Quality of the Diagrams. The more than 200 diagrams are outstanding in content and execution, even without the added feature of color. All are large, striking, simplified and accurate.

UP-TO-DATE CONTENT AND ORGANIZATION

War Motivation. After a careful study of both army and navy pre-induction manuals and other government syllabi, the author and editors have motivated the text throughout with illustrations, references, examples, and applications of value to students who are studying in the midst of war. These motivations and applications have been selected with a view toward clarifying the basic physical principles involved. In many instances, new subject matter entirely has been included, as for example the sections on meteorology, automobiles and machines in general.

1

New Topics. The new, vital topics of today's physics are treated simply yet comprehensively. The following are a few of the topics not ordinarily included in a book of this scope:

1. *Alternating current circuits.* The basic principles of this subject are essential to a true understanding of radio fundamentals. A simplified, extensively illustrated chapter on the topic has therefore been included in this book for the benefit of those students who intend to continue with studies in communications.

2. *Thorough chapter on radio.* Based logically on the previous work in static electricity, electromagnetism, alternating currents, and sound, this chapter presents the fundamentals of radio theory in a form which has real meaning and value for every physics student. It is a complete introduction to more advanced study.

3. *Physics of the airplane.* Chapter 25 provides a complete survey of the basic principles of aviation in terms of fundamental physical concepts.

Emphasis on the Mathematics of Physics. In view of the current emphasis on quantitative physics, this phase of the subject has been given full treatment throughout the text. As an added feature, the more important highlights of the mathematics of physics have been summarized in the first chapter.

Competent Authorship. Both the author and the editor are teachers of long experience, as well as authors and co-authors of several successful texts in the science field.

Thought Questions, Objective Tests, and Problems. Carefully prepared thought questions, which stimulate the student's thinking, and varied objective questions, which check on his grasp of the factual content, appear at the end of each chapter. Abundant problems are also included, since these provide the most adequate drill for the student. Answers (printed in red) are given for all problems. These answers, computed with a slide rule, are accurate to 3 significant figures.

Special acknowledgment is made to Vernon B. Bremenstuhl of North Tarrytown, New York, for his suggestions and criticisms, particularly on the mathematics of physics, and to Harry H. Williams of the Horace Mann School for Boys, New York City, for the chapters on light and aviation.

ONE

Introduction. It would, of course, be impossible to review all the mathematics, from addition and subtraction to trigonometry, which a physics student should know. However, there are a few fundamental operations and principles which appear repeatedly in the study of physics and which it would be worthwhile to review here. This chapter is an attempt to give you a clearer picture not only of the methods of performing the operations involved, but also of the real meaning of those operations, so that when you come across them in this and other books, you will know exactly what is being done and why.

RATIO, PROPORTIONS, FORMULAS, EQUATIONS

Ratio and Proportion. Many investigations in physics are concerned with finding out how one quantity changes when another is changed. For example, it is found by experiment that the pressure of a gas depends on its temperature—if the temperature is doubled, the pressure is also doubled; if the temperature is multiplied by 10, the pressure becomes 10 times as great. We say, then, that *the pressure is directly proportional to the temperature,* or that *the pressure varies directly as the temperature.* This can be expressed mathematically as follows:

$$P \propto T$$

read, "pressure is proportional to temperature."

Suppose that we find the pressure of a gas (P_1) to be 10 lb/in² when the temperature (T_1) is 300° A. If we divide one by the other we obtain the *ratio* between the two quantities. Thus:

$$\frac{P_1}{T_1} = \text{Ratio}; \quad \frac{10}{300} = \frac{1}{30}$$

If we now take a second reading of temperature ($T_2 = 600°$ A) the pressure (P_2) will be found to be 20 lb/in². (Since the temperature has been doubled, and we know that the pressure varies directly with the temperature, the pressure will also be doubled.) If we again divide one by the other we find that *the ratio is the same*:

$$\frac{P_2}{T_2} = \text{Ratio}; \quad \frac{20}{600} = \frac{1}{30}$$

This illustrates the fact that when two measurements are proportional, the ratio between them will be the same for any pair of corresponding values. Thus, we can write:

$$\frac{P_1}{T_1} = \frac{P_2}{T_2} = \frac{P_n}{T_n} = k \text{ (the constant ratio)}$$

The equation $\frac{P_1}{T_1} = \frac{P_2}{T_2}$ is called a *proportion*. Any proportion can be resolved into a *simple equation* by cross-multiplying as shown:

$$\frac{P_1}{T_1} \diagdown \frac{P_2}{T_2}: \quad P_1 T_2 = P_2 T_1$$

Any proportion, $\frac{a}{b} = \frac{c}{d}$, can be cross-multiplied to give $ad = bc$.

Proportions are very useful because the numerical value of any one of the quantities may be found if the numerical values of the other three are known. Thus if we are given $P_1 = 15$ lb/in^2, $T_1 = 450°$A, and $P_2 = 20$ lb/in^2, and have to find T_2:

$$\frac{P_1}{T_1} = \frac{P_2}{T_2}$$

Substitute known values:

$$\frac{15}{450} = \frac{20}{T_2}$$

Cross-multiply:

$$15T_2 = 20 \times 450$$

Solve the equation:

$$T_2 = \frac{20 \times 450}{15} = 600° A$$

Formulas and Equations. A formula is an equation which contains symbols. When numerical values are substituted for these symbols, the value of an unknown can be found. For example, $s = \frac{1}{2}at^2$ is a formula stating the relationship between distance (s), time (t), and acceleration (a). If numerical values for any two of the unknowns are given, we have an equation from which the value of the third unknown can be derived.

The solution of equations depends upon the following axiom: *If equal numbers are added to, subtracted from, multiplied by, or divided into each side of the equation, the resulting equation is still true.* From this axiom we can derive the following two corollaries: (1) When any term is *transposed* from one side of the equation to the other, *its sign must be changed.* (For example, $3x + 9 = 27$; $3x = 27 - 9$.) (2) One side of the equation can be raised to a power if the other side is raised to the *same power;* the root of one side can be extracted if the *same root* is extracted from the other side. (For example, $x = 5$; $x^2 = 25$; $\sqrt{x} = \sqrt{5}$.)

Let us now apply these rules to a typical problem involving the formula for conversion of Fahrenheit to Centigrade degrees.

$$C = \tfrac{5}{9}(F - 32)$$

where C = degrees Centigrade and F = degrees Fahrenheit. If the Centigrade temperature is 30°C, what is the Fahrenheit temperature?

$$C = \tfrac{5}{9}(F - 32)$$

Multiply by 9:

$$9C = 5(F - 32) = 5F - 160$$

Transpose (add) 160:

$$9C + 160 = 5F$$

Divide by 5:

$$\frac{9}{5}C + 32 = F$$

Substitute the value of C (30°):

$$\frac{9}{5} \times 30 + 32 = F$$
$$86° = F$$

UNITS

Units. Every measurement consists of a numerical value and its corresponding units. If the unit of measurement is changed, the numerical value changes—although the actual quantity being measured remains the same. It is therefore absolutely essential to give the units with each numerical value encountered in a measurement or computation.

A weight of 250 means nothing, for 250 lb is entirely different from 250 oz or 250 kg. In simple measurements such as weight or distance, this is obvious. But it is equally important in other quantities for which the units are sometimes overlooked by careless students. Extreme care must be taken to give proper units for such measurements as density, work, acceleration, and many others to be encountered in physics.

Calculations Involving Units. Many measurements are obtained by calculations involving other measurements rather than by direct readings of instruments. In such cases, it is necessary to have some method for determining the units of the answer obtained. For example, density is obtained by dividing the weight of a body by its volume. Suppose a certain volume of water is measured and found to be 5 cubic feet; its weight is found to be 312.5 pounds. Ignoring units, its density then is

$$\frac{\textbf{weight}}{\textbf{volume}} = \frac{312.5}{5} = 62.5$$

If the same volume of water is measured in terms of cubic inches, it is found to have a volume of 8640 cubic inches. Its density now is

$$\frac{\textbf{weight}}{\textbf{volume}} = \frac{312.5}{8640} = 0.0362$$

Which is correct? *Neither is correct without the proper units—both are correct with the proper units:*

$$\textbf{density} = \textbf{62.5} \text{ lb/cu ft} = \textbf{0.0362} \text{ lb/cu in}$$

The units of the answer, in each case, are found by performing the same operations on the units as were performed on their numerical values. Since the weight was divided by the volume, the units of weight are also divided by the units of volume, as follows:

$$\text{density} = \frac{312.5 \text{ lb}}{5 \text{ cu ft}} = 62.5\frac{\text{lb}}{\text{cu ft}} = 62.5\frac{\text{lb}}{\text{ft}^3}$$

Consider the following example:

The kinetic energy of a body is given by the formula, $KE = \frac{1}{2}\frac{Wv^2}{g}$ where W is the weight of a body, v is its speed, and g is a constant whose value is 32 ft/sec². If a body has a weight of 12 lb and a speed of 8 ft/sec, what is its kinetic energy?

$$KE = \frac{1}{2}\frac{Wv^2}{g} = \frac{1}{2} \times \frac{12 \text{ lb} \times \left(8\frac{\text{ft}}{\text{sec}}\right)^2}{32\frac{\text{ft}}{\text{sec}^2}}$$

$$= \frac{1}{2} \times \frac{12 \times (8)^2}{32} \times \frac{\text{lb} \times \left(\frac{\text{ft}}{\text{sec}}\right)^2}{\frac{\text{ft}}{\text{sec}^2}} = 12 \times \frac{\text{lb} \times \text{ft}^2}{\text{sec}^2} \times \frac{\text{sec}^2}{\text{ft}}$$

$$= 12 \text{ ft} \times \text{lb}$$

which is usually written, 12 ft-lb, the hyphen standing for multiplication of the units ft and lb.

As we shall learn, the units of energy are always a distance unit times a weight unit, so that we know that our answer is correct as far as the units are concerned. If the units worked out to be, say, $\frac{\text{ft-lb}}{\text{sec}}$, we would know that an error had been made somewhere, because energy can never have those units.

Conversion of Units. Suppose the speed of the body, instead of being given in ft/sec, had been given in miles/hour—5.46 mi/hr instead of 8 ft/sec. If we tried to substitute 5.46 in the formula, instead of 8, the value of g would still be in ft/sec², and not only would we obtain a different numerical answer, but its units would have feet, miles, seconds, and hours mixed up in it. Therefore, whenever we have measurements expressed in different units (as distance measurements expressed in feet and miles, time in hours and seconds, etc.), before attempting to use them in formulas, all units for the same fundamental measurement (length, time, weight) must be converted to the same basis. In the English system, all lengths, and quantities involving units of length, should be changed to feet; all forces and weights to pounds; all time values to seconds. Similarly in the metric system change all quantities to centimeters, grams, and seconds.

When making this conversion, the numerical value expressed in a unit to be converted must be multiplied or divided by a certain *conversion factor*. For example, to change 12 yards to feet, we must multiply by the conversion factor 3 ft/yd, since there are three feet in a yard. Note how the units work out correctly:

$$12 \text{ yd} = 12 \text{ yd} \times 3\frac{\text{ft}}{\text{yd}} = 12 \times 3 \times \frac{\text{yd} \times \text{ft}}{\text{yd}} = 36 \text{ ft}$$

To change inches to feet, we multiply by the factor 1/12 ft/in, or divide by 12 in/ft:

$$48 \text{ in} = 48 \text{ in} \times \frac{1}{12} \times \frac{\text{ft}}{\text{in}} = 4 \text{ ft, or,}$$
$$48 \text{ in} = 48 \text{ in} \div 12\frac{\text{in}}{\text{ft}} = 48 \text{ in} \times \frac{1}{12} \times \frac{\text{ft}}{\text{in}} = 4 \text{ ft}$$

To change 5.46 mi/hr to ft/sec, use the factors ft = mi × 5280 $\frac{\text{ft}}{\text{mi}}$ and sec = hr × 3600 $\frac{\text{sec}}{\text{hr}}$:

$$5.46\frac{\text{mi}}{\text{hr}} = 5.46 \times \frac{\text{mi} \times 5280\frac{\text{ft}}{\text{mi}}}{\text{hr} \times 3600\frac{\text{sec}}{\text{hr}}} = 8.0\frac{\text{ft}}{\text{sec}}$$

The problems in chapter 3 are worked out with all operations on the units shown. Study these carefully. Note how the units cancel out to give the proper units for the answer, and note when conversions are necessary. In the remainder of the book, the operations on the units are not always shown. The student is advised to work these problems out on separate sheets, checking the units as he goes along and verifying the units given in the answer by the author.

TRIANGLES

Triangles. Two triangles are similar if (1) the angles of one are equal to the corresponding angles of the other; or, (2) their sides are respectively parallel; or, (3) their sides are respectively perpendicular. In similar triangles, corresponding sides are proportional. If ΔABC is similar to $\Delta A'B'C'$, then:

$$\frac{AB}{A'B'} = \frac{BC}{B'C'} = \frac{CA}{C'A'}$$

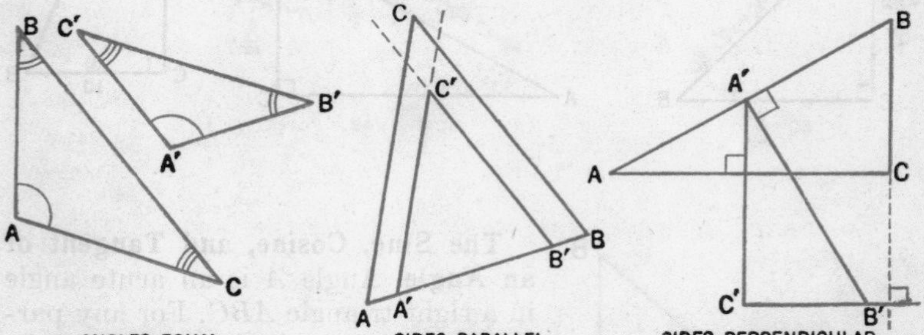

ANGLES EQUAL   SIDES PARALLEL   SIDES PERPENDICULAR

Diagrams in physics problems often show one or the other of these situations, and the student should be prepared to take advantage of the information so obtained.

Right Triangles. A right triangle is one with a right angle. The sides which form the right angle are called the arms; the side opposite the right angle is the hypotenuse. In any right triangle, the sum of the squares of the arms equals the square of the hypotenuse (Pythagorean Theorem):

$$AC^2 + BC^2 = AB^2; \quad \sqrt{AC^2 + BC^2} = AB$$

There are certain right triangles in which the three sides may be whole numbers. The one most frequently encountered is the 3:4:5 triangle $(3^2 + 4^2 = 5^2)$. Another such triangle is the 5:12:13 triangle. Triangles whose sides have either of these proportions are always right triangles.

In addition, the $45° - 45° - 90°$ triangle and the $30° - 60° - 90°$ triangle have definite numerical relationships among their sides which should be remembered. These relationships are shown in the diagram on page 10.

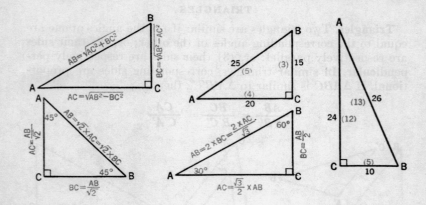

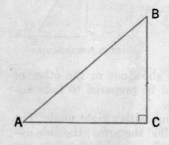

The Sine, Cosine, and Tangent of an Angle. Angle A is an acute angle in a right triangle ABC. For any particular size of angle A, the sides of the triangle have certain definite ratios which have already been calculated by mathematicians. These ratios are useful for finding the lengths of the sides when the angle is known, or for finding the size of the angle when the sides are known. These various ratios (sine, cosine, tangent) as defined in the table below. The numerical values of the ratios (called *trigonometric functions*) for every angle are listed in *trigonometric tables*.

	Definitions	Formulas Derived from Definitions
sine of angle A	$\sin A = \dfrac{BC}{AB}$	$AB = \dfrac{BC}{(\sin A)}$; $BC = AB(\sin A)$
cosine of angle A	$\cos A = \dfrac{AC}{AB}$	$AB = \dfrac{AC}{(\cos A)}$; $AC = AB(\cos A)$
tangent of angle A	$\tan A = \dfrac{BC}{AC}$	$AC = \dfrac{BC}{(\tan A)}$; $BC = AC(\tan A)$

PROBLEMS

1. Solve the following: (a) $97,638 + 25 + 862 + 1001$; (b) $9013 - 797$; (c) $4327 \times 263 \times 30$; (d) $18,762 \div 201$.

Ans. (a) 99,526 (b) 8216 (c) 34,140,030 (d) 93.34

2. Solve the following: (a) $0.168 + 25.23 + 101.62$; (b) $0.976 - 0.231$; (c) 1015×0.37; (d) $139.65 \div 11.312$; (e) $0.0016 \div 0.04$.

Ans. (a) 127.018 (b) 0.745 (c) 375.55 (d) 12.345 (e) 0.04

3. Solve the following: (a) $\frac{1}{3} + \frac{1}{5} + \frac{5}{9}$; (b) $\frac{5}{7} - \frac{3}{8}$; (c) $\frac{2}{3} \times \frac{1}{4}$; (d) $100 \times \frac{1}{4}$; (e) $\frac{3}{4} \div \frac{1}{2}$; (f) $100 \div \frac{1}{4}$.

Ans. (a) $1\frac{4}{45}$ (b) $\frac{19}{56}$ (c) $\frac{1}{6}$ (d) 25 (e) $1\frac{1}{2}$ (f) 400

4. If a machine gun fires 1 tracer bullet in every 10 bullets, what is the ratio of tracers to regular bullets? Express this relationship as a percentage. Ans. $\frac{1}{9}$; 11.1%

5. How many tracer bullets would be fired by the machine gun in a total of 250 bullets? Ans. 25

6. Solve the following proportions: (a) $\frac{15 \text{ in}}{60 \text{ in}} = \frac{x \text{ ft}}{25 \text{ ft}}$; (b) $220 : x = 350 : 17.5$.

Ans. (a) 6.25 (b) 11

7. Solve the following equations for the terms indicated: (a) $I = \frac{E}{R}$ for R; (b) $W = EI$ for I; (c) $s = \frac{1}{2}gt^2$ for g; (d) $v^2 = 2as$ for s; (e) $v = ln$ for l; (f) $\frac{s}{d^2_s} = \frac{x}{d^2_x}$ for x.

Ans. (a) $R = \frac{E}{I}$ (b) $I = \frac{W}{E}$ (c) $g = \frac{2s}{t^2}$ (d) $s = \frac{v^2}{2a}$ (e) $l = \frac{v}{n}$ (f) $x = \frac{sd_x^2}{d_s^2}$

8. In what unit should the answer be stated in each of the following?

(a) $g \times m = ?$ (b) $\frac{kg \times m}{sec} = ?$ (c) $\frac{ft \times sec^2}{sec \times sec} = ?$

(d) $\frac{lb \times \frac{ft}{sec}}{\frac{ft}{sec^2}} = ?$ (e) $\frac{\frac{mi}{hr}}{\frac{min}{hr} \times \frac{sec}{min}} \times sec = ?$

Ans. (a) g — m (b) $\frac{kg - m}{sec}$ (c) ft (d) lb — sec (e) mi

9. Find: (a) hypotenuse of a right triangle with sides of 5 ft and 12 ft; (b) altitude of a right triangle with base of 8 ft and hypotenuse of 17 ft; (c) base of a right triangle with hypotenuse of 30 ft and altitude of 24 ft; (d) altitude of a right triangle with base of 35 ft and hypotenuse of 91 ft. Ans. (a) 13 ft (b) 15 ft (c) 18 ft (d) 84 ft

TWO— FUNDAMENTAL CONCEPTS

Undefined Terms. Suppose you were asked this question: "Do you know what *distance* is?" You would probably answer "yes"; but if you were then asked to explain or describe just what distance is, you would find it to be impossible. Distance is so fundamental to our ideas of the world around us, so much a part of our automatic thought processes, that even though we are positive we do know what it is, we are unable to find simpler terms with which to define it.

So it goes with many of the terms of physical science—matter, force, motion, space, time. We don't know exactly what they are, but we can usually recognize them without much trouble. Moreover, we know a great deal about what they can do and how they behave under various circumstances, and it is this information which is, after all, of the greatest practical importance.

Matter and Energy. The universe that the physicist studies is made up of *matter* and *energy*. Nobody knows what matter "is," but we can give several examples of it—air, water, gold, etc. We can also describe a few of the properties of matter which enable us to recognize it. These properties are listed a few paragraphs below.

Various kinds of matter are commonly spoken of as *materials*. Pure, single materials are called *substances*. Sugar, water, sulfur, aluminum, and oxygen are examples of substances; however, brass is not a single chemical substance and is spoken of simply as a material. Definite pieces of matter are called *bodies*. An iron ball, a quart of water, an atom of oxygen, or the earth itself represent bodies of matter.

Nobody knows what energy is, either, but here too we can give several examples—heat, light, electricity, magnetism, the motion of bodies. We know that these things exist, but we sense somehow that these things are not tangible or "material." *Energy manifests itself only through its effects on matter. Conversely, we become aware of matter only by means of transfer of energy.* Thus the two are related—together they make the entire physical universe.

Some General Properties of Matter. All bodies of matter have the following properties:

1. *Extension in Space.* Every body occupies a region of space— that is, some points in space are definitely inside the body, and others are definitely outside.

2. *Porosity.* Within every body of matter there is a relatively large amount of empty space, into which the particles of another body of matter can sometimes be placed. Thus a pint of alcohol mixed with a pint of water gives less than two pints of mixture. Hydrogen gas has been forced through steel plates 5 inches thick.

3. *Indestructibility.* Except under special conditions, matter cannot be destroyed, although its appearance and other special properties may be changed. When matter *is* destroyed, it is always turned into a definite amount of energy.

4. *Gravitation.* Every particle of matter attracts every other particle of matter in the universe, regardless of how far apart they are and how many other bodies of matter exist in the space between them. The amount of this attraction is given by a definite mathematical formula discovered by Isaac Newton:

$$F = K \frac{m_1 m_2}{d^2}$$

where F is the force of attraction, m_1 and m_2 are the amounts of matter in the two bodies, d is the distance between them, and K is a fixed number which depends on the units in which the other quantities are measured.

The gravitational attraction between the earth and any other body is called *weight*. Since the earth attracts all bodies, it is often said that "matter is anything that has weight."

5. *Inertia.* If a body is at rest, it cannot be made to move unless a force is exerted on it. If a body is moving, its speed or direction cannot be changed unless a force is exerted on it. This property of matter is called *inertia*. Inertia, like gravitation, obeys a definite formula, also discovered by Newton:

$$F = ma$$

where F is the force acting on the body, m is the amount of matter in the body, and a is its acceleration—the rate at which its motion is changing.

Force. In the preceding paragraphs we have mentioned "force" several times. Force is another of those things with which we are all familiar but which we cannot define. About the best we can do is the following:

Force is known to us as a push or a pull. It has the ability to change the motion of a body (either direction or speed), and also to change the shape of a body. Thus a force created by an explosion of powder in a cartridge causes a lead bullet to move at high speed; when the bullet strikes a steel plate a force is produced which not only stops the motion but also changes the shape of the bullet.

Force can be measured by measuring the amount of distortion which the force produces in a coiled spring (the spring scale).

Weight. Weight, as explained above, is the name given to the force of gravitation which exists between the earth and any other body. The weight of a body can be determined with a spring scale. It will be found that the weight of a body varies as it is taken from place to place on the earth's surface, or moved to different altitudes. This occurs because the quantity "d" in the gravitation formula changes as the body is moved about.

Mass. *Mass* is the amount of matter in a body, and is the quantity which has been represented by the letter m in the formulas given above. The mass of a body is, of course, constant, and does not depend on the location of the body. The mass of a body is usually determined by measuring its weight at a definite place on the earth's surface. From the formula for gravitation it is clear that the weight of a body at a given place will be directly proportional to its mass. Thus if Body A weighs 3 pounds, and Body B weighs 6 pounds at the same place, Body B has twice the mass of Body A.

The law of inertia, $F=ma$, may also be used to measure mass, but in most cases is not as convenient as weighing. The weight of a body, in practice, is usually used as a measure of its mass. In fact, weight and mass are measured in the same units. Therefore, in this book we will use the term weight to mean a definite quantity of a substance, even though mass is strictly more accurate. We will assume that the bodies we are talking about have all been weighed at the same place.

Measurement and Units. All measurements are relative—that is, they are comparisons between the quantity being measured and a *standard of measurement*.

As an example, consider the standard meter. The distance between two marks on a certain bar of metal is arbitrarily called *one meter.* If another distance is found to be twice as great, its measurement is *2 meters;* if it is 5.698 times as great, its measurement is *5.698 meters.* Every time we measure a length, we are simply comparing it with the standard length.

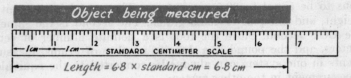

When the object is compared with the standard centimeter scale it is found that the standard centimeter goes into the length 6.8 times; the length is therefore 6.8 centimeters.

The Two Systems of Measurement. There are three fundamental quantities for which we need units of measurement— length (or distance), mass (or weight), and time. Two such sets

English and Metric Systems Compared

Quantity	English System	Metric System	Equivalents
Length	**FOOT** 1 foot = 12 inches 1 yard = 3 feet 1 mile = 5280 feet	**CENTIMETER** 1 centimeter = 10 millimeters 1 decimeter = 10 centimeters 1 meter = 100 centimeters 1 kilometer = 1000 meters	1 in = 2.54 cm 1 ft = 30.5 cm 1 meter = 39.37 in 1 km = 0.62 mile
Weight (Mass)	**POUND** 1 pound = 16 ounces 1 ton = 2000 pounds	**GRAM** 1 gram = 1000 milligrams 1 kilogram = 1000 grams	1 lb = 453.6 g 1 kg = 2.2 lb
Time	**SECOND** 1 second = $\dfrac{1}{86,400}$ of average solar day.	**SECOND** Same as for English system	Time is same in both systems

of units are in widespread use today—the *metric* system, and the *English* system.

The metric system uses units called *centimeter* (length), *gram* (mass), and *second* (time). The metric system is sometimes called the CGS system (from the initials of its units).

The English system simply uses units which have a different size. Thus the *foot* is the unit of length in this system, and happens to be equal to 30.5 centimeters. The *pound* is the unit of weight, and is equal to 453.6 grams. The *second* is the same as the CGS second. Since the foot is a definite number of centimeters, and the pound is a definite number of grams, measurements in one system can always be converted to the equivalent measurement in the other system.

There are other units of measure, such as *area* and *volume*, which are derived from the above fundamental measures, as shown by the following table.

	English System	Metric System	Equivalents
Area	1 sq ft = 144 sq in. 1 sq yd = 9 sq ft	1 sq cm = 100 sq mm 1 sq m = 10,000 sq cm	1 sq in = 6.45 sq cm 1 sq ft = 928.8 sq cm
Volume	1 cu ft = 1728 cu in 1 gallon = 231 cu in 1 gallon = 4 quarts	1 cu m = 1,000,000 cc 1 liter = 1000 cc	1 cu ft = 28.35 liters 1 liter = 1.06 qt

Measurement of Volume. The volume of a liquid can be easily measured by pouring the liquid into a graduated cylinder. The wall of the cylinder is marked off in units of volume, and the volume is read from the level of the liquid. The surface of a liquid in a container is not absolutely level, since the liquid either rises or falls where it touches the wall of the container, depending on whether the liquid wets the container or not. If the edge of the liquid rises, the volume is read from the lowest part of the curved liquid surface (*meniscus*); if it falls, the highest part is read.

The volume of a solid of regular or geometric shape can be calculated by applying the formulas of geometry. The more common formulas are illustrated on page 17.

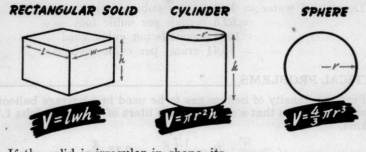

RECTANGULAR SOLID   **CYLINDER**   **SPHERE**

$$V = lwh$$ $$V = \pi r^2 h$$ $$V = \frac{4}{3}\pi r^3$$

If the solid is irregular in shape, its volume can be determined by displacement of liquid in a graduated cylinder as shown. This method is satisfactory only if the solid is not affected by the liquid. Thus the volume of a lump of sugar could *not* be found by displacement of water.

Density. The *density* of a substance is the weight of a unit volume of the substance. For example, each cubic centimeter of water weighs 1 gram; the density of water is therefore 1 gram per cubic centimeter. A cubic foot of water weighs 62.5 pounds; the density of water in the English system is thus 62.5 pounds per cubic foot. The total weight of a body is equal to its density multiplied by its volume:

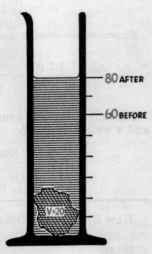

80 AFTER

60 BEFORE

V=20

$$\textbf{weight} = \textbf{volume} \times \textbf{density}$$
$$W = VD$$

On the other hand, the density of a body can be found by dividing its total weight by its volume:

$$D = \frac{W}{V}$$

It is essential to indicate the units in which density is expressed, since the numerical value depends on the units chosen. The density of water may be used as an illustration:

Density of water = 1 gram per cubic centimeter
                = 62.5 pounds per cubic foot
                = 1687.5 pounds per cubic yard
                = 16.41 grams per cubic inch, etc.

TYPICAL PROBLEMS

Find the density of helium gas to be used in a barrage balloon when it is known that a sample of ten liters of the gas weighs 1.7 grams.

$$D = \frac{W}{V}; \quad D = \frac{1.7 \text{ g}}{10 \text{ l}} = 0.17 \frac{\text{g}}{\text{l}}$$

Expressed in smaller units,

$$D = \frac{1.7 \text{ g}}{10 \text{ l}} = \frac{1.7 \text{ g}}{10 \text{ l} \times \frac{1000 \text{ cm}^3}{\text{l}}} = 0.00017 \frac{\text{g}}{\text{cm}^3}$$

Find the volume of a marble object with a density of 2.6 g per cc and a weight of 580 g.

$$V = \frac{W}{D}; \quad V = \frac{580 \text{ g}}{2.6 \frac{\text{g}}{\text{cm}^3}} = \frac{580}{2.6}\left(\text{g} \times \frac{\text{cm}^3}{\text{g}}\right) = 223 \text{ cm}^3$$

How Bodies May Differ. We have considered some of the general properties of all bodies. We shall now mention a few special properties by which substances may be distinguished, and which make some substances more useful than others for a particular purpose.

Physical State. Substances may be solid, liquid, or gaseous. A solid has a fixed volume and a fixed shape. A liquid has a fixed volume, but assumes the shape of its container. A gas has neither a definite volume nor a definite shape; it always fills completely any container in which it is placed.

The same substance may exist in any of the three states of matter, as its temperature and pressure are changed. Thus the solid, ice, melts to water at 0°C, and water changes to a gas at 100°C. Physical state will be treated at greater length in Chapter 12.

Density. Each substance has a definite density (under given conditions of temperature and pressure).

Elasticity. The tendency of a body to resume its original shape when a distorting force is removed is called elasticity. Steel wire is highly elastic, because it can be subjected to forces of thousands of pounds per square inch of cross-section, and still return to its original length when the force is removed. Putty, on the other hand, is inelastic. A small force applied to putty permanently changes its shape. Each substance has an *elastic limit*—the maximum force the substance can stand without being permanently deformed or broken.

The distorting force may be one of several kinds: stretching, compressing, twisting, bending, or tearing. A substance has a different elastic limit for each type of force or *stress.* The amount

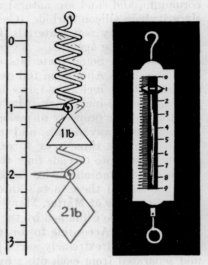

The extension of a spring is proportional to the force acting on it.

of distortion which occurs under a given stress is called *strain.* Robert Hooke (1635–1702), discovered the law (Hooke's Law) that *strain is proportional to stress* if the stress stays within the elastic limit of the material. The spring balance is an application of Hooke's Law—the amount of stretch in the spring is proportional to the force producing it. Hooke's Law must be used in the design of all machines and mechanical structures.

Tenacity. Tenacity is the ability of matter to resist being pulled or torn apart. Some materials can be pulled in two very easily; others require great force. Tenacity per unit area is called *tensile strength,* and is usually stated in pounds per square inch. For example, some alloy steels require a force of over 100,000 lb per sq in to pull them in two. Airplane alloy metals combine high tensile strength with low density.

Hardness. One substance is harder than another when it can scratch the other. The diamond is the hardest substance known; it can scratch all other materials. Very hard materials are used as cutting agents, drill points, abrasives, and the like. Emery, corundum, and sand are natural abrasives; manufactured abrasives include silicon carbide (Carborundum), tungsten carbide, and others. Very soft materials, like chalk, talc, and rouge are used as polishing agents.

Malleability. Some materials may be rolled or beaten into very fine sheets Aluminum foil can be obtained with a thickness of about 0.001 inch. Gold has been beaten into sheets about $\frac{1}{300,000}$ of an inch thick. Many metals have important uses because of their property of malleability.

Ductility. Many metals, and other materials as well, can be drawn into fine threads or wires. Quartz, when highly heated, can be drawn into threads finer than the fibers in a spider's web. Copper and aluminum wire for electrical purposes is made by drawing rods of these metals through smaller and smaller dies.

The Structure of Matter. Many of the properties of matter just described can be explained by the *molecular theory* of the structure of matter. According to this theory, each body consists of a large number of extremely small particles moving at high speed and separated from each other by empty space. These particles are called *molecules.* All the molecules of a given substance are alike, but the molecules of one substance are different from the molecules of every other substance.

This theory of matter is supported by an overwhelming amount of evidence of many different kinds. It is believed that large molecules have already been photographed with the electron microscope. The molecular structure of matter is now considered to be virtually an established fact.

Molecules themselves consist of smaller particles called *atoms,* chemically united within the molecules. There are **92** different kinds of atoms (each called an *element*). All atoms are made up of combinations of certain fundamental particles—*protons, electrons, neutrons,* and possibly a few others. All protons are alike, as are all electrons and neutrons. They are the true building blocks of the material universe. However, the molecule is the smallest particle of a body which has the properties of that body.

Molecular Forces. Gravitational forces exist between all molecules of matter. In addition, there are a number of other forces which act between molecules when they approach one another. The exact nature of these forces is not yet known, except that some are attractions and some repulsions. One of the attractive forces (called *cohesion*) holds the molecules of a body together, as in the case of a steel rod.

In a gas, the attractive or cohesive forces have little effect, because of the great distance between the molecules. Consequently, a gas shows no tendency to "hold together." In a liquid, the molecules are easily separated from one another (the substance is easily "torn"), and they flow more or less freely past each other; but there is enough cohesive force to hold a body of liquid together if the liquid is undisturbed. (*Viscosity* is a measure of the difficulty with which the molecules of a liquid flow past one another. Molasses is a highly *viscous* liquid.) In a solid, the cohesive forces are great enough to hold the molecules within a fairly rigid pattern which is not easily disturbed. That is why distortions or strains tend to disappear when stresses are removed from solids.

Surface Tension. The molecular forces at the surface of a liquid are different from those deep within the liquid, because there are no upward forces at the surface. The action of these forces makes the surface act like a stretched membrane, such as a sheet of rubber. Razor blades will rest on this surface without sinking; certain insects can walk on water; a single drop will contract into the

Surface tension will support a steel needle.

shape of a sphere; thin liquid films will contract. These are all effects of surface tension.

Adhesion. Attractive forces exist between dissimilar molecules also. The effects of these attractive forces are called *adhesion*. The action of glue, concrete, solder, etc., is the result of adhesive forces.

Capillarity. A liquid in contact with the wall of a container experiences two forces—one is its own cohesive force, the other the force of adhesion between the container and the liquid. If the adhesive force is greater, the liquid will "wet" the surface, and climb up it slightly. Otherwise the liquid will be drawn away from the walls, and dip down at the sides. If a tube of small diameter (a *capillary* tube) is dipped into water, the water immediately wets the walls of the tube, and begins to climb the sides. In capillary tubes this climbing force is sufficient to pull a column of water up the tube a considerable distance. The finer the tube, the higher will be the column.

If the tube is placed in a liquid which does not wet the tube, the opposite action results—the liquid is depressed inside the tube. Mercury is an example of a liquid which does not wet glass.

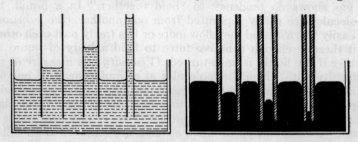

Water rises in a capillary glass tube; mercury is depressed. The change in level is greater the smaller the diameter of the tube.

Examples of capillary action are the penetration of oil between the leaves of automobile springs when sprayed on the surface; the rise of water in soil and in the roots and stems of plants; the rise of oil in the wick of an oil lamp; the absorption of water by filter paper or a towel.

Effect of Temperature on Cohesive Forces. A rise in the temperature of a body usually reduces its cohesive forces. Thus when solids are heated they eventually become liquids, and liquids heated sufficiently become gases. Two steel plates placed in contact will not stick together; but if the plates are strongly heated, as by the passage of an electric current through them, the cohesive forces are temporarily weakened, and the plates fuse together, making a permanent joint. This is the process of *welding*. Metals may be welded by pouring molten metal between the surfaces to be joined. The explanation is the same.

Cold solder is, of course, useless. When the solder is heated, however, adhesive forces are given an opportunity to act between the solder and the surfaces to be joined.

PROBLEMS

1. Find the metric or English equivalent in each of the following:
(a) 1 foot in cm; (b) 1 oz in g; (c) 100 meters in yards; (d) 1 yd² in
cm²; (e) 1 gal in liters.

> Ans. (a) 30.5 cm (b) 28.4 g (c) 109.5 yd (d) 8370 (e) 0.264 l

2. What is the weight in kilograms of a 2-ton "block buster"?

> Ans. 1820 kg

3. What would half a pound of platinum cost at $4.00 a gram?

> Ans. $908

4. How much does a liter of mercury weigh (a) in g; (b) in kg?
(Density of mercury = 13.6 g/cm³.)   Ans. (a) 13,600 g (b) 13.6 kg

5. What is the density of a cube of aluminum, 10 cm on an edge,
that weighs 2.6 kg?   Ans. 2.6 g/cm³

6. How many liters of alcohol will weigh 10 kg? (Density of alcohol = 0.8 g/cm³.)   Ans. 12.5 l

7. A beam of pine wood 10 ft long, 1 ft wide, and 6 in thick weighs
150 lb. Calculate its density.   Ans. 30 lb/ft³

8. A cylinder 2 cm in diameter and 20 cm long is made of brass (density = 8.5 g/cm³). Calculate its weight.   Ans. 535 g

9. What will be the weight of a rectangular steel bar 25 ft long, 6 in
wide, and 2 in thick? (Density of steel = 461 lb/ft³)   Ans. 960 lb

10. A metal ball is 20 cm in diameter and weighs 32 kg. Calculate the
density of the metal.   Ans. 7.64 g/cm³

CLASSIFICATION TEST

*Give the number of the term in each of the following groups which
includes all the others.*

11. (1) wood; (2) air; (3) matter; (4) ice; (5) smoke; (6) gasoline.

12. (1) force; (2) gravitation; (3) magnetism; (4) push; (5) adhesion.

13. (1) heat; (2) light; (3) electricity; (4) flying bullet; (5) energy.

14. (1) lb/ft³; (2) g/cm³; (3) density; (4) kilograms per liter.

15. (1) gravitation; (2) inertia; (3) matter; (4) extension.

COMPLETION TEST

*Complete the following statements by writing the word or expression
which, if inserted in the blank, will make a true statement.*

The attraction between like molecules is termed _____(16)_____.
One kilogram is equal to about _____(17)_____ pounds. Internal
resistance to the flow of liquids is termed _____(18)_____. Small
drops of mercury assume a spherical shape because of _____(19)_____.
As a body is moved to various locations on the earth, its _____(20)_____
undergoes slight changes, but its _____(21)_____ remains the
same. One unit of measurement that is the same in both the metric and
the English systems is the _____(22)_____. The formula for calculating the volume of a cylinder is _____(23)_____. The effect
of a decrease in temperature on molecular motion is to _____(24)_____.
The property of a material that enables it to scratch another material
is _____(25)_____.

Force and Pressure. To understand the action of gravitational force in fluids, we must know what *force* and *pressure* are and how they are related to each other. We can think of force as a push or a pull, which can be measured in pounds, grams, kilograms, tons, or any other unit of weight.

Suppose a rectángular tank 2 ft square and 5 ft deep is filled with water. The area of the bottom surface is 4 sq ft (4 ft²); and the volume of the tank is 20 cu ft (20 ft³). Because water weighs 62.5 lb per cu ft ($62.5\frac{lb}{ft^3}$), the *total force* exerted by the water against the bottom of the tank is 1250 lb:

$$\text{total force} = \text{area} \times \text{height} \times \text{density}$$
$$F = A \times H \times D$$
$$= 4 \text{ ft}^2 \times 5 \text{ ft} \times 62.5\frac{lb}{ft^3} = 1250\text{ lb}$$

The bottom of the tank has an area of 4 ft², so that the force on each square foot is $\frac{1250}{4} = 312.5$ lb. *Pressure is the force exerted on a unit area of a given surface;* therefore, *total force equals pressure multiplied by the total area.*

$$\text{pressure} = \frac{\text{total force}}{\text{area}}; \quad \text{total force} = \text{pressure} \times \text{area}$$
$$P = \frac{F}{A} \qquad F = P \times A$$
$$\text{since } F = AHD, \text{ and also } F = PA,$$
$$PA = AHD$$
$$P = HD$$

Pressure Depends on Depth and Density. This is the meaning of the formula, $P = HD$. If the tank described above were filled with kerosene (density $= 50\frac{lb}{ft^3}$) instead of water, the kerosene,

24

weighing less than the same volume of water, would exert a smaller total force on the bottom; and the pressure at a depth of 5 ft would be less, as shown by the following calculations. (The units cancel out to give the correct unit for the numerical answer.)

$$\textbf{(1)}\ F = AHD$$
$$= 4\ \text{ft}^2 \times 5\ \text{ft} \times 50\frac{\text{lb}}{\text{ft}^3} = \textbf{1000 lb}$$

$$\textbf{(2)}\ P = \frac{F}{A} = \frac{1000\ \text{lb}}{4\ \text{ft}^2} = 250\frac{\text{lb}}{\text{ft}^2}$$

$$\textbf{(3)}\ P = HD = 5\ \text{ft} \times 50\frac{\text{lb}}{\text{ft}^3} = 250\frac{\text{lb}}{\text{ft}^2}$$

Suppose we wish to calculate the pressure in pounds per square inch. Since one square foot = 144 square inches, we must divide the previous answer by $144\ \dfrac{\text{in}^2}{\text{ft}^2}$.

$$\frac{\text{lb}}{\text{in}^2} = \frac{\frac{\text{lb}}{\text{ft}^2}}{144\frac{\text{in}^2}{\text{ft}^2}} = \frac{250\frac{\text{lb}}{\text{ft}^2}}{144\frac{\text{in}^2}{\text{ft}^2}} = \frac{250}{144} \times \frac{\text{lb}}{\text{ft}^2} \times \frac{\text{ft}^2}{\text{in}^2} = 1.7\frac{\text{lb}}{\text{in}^2}$$

Because the pressure of liquids varies as the depth, dams and levees are built much thicker at their bases than at their tops. For the same reason, submarines must be so constructed as to withstand the tremendous pressure encountered when they submerge. Sea water has a density of $64\ \dfrac{\text{lb}}{\text{ft}^3}$; the pressure in pounds per square inch at a depth, for example, of 300 ft would be:

$$P = HD = 300\ \text{ft} \times 64\frac{\text{lb}}{\text{ft}^3} = 19{,}200\frac{\text{lb}}{\text{ft}^2} = \frac{19{,}200}{144}\ \frac{\text{lb}}{\text{in}^2} = \textbf{133.3}\frac{\text{lb}}{\text{in}^2}$$

The depth charges used to sink or destroy enemy submarines are timed to explode at predetermined depths. The firing mechanism is adjusted so that it acts as soon as the water pressure reaches a value corresponding to the chosen depth.

Other Characteristics of Liquid Pressure. Experiments prove that at any point beneath the surface of a liquid *the pressure is the same in all directions*: sidewise, upward, and downward.

The pressure exerted by a liquid, on any of its surfaces, is not affected by the size or shape of the vessel or by the volume of water. The size of the pond behind a dam has no effect on the total force against the dam, provided, of course, that the depth of the water remains the same.

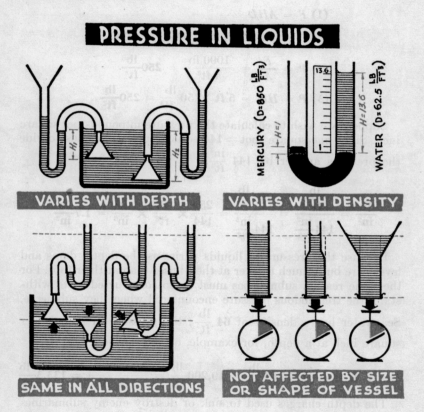

PRESSURE IN LIQUIDS

VARIES WITH DEPTH

VARIES WITH DENSITY

SAME IN ALL DIRECTIONS

NOT AFFECTED BY SIZE OR SHAPE OF VESSEL

Pressure on a Vertical Surface. In calculating how much force a dam or other *vertical* surface must withstand, we should realize that the pressure is not the same at all points but increases with the depth. The *average* pressure on a vertical surface is the pressure at its midpoint or average depth. We may, therefore, modify our formulas as follows:

$$P_{ave} = H_{ave} \times D, \text{ or } P_{ave} = \frac{H \times D}{2}$$

$$F = A \times P_{ave}, \text{ or } F = \frac{A \times H \times D}{2}$$

TYPICAL PROBLEMS

To what pressure, in pounds per square inch, is a diver subjected when he descends to an ocean depth of 80 feet?

$$P = HD = \frac{80 \text{ ft} \times 64 \frac{\text{lb}}{\text{ft}^3}}{144 \frac{\text{in}^2}{\text{ft}^2}} = \frac{5120 \text{ ft}}{144} \times \frac{\text{lb}}{\text{ft}^3} \times \frac{\text{ft}^2}{\text{in}^2} = 35.5 \frac{\text{lb}}{\text{in}^2}$$

A rectangular vessel measuring 30 cm wide, 50 cm long, and 15 cm deep is filled with mercury (density = 13.6 grams per cubic centimeter). (a) What is the total force on the bottom? (b) What is the pressure on the bottom? (c) What is the average pressure on one side? (d) What is the total force against one end?

(a) $F = AHD = 1500 \text{ cm}^2 \times 15 \text{ cm} \times 13.6 \frac{\text{g}}{\text{cm}^3} = 306,000 \text{ g}$

(b) $P = HD = 15 \text{ cm} \times 13.6 \frac{\text{g}}{\text{cm}^3} = 204 \frac{\text{g}}{\text{cm}^2}$

(c) $P_{ave} = H_{ave} \times D = 7.5 \text{ cm} \times 13.6 \frac{\text{g}}{\text{cm}^3} = 102 \frac{\text{g}}{\text{cm}^2}$

(d) $F = \frac{AHD}{2} = \frac{450 \text{ cm}^2 \times 15 \text{ cm} \times 13.6 \frac{\text{g}}{\text{cm}^3}}{2} = 46,000 \text{ g}$

If the firing mechanism of a depth bomb is set to act at a pressure of 50 lb per sq in, at what depth will the bomb explode?

$$P = HD \text{ ;} 50 \frac{\text{lb}}{\text{in}^2} = \frac{H \times 64 \frac{\text{lb}}{\text{ft}^3}}{144 \frac{\text{in}^2}{\text{ft}^2}};$$

$$H = \frac{50 \times 144}{64} \times \frac{\text{lb}}{\text{in}^2} \times \frac{\text{in}^2}{\text{ft}^2} \times \frac{\text{ft}^3}{\text{lb}} = 112.5 \text{ ft}$$

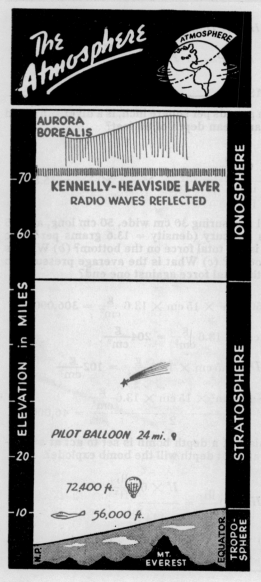

The Earth's Atmosphere. Man lives at the bottom of an ocean of air which extends outward all around the earth and which thins gradually into the vast emptiness of space. Explorations of this air ocean have revealed that the density of the air decreases as the height above the earth increases. The density is almost zero at an altitude of probably 150 or 200 miles. Fifty per cent of the air by weight is found below an altitude of 18,000 feet.

The earth's atmosphere is divided rather sharply into definite zones. The layer next to the earth is called the *troposphere*. It is about 4 miles thick at the poles, about 11 miles thick at the equator, and an average of about 7 miles thick in the middle latitudes. The troposphere is of special interest because in it occur all the things which make up our weather—such as clouds, winds, vertical air currents, storms, fog, rain, snow, and temperature changes. In this zone, aviators frequently encounter weather hazards. Above the troposphere, however, is a region which offers excellent flying conditions—the *stratosphere*. This zone is cloudless, with steady winds and a nearly constant temperature of about 70 degrees below zero Fahrenheit. The stratosphere extends to a height of at least 50 miles. Above it is still another layer of the atmosphere, the *ionosphere*. This layer reflects certain radio waves back to the earth and thus increases the range of some radio transmitters. The aurora borealis (northern lights) occurs in the ionosphere, at an altitude of about 600 miles. How much higher than this the atmosphere extends is unknown.

Weight and Pressure of the Air. To prove that air has weight, pump the air out of a glass flask fitted with a one-hole stopper and pinch clamp. Weigh the exhausted flask on a sensitive balance. Open the valve to let the air rush in, and weigh the flask

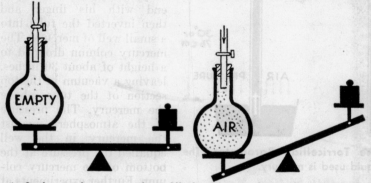

A flask weighs more when filled with air than when partially evacuated.

again. Note that the weight has increased. The density of air under standard conditions is about 1.29 grams per liter, or 1.22 ounces per cubic foot. The air is "stacked in layers" to a very great height, so that its total weight is enormous. At sea level, more than a ton of air presses against each square foot of the earth's surface. Standard sea level pressure is 14.7 $\frac{\text{lb}}{\text{in}^2}$. Air is a gas and, therefore, this pressure is exerted equally in all directions—upward and sidewise as well as downward. The total force (resulting from the air above) exerted on a table top 5 feet by 3 feet in size is enormous.

$$F = P \times A$$
$$= 14.7 \frac{lb}{in^2} \times 15\,ft^2 \times 144 \frac{in^2}{ft^2} = 31,800\,lb$$

Still, because the upward (and sidewise) pressure is equal to the downward pressure, the table legs do not break.

Measuring Atmospheric Pressure. The first practical measurement of atmospheric pressure was made by an Italian, Torricelli, in 1643. He used a glass tube about three feet long and closed at one end. Having filled the tube with mercury, he covered the open end with his finger and then inverted the tube into a small well of mercury. The mercury column dropped to a height of about 30 inches, leaving a vacuum in the top section of the tube, above the mercury. The pressure of the atmosphere against the mercury in the well equalled the pressure at the bottom of the mercury column. Further experiments at different altitudes revealed that the mercury was supported by air pressure, for the height of the column varied with the altitude.

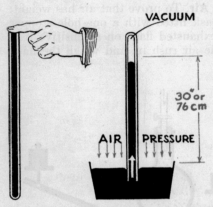

The Torricellian Barometer. The liquid used is mercury.

Under normal conditions (sea level pressure, and 0°C), a column of mercury 76 cm high remains in the tube. The air supporting this column presses down on the surface of the mercury in the well. This mercury, in turn, transmits the pressure to the mercury in the tube. The mercury column must be high enough so that the pressure due to its weight just balances the transmitted air pressure. When this condition has been reached,

$P = HD$. Since the density of mercury is $13.6 \frac{g}{cm^3}$, and the height of the column is 76 cm,

$$P = 76 \text{ cm} \times 13.6 \frac{g}{cm^3} = 1033.6 \frac{g}{cm^2}$$

Using the formula, $P = HD$, we find that since the density of mercury remains constant, any variations in atmospheric pressure must appear as variations in the height of the mercury column. The modern *mercurial barometer* for measuring air pressure operates on this principle. A vernier scale is provided so that the height of the mercury in the tube can be read easily and accurately. An attached thermometer and table of corrections enable the observer to allow for the expansion of the mercury from heat, and thus to get the corrected height of the mercury column. A statement that the atmospheric pressure is, for example, 29.6 inches of mercury means that the atmospheric pressure can support a column of mercury 29.6 inches high. Atmospheric pressure varies with changes in the weather and with changes in the altitude above (or below) sea level.

Standard air pressure may be stated not only as 76 cm of mercury, or 1034 grams per square centimeter, but also as 29.92 (or 30) inches of mercury, or 14.7 lb per square inch. In meteorology another unit of pressure, the *millibar*, has recently come into widespread use. The pressure of one inch of mercury corresponds to about 34 millibars, and the standard pressure (29.92 in) may, therefore, also be stated as 1013.2 millibars.

The Aneroid Barometer. Because of its size and weight, the mercury barometer, despite great accuracy, is not always convenient to use. The aneroid barometer, which can be made in various sizes, is accurate enough for most purposes and is less costly than the mercury barometer. *Aneroid* means "without liquid." The working part of such a barometer contains a sealed corrugated metal box from which most of the air has been removed. To keep the box from collapsing, a curved metal spring is attached to the top. Variations in external atmospheric pressure cause the top of the box to move slightly up or down. A system of levers magnifies these motions, and a chain, or a series of links, causes a pointer to move over a circular scale. The scale readings, which correspond to the readings of a mercury barometer, indicate the pressure in inches, centimeters, or milli-bars. Inasmuch as air pressure decreases (more or less regularly) with gain in altitude, the scale may be modified to indicate altitude instead of pressure. A sensitive aneroid barometer so calibrated is called an *altimeter*. From such instruments, used with care, pilots can obtain accurate information as to their elevation above sea level (or, if added information is available, as to their elevation above the ground over which they are flying).

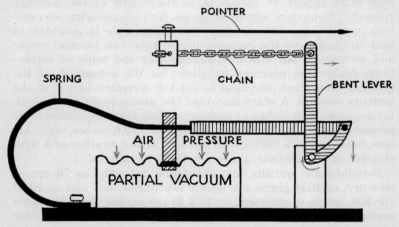

The Aneroid Barometer. As the air pressure changes, the spring moves up and down, causing the pointer to turn.

Relation of Pressure to Altitude. As indicated, atmospheric pressure decreases with gain in altitude. Near sea level, the de-crease is at the rate of 1 inch of mercury (34 millibars) for each 1,000 feet of ascent. If an airplane takes off near sea level and climbs until the barometer reading drops 2.8 inches, its altitude above sea level will be about 2,800 feet. Air is a gas, and the weight of the layers above compresses (and increases the density of) the layers below. The higher the altitude, the lower is the density of the air. A pressure decrease at the rate of 1 inch for each 1,000 feet of ascent holds closely only for the lower levels of altitude. At 10,000 feet, for example, standard pressure is actually 20.58 inches, instead of the 19.92 inches theoretically expected on the basis of 1 in drop per 1000 ft.

Atmospheric Pressure and the Weather. The United States Weather Bureau is the world's largest agency for collecting and analyzing weather data and predicting the weather. More than 550 reporting stations are maintained along civil airways alone, and about 250 other stations are located elsewhere throughout the country. Weather information, collected at frequent intervals, is forwarded to the various forecasting centers by telegraph, telephone, radio, and teletype. From the data so assembled, a daily weather map is prepared and numerous forecasts, warnings, summaries, and bulletins are completed for distribution.

Among the items of weather data reported by each station— such as temperature, pressure, wind direction and velocity, visibility, ceiling, and other items—perhaps the most important is pressure. Experience has shown that when the barometer reading is 30.0 inches or higher, the coming weather is likely to be settled and dry. In nearly all cases, a barometer reading of 29.0 inches or lower signifies stormy or unsettled weather. One cause of the low barometric pressure during such weather is the high moisture content of the air. A cubic foot of water vapor weighs less than a cubic foot of air. Contrary to popular belief, very moist air is lighter, volume for volume, than dry air; although it may be oppressive, moist air is not heavy.

Marked changes in atmospheric pressure usually forebode a change in weather. A falling barometer indicates the approach of a cyclonic storm (or a "low"), and the more rapidly the pressure drops, the more severe is the storm likely to be. Rising pressures precede the onset of a "high" with clearing, cooler, and fair weather. Continued high pressures generally indicate continued cool and fair weather. When a low-pressure area or cyclone has developed over the United States, it then moves in a general easterly direction across the country, carrying its typical brand of weather with it. As the cyclone goes by, higher barometric pressures follow in its wake. The high-pressure regions located between lows are called *anticyclones,* or simply "highs." Low-pressure areas move across the country at a speed of about 500 miles a day, in summer, and about 700 miles a day, in winter. Highs move somewhat faster than lows.

The pressure readings reported by weather observation stations are entered on the weather map. Lines are drawn through all places having the same pressure. These lines, called *isobars,* clearly show areas of high and low pressure. Isobars drawn close together represent sharp changes in pressure and indicate regions having strong winds. These winds blow away from high pressure areas, toward areas of low pressure, but are deflected somewhat by the spin of the earth. Pilots locate the centers of cyclones by applying a useful rule based on wind direction: in the Northern Hemisphere face the wind, and the center of the low pressure area will be to your right and some distance behind you; for the Southern Hemisphere, the reverse is true,—the pressure decreases toward your left and increases toward your right.

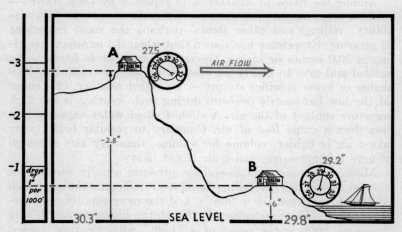

Air flows from A to B because, at any level, the pressure at A is greater than at B, as the correction to sea level shows.

Reducing Pressures to Sea Level. To compare the barometric pressure readings of many stations, each located at a different altitude above sea level, we must reduce all the readings to some common basis. For this purpose, the plane selected is generally sea level. The correction needed to reduce each station pressure reading to what it would be at sea level, is based on the fact that each 1,000 feet of elevation causes a pressure reduction of 1 inch of mercury. If a station is located 3,500 feet above sea level and the station pressure is 26.9 inches, the pressure reduced to sea level and reported to the forecast center is 30.4 (26.9 + 3.5) inches. All stations report these reduced pressures, so that the isobars on a weather map provide a horizontal, sea level, cross-section of pressure distribution over the United States.

The value of this method of reporting pressures becomes apparent when we try to predict the direction of wind flow (as an aviator might have to do in planning a flight). As shown in the illustration, station *A* is 2,800 feet above sea level and has a station pressure of 27.5 in. Station *B* is 600 feet above sea level and has a station pressure of 29.2 in. Apparently, the air should flow from *B* to *A*. But when corrections for altitude are made, the equivalent sea level pressure for station *A* becomes 30.3 in (27.5 + 2.8), while the reading at station *B* becomes 29.8 in (29.2 + 0.6). Hence the air will actually tend to flow from *A* to *B*. Note that the same pressure difference of 0.5 in exists at any altitude. For example, at the level of Station A (2800 ft) the pressure at A is 27.5 in, and above Station B it is 29.8 − 2.8 = 27.0 in.

BEST ANSWER TEST

In each of the following exercises, select the word or phrase that provides the best completion answer for the introductory words.
   1. The height to which air pressure will force mercury in a barometer (1) is about 76 inches; (2) is about 34 feet; (3) depends upon the diameter of the barometer tube; (4) depends upon the altitude of the barometer.
   2. High pressure areas usually have (1) barometric readings around 40 inches; (2) the effect of producing clearing weather; (3) the effect of producing fog or rain; (4) harmful effects on people with high blood pressure.
   3. When an airplane flies from a region of low pressure to one of high pressure, its altimeter (1) will indicate a loss in altitude; (2) will indicate a gain in altitude; (3) will reveal the true elevation above sea level; (4) will not be affected.
   4. The base of a dam is made thicker than the top because (1) pressure varies with depth; (2) pressure varies with density; (3) downward pressure is greater than upward pressure; (4) this type of construction produces a better appearing structure.
   5. The average pressure against the vertical surface of a cylindrical gasoline storage tank (1) is the same as the pressure on the bottom; (2) is twice the pressure at the top; (3) is one-half the pressure on the bottom; (4) depends on the diameter of the tank.

QUESTIONS

   1. How does the length of a river affect the force against the breast of a dam built across it?

2. Explain how it is possible for the pressure at the point of a phonograph needle to be hundreds of pounds per sq in when the reproducer weighs only a few oz.

3. Must the bore of a barometer tube be uniform? Explain.

4. Strictly speaking, there is no such thing as "suction." Explain how a rug is cleaned by "suction."

5. Decide whether each of the following statements is true or false and explain your reasons: (*a*) Pressure depends upon the density and viscosity of a liquid; (*b*) The mercury column in a barometer would rise if the instrument were carried into a deep mine; (*c*) A rising barometer usually indicates that rainy weather is on its way.

PROBLEMS

1. A depth bomb is set to explode in sea water when the pressure becomes 75 lb per sq in. At what depth will it explode?   Ans. 169 ft

2. Calculate (*a*) the pressure, (*b*) the force, on the bottom of an aquarium 80 cm long and 50 cm wide when filled to a depth of 30 cm with water.   Ans. (a) 30 g/cm^2 (b) 120,000 g

3. What is the force on the bottom of a tank 3 ft by 3 ft filled to a depth of 42 in with acid whose density is 80 lb per cu ft?   Ans. 2520 lb

4. What is the total force against a dam 100 ft wide when the water behind it is 50 ft deep?   Ans. 156,250 lb

5. A weather station *A* situated 2200 ft above sea level has a barometric pressure of 28.3 in of mercury, while station *B* situated 900 ft above sea level has a barometric pressure of 29.7 in. (*a*) What is the apparent direction of air flow? (*b*) What is the direction of actual tendency of airflow?   Ans. (a) B to A (b) B to A

6. An airplane takes off from an airport located 800 ft above sea level. The local barometric pressure is 29.2 in. After gaining sufficient altitude, the barometric pressure was found to be 25.6 in. What was the approximate height of the plane above sea level?   Ans. 4400 ft

7. A swimming pool is 60 ft long and 30 ft wide and has a sloping bottom. The water is 3 ft deep at one end, and 9 ft deep at the other end. What is the force against (*a*) the shallow end of the pool? (*b*) The deep end of the pool? (*c*) The bottom of the pool?   Ans. (a) 28,100 lb (b) 84,400 lb (c) 675,000 lb

8. The elevation of the lake behind Boulder Dam is 530 ft above the river below the dam, and the power house is located at the river edge. What is the pressure at the power house?Ans. 33,100 lb/ft^2, or 230 lb/in^2

9. If a barometer were constructed to operate with oil (density = 0.9 g per cu cm) instead of mercury, what height of oil would standard atmospheric pressure support?   Ans. 1150 cm

10. (*a*) What is the pressure in lb per sq in on the bottom of a tank filled with gasoline to a depth of 12 ft? (Density of gasoline = 45 lb/ft^3). (*b*) If the tank is cylindrical and 20 ft in diameter, what is the total force on the bottom of the tank?   Ans. (a) 3.75 lb/in^2 (b) 170,000 lb

Buoyant Effect of Liquids. An object wholly or partially submerged in a liquid seems to weigh less than it weighs in air. A stone that feels light under the water feels much heavier when lifted out of the water. Does water lift the stone, or does gravity pull the stone down with less force when it is in the water? It is easy to prove that the force of gravity doesn't change, but rather that the liquid exerts a buoyant force (or lift) on a submerged object.

Imagine a 1-foot cube of aluminum submerged in water so that the top of the cube is 3 feet below the surface of the water. There is a downward force on the top of the cube; also, the liquid exerts an upward force against the bottom of the cube. Is there any difference between these two forces?

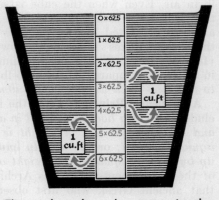

The numbers down the center give the pressure in lb per sq ft at each foot below the surface. As can be seen, the difference between the pressure on the bottom face and the pressure on the top face of a 1-ft cube is the same at any depth.

On the bottom of the cube,

$$F = AHD = 1 \text{ ft}^2 \times 4 \text{ ft} \times 62.5 \frac{\text{lb}}{\text{ft}^3} = \textbf{250.0 lb}$$

On the top of the cube,

$$F = AHD = 1 \text{ ft}^2 \times 3 \text{ ft} \times 62.5 \frac{\text{lb}}{\text{ft}^3} = \underline{\textbf{187.5 lb}}$$
$$\text{Difference} = \overline{62.5 \text{ lb}}$$

The difference between the upward force and the downward force is a force of 62.5 lb exerted upward. This force buoys up the submerged cube. Note that the 1-foot cube of aluminum displaces 1 cubic foot of water, which weighs 62.5 lb, and that the buoyant force is the same at any depth.

If the upward push on the cube is 62.5 lb more than the downward push, why doesn't the upward force push the cube to the surface of the water? One cubic foot of aluminum weighs 168.75 lb in air. Even when the cube is submerged, gravity continues to pull it down with this same force, but the net upward (buoyant) force exerted by the water is only 62.5 lb. The effect of these two forces is a final downward force of 106.25 lb (168.75 − 62.5). The cube of aluminum will weigh 106.25 lb in water, as compared with 168.75 lb in air. *The cube will appear to lose 62.5 lb in weight when submerged.*

Archimedes' Principle. From the foregoing discussion, we conclude that (1) *a body immersed in a liquid seems to lose weight, and the apparent loss in weight is equal to the weight of the liquid displaced;* or (2) *a body immersed in a liquid is buoyed up by a force equal to the weight of the liquid displaced.* Each of these statements expresses Archimedes' principle, named for that ancient Greek who first observed and clearly stated the relationship between the weight of the liquid displaced by a body and the buoyant force exerted on the body by the liquid.

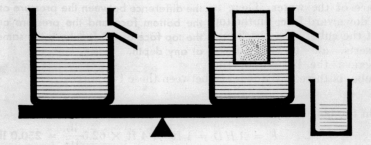

The Law of Flotation. The scale remains balanced when the floating body is placed in the overflow can because the weight of the body is exactly equal to the weight of liquid displaced.

Archimedes' principle applies also to floating bodies. Because *a floating object* loses all its weight, it *displaces a weight of liquid equal to its entire weight.* This relationship is known as the *law of flotation.* For example, in order to float, a 50-lb canoe containing a 180-lb man must displace 230 lb of water. What volume of water must be displaced?

$$\frac{230 \text{ lb}}{62.5 \dfrac{\text{lb}}{\text{ft}^3}} = \frac{230 \text{ lb}}{62.5} \times \frac{\text{ft}^3}{\text{lb}} = 3.68 \text{ ft}^3$$

The canoe floats because its volume is considerably more than 3.68 ft³. In order to float, a body must have an average density less than that of the liquid. The floats on a seaplane must be made large enough so that before they sink too deep they will displace a weight of water equal to the entire weight of the plane. A rubber life raft has a large volume but small weight, so that it can support several occupants without submerging.

The Submarine and Archimedes' Principle. The average density of a floating submarine is less than that of the water. To submerge the submarine, its ballast tanks are allowed to fill, partially, with water. The added liquid makes the total weight of the submarine just about equal to or slightly more than that of the water. Propellers then drive the boat forward, and diving rudders are set at an angle to send it downward. To "surface," compressed air is pumped into the tanks to expel the added water

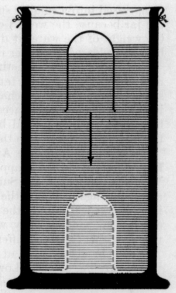

The Cartesian Diver. When the rubber diaphragm is depressed to the position shown in red, the increased air pressure forces more liquid into the diver, causing it to sink to the bottom.

so that the overall weight and density decrease again and the submarine rises. When the average density exceeds that of the water, the boat tends to sink until it reaches bottom. To keep the submarine from sinking too deep, the propellers are kept running with the rudders properly set.

The so-called Cartesian diver illustrates the principle of the submarine. The apparatus shown in the drawing consists of a tall jar nearly full of water, an inverted test tube (the "diver") containing just enough air to make it float, and a rubber membrane stretched tight across the top of the jar. When the finger presses the membrane downward, increased air pressure causes more water to enter the test tube. The air in the test tube is thus compressed into a smaller space. The diver sinks to the bottom of the jar because the weight of the test tube becomes greater than the weight of the water it displaces. When pressure on the membrane is released, the diver rises to the surface.

Sunken ships are sometimes raised by application of Archimedes' principle. Large tanks are filled with enough water to sink them and are then chained to the sunken vessel. The water in the tanks is then replaced by compressed air. If enough tanks have been used, the total buoyant force will suffice to lift both the tanks and the ship to the surface.

Experiments to Prove Archimedes' Principle and the Law of Flotation. Arrange the apparatus suggested by the illustration. Weigh the weight in air. Submerge the weight in the overflow can and weigh again. Weigh the water that overflows when the weight is submerged. Compare the weight of this water with the apparent loss in weight. They will be equal. Repeat the experiment using another liquid of different density, such as kerosene.

Weigh in air a block of some solid that floats, such as pine wood, paraffin, or cork. Lower the block carefully into the overflow can until the block floats in the water. Weigh the water that overflows. Compare with the weight of the block in air. The two weights will be equal. Repeat the experiment using another liquid, such as kerosene.

The greater the density of the liquid, the greater is the buoyant force which it exerts on objects submerged in it, since the buoyant force equals the weight of liquid displaced. Ships float deeper in fresh than in salt water because fresh water is less dense than salt water; to displace their own weight, they must sink deeper in the fresh water.

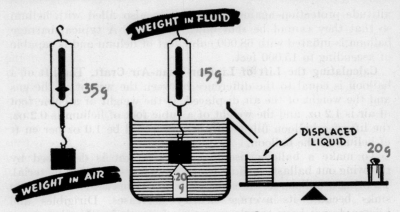

BUOYANT FORCE = Weight of Displaced Liquid

Archimedes' Principle. The weight of the liquid displaced by a submerged body is exactly equal to the apparent loss in weight or buoyant force on the body.

Buoyant Effect of Air. All these facts about the buoyant effect of liquids apply to every fluid, that is, to gases as well as liquids. A balloon is buoyed up by a force equal to the weight of the air it displaces. Balloons are submarines of the atmosphere. Balloons and dirigibles are filled with a gas, usually hydrogen or helium, which is much less dense than air. A balloon on the ground weighs less than the air displaced. Unless the balloon is tied down, the air around it will push it upward, just as water pushes a cork upward when released beneath the surface.

According to Archimedes' principle, the balloon will be buoyed upward by a force equal to the weight of the displaced air. When released, the balloon will rise until it displaces its own weight of air. Because the density of air decreases with gain in altitude, the balloon will rise to a height at which the density of the air equals the average density of the balloon. At that altitude it will float in the air much like a cork on water.

Dirigibles and most balloons designed to carry passengers are filled with helium. Helium is not flammable, whereas hydrogen and air form an explosive mixture. Barrage balloons for high-altitude protection against bombing are also filled with helium so that they cannot be shot down in flames. A typical barrage balloon is inflated with 68,000 cubic feet of helium and is capable of ascending to 15,000 feet.

Calculating the Lift of Lighter-Than-Air Craft. The lift of a balloon is equal to the difference between the weight of the gas and the weight of the air displaced. If the weight of a cubic foot of air is 1.2 oz, and the weight of a cubic foot of helium is 0.2 oz, the lift of a balloon filled with helium would be 1.0 oz per cu ft of helium in the balloon.

To make a balloon rise higher, its weight is decreased by throwing out ballast, such as water, sand bags, or other material. To bring a balloon down, some of its gas is released: the balloon sinks because its average density decreases. Dirigibles and blimps do not have to release gas to descend, for they have motors which propel them downward against the buoyant force of the air.

SPECIFIC WEIGHT

Specific Weight. Frequently it is necessary to compare the densities of two kinds of material. The standard of comparison for liquids and solids is water, which weighs 1 gram per cubic centimeter and 62.5 lb per cubic foot. *The number stating how many times denser than water a certain material is, is called the specific weight (or specific gravity) of that material.* For example, the specific weight of aluminum is 2.7; that is, aluminum is 2.7 times as dense as water, and any volume of aluminum weighs 2.7 times as much as an equal volume of water. Since 1 cc of water weighs 1 gram, 1 cc of aluminum weighs 2.7 grams. A cubic foot of aluminum weighs 168.75 lb, or 2.7 times as much as 1 cubic foot of water $(2.7 \times 62.5 = 168.75$ lb$)$. The specific gravity of platinum is 21.5. Hence, 1 cc of platinum, being 21.5 times as dense as water, weighs 21.5 grams. Because the specific weight of the human body is 1.07, the body does not quite float in fresh water.

Specific weight has no units. It has the same numerical value for the English system, metric system, and any other system of weights and measures. Density is weight per unit volume; its numerical value varies from one system to another.

Determining Specific Weight. *Specific weight is calculated by comparing the weight of a definite volume of the given material with the weight of the same volume of water.*

$$\text{specific weight} = \frac{\text{weight of definite volume of given material}}{\text{weight of the same volume of water}}$$

There are several methods of finding the weight of an equal volume of water.

Specific Weight of Solids Denser Than Water. The method depends on Archimedes' principle and the facts that (1) a sinking object displaces its own volume of water, and (2) the loss in weight of the object equals the weight of the water displaced. If we find the weight of the object in air, then:

$$\text{specific weight of a sinking solid} = \frac{\text{weight of object in air}}{\text{loss of weight in water}}$$

TYPICAL PROBLEM

A piece of metal weighs 500 g in air and 430 g in water. What is its specific weight?

$$\text{specific weight of metal} = \frac{\text{wt. of metal in air}}{\text{loss of wt. in water}} = \frac{500}{(500 - 430)} = 7.14$$

Specific Weight of Solids Less Dense Than Water. There is only one difference between this method and the preceding one: to make floating objects sink, we must attach a sinker to them. To find the weight of an equal volume of water, we must weigh the object with sinker attached: (*a*) when only the sinker is immersed, and (*b*) when both object and sinker are immersed. The loss in weight is caused by the buoyant force of the water displaced by the object.

$$\text{specific weight of floating object} =$$

$$\frac{\text{weight of object in air}}{\text{loss of weight caused by immersion of object in water}}$$

TYPICAL PROBLEM

A piece of material weighs 100 g in air (*a*). When a sinker is attached, but only the sinker is immersed in water, the combined weight is 170 g (*b*). When both sinker and material are immersed in water, the combined weight is 40 g (*c*). (1) What is the specific weight of the material? (2) What is the weight of 1 cubic foot of the material?

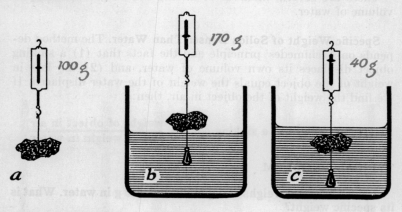

(1) specific weight of unknown material =

$$\text{specific weight of unknown material} = \frac{\text{wt. of object in air}}{\text{loss of weight caused by immersion of object in water}}$$

$$= \frac{100}{(170 - 40)} = 0.77$$

(2) weight of 1 cu ft = specific weight × weight of 1 cu ft of water

$$= 0.77 \times 62.5 \text{ lb} = 48.1 \text{ lb}$$

Specific Weight of Liquids. *The Bottle Method.* To compare the weight of a liquid with the weight of an equal volume of water, we need merely weigh the same volume of each. Weigh an empty bottle; then fill it with water and weigh it again. The difference in weight equals the weight of the water. Now empty the bottle and dry it. Fill it with the liquid whose specific weight is to be determined, and weigh it again. This difference in weight is equal to the weight of the liquid. Because the volume is constant,

$$\text{specific weight of the liquid} = \frac{\text{weight of liquid}}{\text{weight of water}}$$

The Hydrometer Method. A hydrometer is a hollow glass tube weighted with enough lead shot to make it float upright so that its stem is out of the liquid. The specific weight of the liquid can be read on the scale in the stem of the float. The hydrometer must displace its own weight of liquid in order to float, and therefore sinks deeper in liquids of lesser density than in liquids of greater density. Hence, the larger numbers are at the bottom and the smaller numbers at the top of the scale.

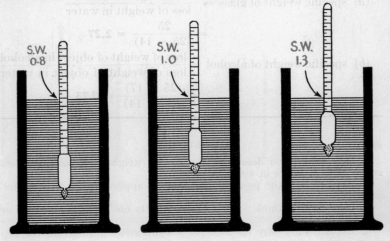

S.W. 0·8   S.W. 1·0   S.W. 1·3

The liquid in the center is water. The liquid on the left is less dense than water, that on the right is more dense. Note the relative depths of the floating hydrometers.

The Displacement Method. An insoluble solid object is used that will sink both in water and in the liquid whose specific weight is to be determined. The object is first weighed in air. It is then weighed while immersed in water, and again while immersed in the other liquid. The object displaces the same volume (its own volume) in water as in liquid, but it displaces different weights, i.e., it loses different amounts of weight in the two liquids. Since the weight lost in each liquid is equal to the weight of the liquid displaced, we see that the specific weight of the unknown liquid is given by the following formula:

$$\text{specific weight of the liquid} = \frac{\text{loss of weight of object in liquid}}{\text{loss of weight of object in water}}$$

TYPICAL PROBLEM

A piece of glass weighs 25 g in air, 14 g in water, and 17 g in alcohol. Find the specific weight (*a*) of the glass, (*b*) of the alcohol.

(*a*) specific weight of glass $= \dfrac{\text{weight in air}}{\text{loss of weight in water}}$

$$= \frac{25}{(25-14)} = 2.27$$

(*b*) specific weight of alcohol $= \dfrac{\text{loss of weight of object in alcohol}}{\text{loss of weight of object in water}}$

$$= \frac{(25-17)}{(25-14)} = 0.73$$

QUESTIONS

1. How would you determine the specific weight of a solid, such as sugar, that dissolves in water?

2. Explain how the pontoon bridge is an application of Archimedes' principle?

3. How do you think a deep breath affects one's ability to swim or float?

4. Explain fully why the scale of a hydrometer reads from the top downward.

5. What happens to the specific weight of milk (*a*) when the cream is removed? (*b*) when water is added? How could a hydrometer be used in testing milk?

6. If the *American Clipper* weighs 82,500 lb, fully loaded, why doesn't it sink when it lands on the sea?

7. Describe a laboratory experiment giving proof of Archimedes' principle.

8. Compare in as many ways as you can the descent of Beebe's bathysphere with the ascent of a stratosphere balloon.

PROBLEMS

1. A body weighs 100 g in air and 84 g in water. (*a*) What weight of water does it displace? (*b*) What volume of water does it displace? (*c*) What is its specific weight?   Ans. (a) 16 g (b) 16 cc (c) 6.25

2. Calculate the buoyant force on a 5-cm cube immersed in alcohol (density 0.8 g per cc) (*a*) to a depth of 10 cm; (*b*) to a depth of 25 cm.
Ans. (a) 100 g (b) 100 g

3. Two cubic feet of marble weigh 180 lb when submerged in water. (*a*) What volume of water does the marble displace? (*b*) What weight of water does the marble displace? (*c*) What is the weight of the marble in air? (*d*) What is the specific weight of the marble?
Ans. (a) 2 cu ft (b) 125 lb (c) 305 lb (d) 2.44

4. Hydrogen weighs 0.09 g per liter, helium 0.17 g per liter, and air 1.29 g per liter. Calculate the lift of 1000 liters (1 cubic meter) of (*a*) hydrogen, (*b*) helium. (*c*) Give the ratio between the lifting values of hydrogen and helium. Ans. (a) 1200 g (b) 1120 g (c) 1200:1120, or 1.07:1

5. (*a*) *The American Clipper,* one of the world's largest flying boats, weighs 82,500 lb fully loaded. How many cu ft of water does it displace when it lands on the sea? (*b*) The *Queen Elizabeth,* one of the world's largest ocean liners, weighs about 82,500 tons. How many cu ft of water does this ship displace? Ans. (a) 1320 cu ft (b) 2,640,000 cu ft

6. A barge 60 ft long and 20 ft wide is floating in sea water. Coke is loaded into the barge until it sinks 2 ft deeper into the water. What weight of coke was added to the barge? Ans. 153,500 lb

7. An empty bottle weighs 0.5 lb. Full of water it weighs 2.5 lb. Full of sulfuric acid it weighs 4.1 lb. What is (*a*) the specific weight of the acid? (*b*) the density of the acid? (*c*) the volume of the bottle?
Ans. (a) 1.8 (b) 112.5 lb/cu ft (c) 0.032 cu ft

8. A 100-g brass weight weighs 88 g in water and 85 g in brine. Find (*a*) the specific weight of the brass; (*b*) the specific weight of the brine.
Ans. (a) 8.33 (b) 1.25

9. A cube of steel 10 cm on each edge is weighed in air, and then when immersed in water, in carbon tetrachloride (specific weight = 1.6), and in turpentine. The cube weighed 6800 g in water, and 6920 g in turpentine. Find (*a*) the weight of the cube in air; (*b*) the weight of 1 cu ft of steel; (*c*) the weight of the cube in carbon tetrachloride; (*d*) the specific weight of the turpentine.
Ans. (a) 7800 g (b) 488 lb (c) 6200 g (d) 0.88

10. A block of paraffin weighs 50 g in air and a sinker weighs 270 g in water. When both are attached and submerged in water they weigh 264 g. (*a*) What is the weight of the sinker in water and the paraffin in air? (*b*) What is the weight of water displaced when the paraffin is submerged? (*c*) What volume of water does this weight represent? (*d*) What is the volume of the paraffin? (*e*) Calculate the specific weight of the paraffin. Ans. (a) 320 g (b) 56 g (c) 56 cc (d) 56 cc (e) 0.893

FIVE

SIMPLE AND COMPOUND MACHINES

Work. You have probably seen a heavy safe being hoisted by a block and tackle. The pull of gravity keeps the safe down until enough force (*pull* or *push*) is used to lift the safe. Force is needed to lift the safe from one point to another against the *resistance of gravity*. While the safe is at rest, either on the ground or in mid-air, no work is being done. Work is done only while the force, which overcomes the downward pull of gravity, moves the safe upward. In the same way, when you push a book with your finger, you do no work if you fail to move the book. But if you exert enough force, you will overcome the *resistance of friction* and succeed in moving the book, thereby doing work. *Work may, therefore, be defined as the overcoming of resistance through any distance.*

TYPICAL PROBLEM

How much work is done when you apply a force of ten pounds to pull a cart three feet?

Multiply the force (10 lb) by the distance through which the force acts (3 ft).

$$\text{work} = \text{force} \times \text{distance}$$
$$= F \times D$$
$$= 10 \text{ lb} \times 3 \text{ ft} = \textbf{30 ft-lb}$$

Further examples:

1. A weight is lifted 10 ft by a force of 10 lb. To find the amount of work done, multiply the force by the vertical distance through which the weight moves. The amount of work done is:

$$W = F \times D = 10 \text{ lb} \times 10 \text{ ft} = \textbf{100 ft-lb}$$

2. A table exerts an upward force to support a book. Because the book is not moved, no work is done.

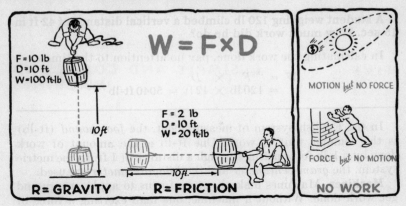

The Principle of Work

3. Work is done only when the force acts *in the direction of motion*. If a body moves at right angles to a force acting on it, no work is done by that force. Thus the force of gravitation holds the earth in its orbit around the sun, but this force is at right angles to the earth's motion—hence no work is done.

TYPICAL PROBLEMS

To be loaded into a gun, a shell weighing 60 lb was lifted 4 ft from the ground. How much work was done?

It takes a force of 60 lb to lift the shell vertically. Multiply this force by the distance through which the force acts:

$$W = F \times D$$
$$= 60\,\text{lb} \times 4\,\text{ft} = \textbf{240 ft-lb}$$

A force of 50 lb, exerted parallel to the slope of a hill, pushed a loaded cart weighing 300 lb a distance of 10 ft along the hill. How much work was done?

$$W = F \times D$$
$$= 50\,\text{lb} \times 10\,\text{ft} = \textbf{500 ft-lb}$$

Note: It is the force in the direction of motion (50 lb), not the weight, that determines the work done.

A student weighing 120 lb climbed a vertical distance of 42 ft in 15 sec. How much work did he do?

In calculating the work done, pay no attention to the time.

$$W = F \times D$$
$$= 120\,\text{lb} \times 42\,\text{ft} = \textbf{5040 ft-lb}$$

In the English system of measurement, the *foot-pound* (ft-lb) is the common unit of work. One ft-lb is the amount of work done by a 1-lb force acting through a distance of 1 ft. In the metric system, the *gram-centimeter* and the *kilogram-meter* are used.

Machines. Machines make it easier for us to apply energy and get work done. Without a machine, one man exerting a force of 100 lb could not lift a 500-lb piano; the weight offers too much resistance to his effort. By using a *machine,* such as a system of pulleys and ropes, he can raise the piano with the same force of 100 lb. The machine multiplies the force he applies and thus overcomes the resistance of gravity. Machines may also be used to increase the *speed* of work. You can carry a package a mile in about 20 minutes. But you can do the same errand in about 5 min if you use a bicycle. Sometimes, a machine is used only because it changes the direction of the force, without multiplying either force or speed. With a single fixed pulley, for example, we can lift a weight by pulling down instead of up.

Force and Speed in Machines. Whenever a machine multiplies the effort force, and produces motion against a greater resistance, it will be found that the effort force moves through a greater distance than the resistance does. In the simple lever on page 51, a small effort (E) moving through a relatively large distance (D_E), causes the large resistance (R) to move through the smaller distance (D_R). Since both movements occur in the same time interval, it is clear that the effort had to move *faster* (as well as farther) than the resistance. In other words, we have obtained an increase in force with a reduction in speed.

The converse is true of machines used to *increase* the speed. In such machines, the motion against the resistance occurs at greater speed, but the resistance is then smaller than the applied effort. We have gained speed at the expense of force. The bicycle is an example of a machine used to multiply speed of motion.

A machine cannot multiply both force and speed at the same

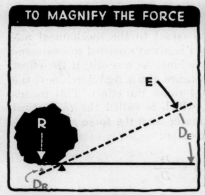

TO MAGNIFY THE FORCE

E

R

D_E

D_R

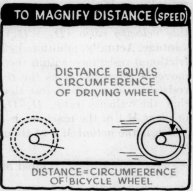

TO MAGNIFY DISTANCE (SPEED)

DISTANCE EQUALS
CIRCUMFERENCE
OF DRIVING WHEEL

DISTANCE = CIRCUMFERENCE
OF BICYCLE WHEEL

Machines Magnify Force or Speed. In the bicycle, the effort is applied to the chain which exerts a turning force on the small driving wheel. When the chain unwinds a distance equal to the circumference of the small wheel, the large wheel also makes one revolution and the whole bicycle moves forward a distance equal to the circumference of the large wheel. The bicycle moves forward much faster than the speed at which the chain moves.

time. If a small force moving through a small distance could move a large force through a large distance, the work done by the machine ($W = F \times D$) would be greater than the work put into the machine. This is never possible, since work (which is really energy) can never be created—it can only be transferred from one place to another by machines. (See "Law of Conservation of Energy," pp. 87–88.)

Mechanical Advantage. If an effort force of 5 lb is sufficient to move a resistance of 20 lb, the machine which enables us to do that is said to have a *mechanical advantage* of 4 (obtained by dividing the resistance, 20, by the effort, 5). In general, the mechanical advantage of a machine is the ratio between the resistance overcome and the effort applied:

$$MA = \frac{\text{resistance}}{\text{effort}} = \frac{R}{E}$$

This is the *actual MA* of the machine.

In the preceding section we saw that a machine which theoretically multiplies the force by 4 requires the effort to move 4 times as far (or as fast) as the resistance. Thus, theoretically, this *velocity ratio* $(D_E \div D_R)$ is equal to the mechanical advantage. Actually, additional effort is always needed to overcome frictional resistance within the machine. As a result, if the effort moves 4 times as far as the resistance (in a real machine), the resistance overcome is *less* than 4 times the effort. This means that the velocity ratio, D_E/D_R, which is called the *theoretical* or *ideal MA* of the machine, is greater than the force ratio, R/E, which is the *actual MA* of the machine:

$$\text{ideal } MA = \frac{D_E}{D_R}$$

$$\text{actual } MA = \frac{R}{E}$$

$$\text{ideal } MA > \text{actual } MA$$

The Law of Machines. The work done *on* a machine is called *input,* and equals the product of the effort force and the effort distance. The work done *by* a machine is called *output,* and is equal to the product of the resistance and the resistance distance. In other words,

$$\text{input} = E \times D_E$$
$$\text{output} = R \times D_R$$

Theoretically, input should equal output; actually, *input is always greater than output,* because some of the input is used to overcome the friction of the machine. The energy lost turns into heat, so that there is no violation of the law of conservation of energy. The law of machines may be stated as follows:

input = useful work output + losses caused by friction

Friction. Friction is a force which interferes with the sliding or rolling of one body over another. Because of the friction in machines,

$$\frac{D_E}{D_R} \text{ (ideal } MA) > \frac{R}{E} \text{ (actual } MA)$$

$$E \times D_E \text{ (work input)} > R \times D_R \text{ (useful work output)}$$

When choosing a machine for a given task, we consider the *efficiency* of the machine, that is, what percentage of the input will be changed into useful work. A machine that does 75 ft-lb of work when 100 ft-lb of work is done on the machine, is 75% efficient. To determine the efficiency of any machine, *divide the output by the input*:

$$\text{efficiency} = \frac{\text{output}}{\text{input}} = \frac{R \times D_R}{E \times D_E}$$

Actual $MA = R/E$; ideal $MA = D_E/D_R$. Therefore,

$$\frac{\text{actual } MA}{\text{ideal } MA} = \frac{R}{E} \div \frac{D_E}{D_R} = \frac{R}{E} \times \frac{D_R}{D_E} = \text{efficiency}$$

Thus we see that the efficiency of a machine can be determined by dividing its actual MA by its ideal MA.

The efficiency is usually expressed as a per cent, rather than as a decimal or fraction. A machine with an efficiency of .75 has an efficiency of 75%.

Advantages and Disadvantages of Friction. Friction in machines wastes energy. Furthermore, as one surface of any body is moved over another, the energy used up by friction is transformed into heat. "Hot boxes" on axles, and burned-out bearings (really melted bearings) on machines, are among the harmful results of frictional heating.

But friction is often advantageous—in fact, necessary. Friction is used to start and stop machines. If there were no friction, the wheels of automobiles and locomotives would fail to grip the surface and would spin uselessly. Brakes for stopping these vehicles depend on friction for their action. The clutch, which relays driving power from the engine to the driving shaft, utilizes friction. Without friction, the clutch would spin around and fail to catch. The chains on automobile wheels and the treads on tanks produce much desirable friction. When sand or ashes are put on wet, slippery roads, icy pavements, etc., the increased friction helps to prevent slipping or skidding. Without friction, all ordinary activities would be impossible.

Factors on Which Friction Depends. The primary cause of friction is the minute irregularities on the rubbing surfaces. Rough surfaces offer more friction than smooth ones. If the surfaces rubbing against each other are highly polished, or if oil, grease, soap, graphite, or other lubricant is used between them, friction will be greatly reduced. In the latter case, the surfaces slide on the lubricant instead of on each other. It is important to select a lubricant of the correct grade (viscosity); if it is too "thin," the lubricant will be squeezed out from between the two surfaces; if it is too "sticky," its own internal friction will retard the motion of the surfaces.

Because certain alloys, such as Babbitt metal, give comparatively little friction, these alloys are used as bearing surfaces in automobile and aircraft engines and around the axles of heavy machinery.

An airplane in flight offers resistance to the airflow. Part of this resistance consists of the friction of air as it passes over the surfaces of the fuselage, vertical and horizontal tail surfaces, etc. Such friction is known as *skin friction*. To reduce skin friction, the skin of airliners is waxed frequently. Another kind of friction is *ground friction*. On take-off runs, ground friction is produced as the airplane tires roll along the surface of the airfield. The amount of friction depends on the type of surface. If the surface is hard and smooth, there is less ground friction, and the take-off run may be comparatively short; if the surface is uneven or soft, as in the case of soft earth, long grass, or turf, there is more ground friction, and the take-off run has to be longer.

1. The first factor upon which friction depends is, therefore, the *nature of the substances in contact*. This factor can be expressed mathematically, as shown later, by the coefficient of friction between the two surfaces.

2. The amount of friction between two objects depends also on the *force pressing their surfaces together*.

A spring holds the plates of an automobile clutch in tight contact, thus producing enough friction to transmit the engine force to the drive shaft. When the clutch pedal is depressed slightly, the force pressing the plates together is relaxed, and the clutch begins to slip—less friction is being developed. As the pedal is depressed further, less friction is produced and more slipping occurs. Vises, set screws, nuts and bolts prevent slipping when they are tightened because they exert greater force on the surfaces in contact.

Starting friction is greater than sliding friction. Apart from the force needed to overcome inertia, it takes more force to start a sled in motion over snow than to keep it moving. This is true because once started, the surfaces tend to "ride up" on each other, so that the "gripping action" of the hills and depressions in the surfaces is reduced.

Sliding friction is greater than rolling friction, when the surfaces are hard,—hence the use of wheels, ball bearings, and roller bearings. In soft ground, however, sliding friction is less than rolling friction, because wheels tend to sink into soft ground, while flat treads and skis ride the surface without sinking. Airplanes designed to land and take off on snow are equipped with skis instead of wheels.

3. The third factor in friction is thus the *kind of motion* involved.

Coefficient of Friction. In dry friction (friction between dry surfaces) the amount of the frictional force depends only on the force pressing the surfaces together; it is *not* affected by the *area* of the surfaces in contact. Thus it takes just as much force to drag a brick along on a narrow side as it does when the brick is resting on a wide side, because the force (weight of the brick) pressing the surfaces together is the same in each case. The frictional resistance is doubled, however, for a brick which weighs twice as much. Thus the resistance of friction is proportional to the force perpendicular to the surfaces, as expressed by the following formula:

$$\text{force of friction} = K \times \text{force perpendicular to surface}$$

The constant, K, is called the *coefficient of friction*. From the equation above, we see that:

$$\text{coefficient of friction } (K) = \frac{\text{force of friction}}{\text{force perpendicular to surface}}$$

When a body is resting on a horizontal surface, the force perpendicular to the surface is the weight of the body.

TYPICAL PROBLEMS

A trunk weighing 200 lb is to be dragged across a wooden floor. What force is needed if the coefficient of sliding friction is 0.20?

force of friction = coefficient of friction × force perpendicular to surface

$$= 0.20 \times 200 = \textbf{40 lb}$$

What force is needed to start the trunk moving, if the coefficient of static friction is 0.22?

$$\text{force needed} = 0.22 \times 200 = \textbf{44 lb}$$

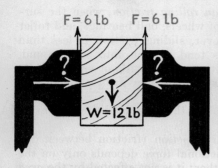

A block weighing 12 lb is to be supported in a vise as shown. What force must the vise exert on each face of the block if the coefficient of friction is 0.18? (*Note: Friction is produced on both faces.*)

Total force of friction must equal weight of block; friction on each face must be half the weight of block (6 lb on each face).

$$\text{perpendicular force} = \frac{\text{force of friction}}{\text{coefficient of friction}}$$

$$= \frac{6}{0.18} = \textbf{33.3 lb}$$

Simple Machines. Most machines consist essentially of combinations of certain fundamental machine types. There are six such simple machines: the pulley, the wheel-and-axle, the inclined plane, the wedge, the screw, and the lever. A can opener, a screwdriver, a knife blade, a nut and bolt, and an airplane propeller are examples of simple machines. When one simple machine acts upon another so that they work together to perform a given task, the combination is called a *compound machine.* The most complicated machines are merely combinations of simple machines. The typewriter is a compound machine composed chiefly of levers.

In analyzing the characteristics of any machine, whether simple or compound, we need to consider only four factors: effort force (E), resistance force (R), effort distance (D_E), and resistance distance (D_R). We have already seen that these factors are related as shown by the following formulas:

(1) ideal $M A = \dfrac{D_E}{D_R}$

(2) actual $MA = \dfrac{R}{E}$

(3) input $= E \times D_E$

(4) output $= R \times D_R$

(5) efficiency $= \dfrac{\text{output}}{\text{input}} = \dfrac{R \times D_R}{E \times D_E}$

(6) efficiency $= \dfrac{\text{actual } MA}{\text{ideal } MA}$

The Pulley. The pulley is a grooved wheel or disc mounted on a fixed axis and supported by a frame. A rope is fitted into and runs over the grooved wheel. The grooved wheel is called the *sheave* (or *sheaf*). The frame is called the *block*. In a *block and tackle*, there is a pair of blocks each of which contains one or more pulleys, and a rope connecting the pulleys. The block and

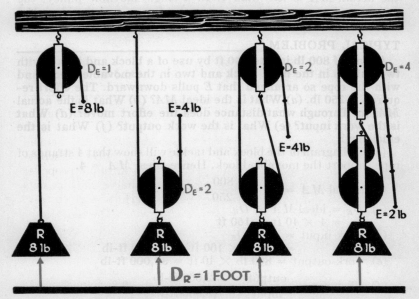

Several Pulley Combinations. The number of feet of rope pulled out when the resistance moves up 1 foot is equal to the ideal MA of the machine. Compare with the number of strands supporting the load in each case.

tackle is widely used on the farm; in the factory, shop, and garage; around docks, for loading and unloading ships; and elsewhere, for such tasks as hoisting pianos, painter's scaffoldings, safes, and derricks.

There are two ways to find the ideal mechanical advantage (velocity ratio) of any pulley system: (1) measure the number of feet of rope pulled out when the resistance moves 1 ft; or (2) count the number of rope strands that support or move the *movable* block. The actual mechanical advantage is found, of course, by measuring the effort and the resistance, and dividing R by E. As indicated in the illustrations, pulleys may be used either singly or in various combinations. The velocity ratio of a single fixed pulley is 1; only one strand of rope supports the load, and $D_E = D_R$. Actually, because of friction, $E > R$; hence, the actual MA is less than 1. In a single movable pulley, the resistance is supported by two strands of rope, and the ideal MA is 2. The other pulley systems are analyzed in similar fashion.

TYPICAL PROBLEM

A load of 800 lb is lifted 40 ft by use of a block and tackle with two pulleys in the fixed block and two in the movable block, and with the rope so arranged that E pulls downward. The effort required is 250 lb. (*a*) What is the ideal MA? (*b*) What is the actual MA? (*c*) Through what distance does the effort move? (*d*) What is the work input? (*e*) What is the work output? (*f*) What is the efficiency?

(*a*) A diagram of the block and tackle will show that 4 strands of rope support the movable block. Hence, ideal $MA = 4$.

(*b*) actual $MA = \dfrac{R}{E} = \dfrac{800}{250} = 3.2$

(*c*) $D_E = \text{ideal } MA \times D_R$
$= 4 \times 40 \text{ ft} = 160 \text{ ft}$

(*d*) work input $= E \times D_E$
$= 250 \text{ lb} \times 160 \text{ ft} = 40{,}000 \text{ ft-lb}$

(*e*) work output $= 800 \text{ lb} \times 40 \text{ ft} = 32{,}000 \text{ ft-lb}$

(*f*) efficiency $= \dfrac{\text{output}}{\text{input}} = \dfrac{32{,}000 \text{ ft-lb}}{40{,}000 \text{ ft-lb}} = 0.8$

$$0.8 \times 100 = 80\%$$

Also, efficiency $= \dfrac{\text{actual } MA}{\text{ideal } MA} = \dfrac{3.2}{4.0} = 0.8$

$$0.8 \times 100 = 80\%$$

Wheel-and-Axle. The wheel-and-axle is used either to overcome a great resistance with a small force, or to produce rapid motion. To gain force, the effort is applied on the wheel; to gain speed, the effort is applied on the axle. The wheel-and-axle arrangement is found in such devices as: the windlass for drawing water from a well; the steering wheel of an automobile; the driving wheel-and-axle of an automobile; the capstan for raising a ship's anchor; the doorknob; and the gears in watches, clocks, and various kinds of machinery. Note that a wheel-and-axle consists of two parts: (1) either a wheel or a crank; and (2) either an axle or a smaller wheel. Both parts, rigidly attached to each other, turn together about a common center.

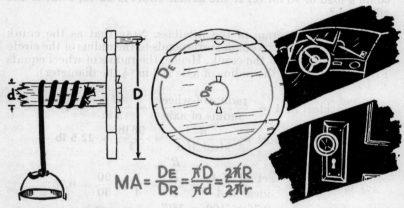

$$MA = \frac{D_E}{D_R} = \frac{\pi D}{\pi d} = \frac{2\pi R}{2\pi r}$$

The Wheel-and-Axle. D_E and D_R for one revolution of the machine are shown in red. Note that these distances are proportional to the diameters (and radii) of the wheels.

As in all machines, to find the MA, divide D_E by D_R. For each revolution of the wheel, the axle also makes one revolution. The effort force moves around the circumference of the wheel (or the crank), while the resistance force moves around the circumference of the axle. Hence,

$$\text{ideal } MA = \frac{D_E}{D_R} = \frac{\text{circumference of wheel}}{\text{circumference of axle}} =$$

$$\frac{\pi \times \text{diam. of wheel } (D)}{\pi \times \text{diam. of axle } (d)} = \frac{2\pi \times \text{radius of wheel } (R)}{2\pi \times \text{radius of axle } (r)}$$

Since π and 2π cancel out:

$$\text{ideal } MA = \frac{\text{diameter of wheel}}{\text{diameter of axle}} = \frac{\text{radius of wheel}}{\text{radius of axle}}$$

$$\text{ideal } MA = \frac{D}{d} = \frac{R}{r}$$

TYPICAL PROBLEM

The crank of a windlass is 1 ft long. The axle, on which the rope is wound, has a diameter of 6 in. (*a*) What is the ideal *MA*? (*b*) What force applied to the crank is theoretically needed to overcome a load of 90 lb? (*c*) If the actual effort is 30 lb, what is the efficiency?

(*a*) Draw a diagram of the windlass. Note that as the crank turns, the length of the crank corresponds to the radius of the circle formed by the end of the crank. Hence, the radius of wheel equals 1 ft, or 12 in, while the radius of axle is 3 in ($\frac{1}{2}$ the diameter).

$$\text{ideal } MA = \frac{\text{radius of wheel}}{\text{radius of axle}} = \frac{12 \text{ in}}{3 \text{ in}} = 4$$

$$(b) \text{ theoretical effort} = \frac{R}{\text{ideal } MA} = \frac{90 \text{ lb}}{4} = 22.5 \text{ lb}$$

$$(c) \text{ efficiency} = \frac{\text{actual } MA}{\text{ideal } MA} = \frac{\dfrac{R}{E}}{4} = \frac{1}{4} \times \frac{90}{30} = 0.75;$$

$$0.75 \times 100 = 75\%$$

The Inclined Plane. Anyone who rolls or slides an object up a slanting plank which extends from the ground to a higher level,

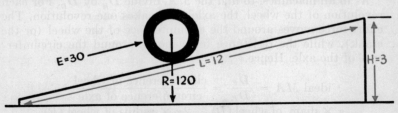

The Inclined Plane

is using the inclined plane. This arrangement is used because the object is too heavy to be lifted vertically against the pull of gravity. The resistance force (gravity) is overcome through the vertical height of the plane. The effort force, however, acts through the entire length of the plane. For this simple machine,

$$\text{ideal } MA = \frac{D_E}{D_R} = \frac{\text{length of plane}}{\text{height of plane}}$$

As in all machines, actual $MA = \dfrac{R}{E}$.

Ramps and stairways are examples of the inclined plane; so is an automobile road or railroad bed winding up a mountain. The "grade" or slope of a road is calculated as a per cent which gives the ratio of the height to the length of the inclined plane. Thus, a 4% grade is one which rises 4 ft for each 100 ft of length. The more gradual the slope, the greater is the mechanical advantage of the inclined plane. For this reason, mountain roads wind back and forth as they ascend gradually to higher levels.

TYPICAL PROBLEM

A plank 12 ft long extends from the ground to a platform 4 ft high. A push of 120 lb is required to roll a 270-lb barrel up the plank. (*a*) What is the ideal *MA* of the incline? (*b*) What is the actual *MA*? (*c*) What is the efficiency? (*d*) How much work is done against gravity? (*e*) How much work is done in overcoming friction?

(*a*) ideal $MA = \dfrac{D_E}{D_R} = \dfrac{12 \text{ ft}}{4 \text{ ft}} = 3$

(*b*) actual $MA = \dfrac{R}{E} = \dfrac{270 \text{ lb}}{120 \text{ lb}} = 2.25$

(*c*) efficiency $= \dfrac{\text{actual } MA}{\text{ideal } MA} = \dfrac{2.25}{3} = 75\%$

(*d*) work output $= R \times D_R = 270 \text{ lb} \times 4 \text{ ft} = 1080 \text{ ft-lb}$

(*e*) work to overcome friction $=$ work input $-$ work output

$\qquad\qquad = (E \times D_E) - (R \times D_R)$

$\qquad\qquad = (120 \text{ lb} \times 12 \text{ ft}) - (270 \text{ lb} \times 4 \text{ ft})$

$\qquad\qquad = 360 \text{ ft-lb}$

The Wedge. This machine consists of two inclined planes with their bases together. Examples are: the prow of a boat; the edge of a knife, ax, chisel, or other cutting tool; a pin, needle, or nail. The mechanical advantage of the wedge depends on the ratio of its length to its thickness. A long, thin wedge gives a larger mechanical advantage than a short, thick one. In actual use, friction of the wedge is so great and so variable that any attempt to calculate its theoretical *MA* would have no practical meaning.

The Screw. The various types of screws, such as the jackscrews used to support a building during repairs, may also be regarded as modifications of the inclined plane. If unwound, the thread of the screw would assume the shape of an inclined plane. Among examples of the screw are: the turnbuckle, the mechanic's vise, a nut and bolt, a micrometer caliper, a corkscrew, and the propeller of an airplane or of a boat.

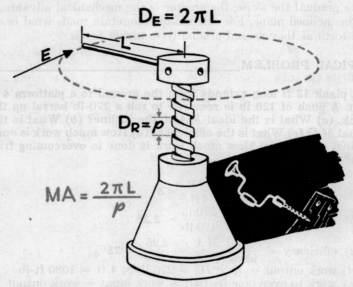

$$D_E = 2\pi L$$

$$D_R = p$$

$$MA = \frac{2\pi L}{p}$$

The Jackscrew. Effort distance and resistance distance for one revolution are shown in red.

The ordinary jackscrew has a large, stationary base and a cylindrical screw which fits into the base. There are openings in the head of the screw, so that a strong rod of suitable length can be inserted to turn the screw. The object to be lifted is supported by the head of the screw. The velocity ratio of the screw is calculated on the basis of one revolution of the screw. During this revolution, the effort moves through a distance equal to the circumference of the circle described by the point of application; that is,

$$D_E = 2\pi \times \text{length of handle}$$

Meanwhile, the resistance is lifted against gravity through the distance between two successive threads of the screw; this distance is called the *pitch* of the screw. Hence,

$$\text{ideal } MA = \frac{D_E}{D_R} = \frac{2\pi \times \text{length of handle}}{\text{pitch}} = \frac{2\pi L}{p}$$

Actual MA, of course, equals R divided by E.

TYPICAL PROBLEM

A jackscrew has a pitch of 0.25 in and a lever arm 16 in long. A load of 2 tons is to be lifted. (*a*) What theoretical effort (in lb) is needed? (*b*) If an actual effort of 65 lb is required, what is the actual MA of the jack? (*c*) Calculate the efficiency. (*d*) Calculate the work done to overcome friction for one turn of the screw.

(*a*) ideal $MA = \dfrac{2\pi L}{p} = \dfrac{2 \times 3.14 \times 16 \text{ in}}{0.25 \text{ in}} = 402$

theoretical $E = \dfrac{R}{\text{ideal } MA} = \dfrac{4000 \text{ lb}}{402} = $ **9.95 lb**

(*b*) actual $MA = \dfrac{R}{\text{actual } E} = \dfrac{4000 \text{ lb}}{65 \text{ lb}} = $ **61.5**

(*c*) efficiency $= \dfrac{\text{actual } MA}{\text{ideal } MA} = \dfrac{61.5}{402} \times 100 = $ **15.3%**

(*d*) work against friction = input − output

$= (E \times D_E) - (R \times D_R)$
$= (65 \text{ lb} \times 2 \times 3.14 \times 16 \text{ in}) - (4000 \text{ lb} \times 0.25 \text{ in})$
$= 6540 \text{ in-lb} - 1000 \text{ in-lb} = $ **5540 in-lb**

$\dfrac{5540 \text{ in-lb}}{12 \dfrac{\text{in}}{\text{ft}}} = $ **462 ft-lb**

The screw gives the largest *MA* of all the simple machines, but it also has the greatest amount of friction. Consequently, in the jackscrew, the actual *MA*, although large, is considerably below expectation, and the efficiency of this machine is comparatively low. However, the high friction is desirable to keep the machine from slipping backward under a heavy load.

Levers. A lever is a rigid bar upon which a force, the effort, is applied to overcome a second force, the resistance. The fulcrum (*F*) is the point of support, or pivot point (usually fixed) about which the lever turns or tends to turn. The *effort arm* (*EF*) of a lever is the distance from the fulcrum to the point at which the effort is applied. The *resistance arm* (*RF*) is the distance from *R* to *F*. Note that, as indicated in the illustrations on the following page, levers are divided into three classes according to the relative positions of fulcrum, resistance, and effort.

Mechanical Advantage of the Lever. Study the following diagram. The black line shows the original position of the lever.

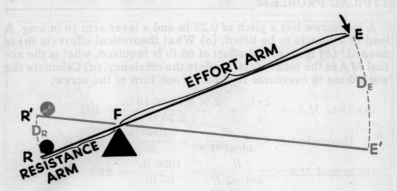

When the lever is moved to the position shown in red, the effort has moved through the distance D_E, and by action of the lever has caused the resistance to be lifted through the distance D_R. The distance D_E is an arc of a circle whose radius is EF; similarly, the distance D_R is an arc of a circle whose radius is RF. Since angle $EFE' = RFR'$, it can be seen that

$$\frac{D_E}{D_R} = \frac{EF}{RF} = \frac{\text{effort arm}}{\text{resistance arm}}$$

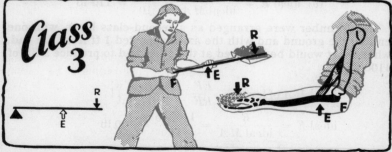

Therefore the ideal MA of a lever is:

$$\text{ideal } MA = \frac{D_E}{D_R} = \frac{\text{effort arm}}{\text{resistance arm}}$$

If we experiment with three levers equal in length but arrange one as a first-, one as a second-, and one as a third-class lever, we shall discover the following results.

1. The first-class lever can be arranged to give an ideal MA either more or less than 1.

2. The second-class lever can be arranged to give a greater mechanical advantage than either of the other two classes, because the effort arm in the second-class lever can be made longer than the effort arm in either of the other classes. Furthermore, the effort arm of a second-class lever is always longer than its resistance arm; hence, levers of this class cannot be used to multiply speed.

3. In the third-class lever, the effort arm is always shorter than the resistance arm. Levers of this class, therefore, multiply speed at the expense of force; their velocity ratio must be less than 1.

TYPICAL PROBLEMS

A timber 11 ft long, arranged as a first-class lever, is used to lift the wheel of a truck out of the mud. The fulcrum is placed 1 ft from the axle, and the axle is at the end of the timber. Effort is exerted at the other end of the timber. (*a*) What is the ideal MA of the lever? (*b*) What effort is needed to lift the wheel if the wheel supports a load of 1100 lb?

$$(a) \text{ ideal } MA \text{ of lever} = \frac{EF}{RF} = \frac{10\,\text{ft}}{1\,\text{ft}} = 10$$

$$(b) \text{ ideal } E = \frac{R}{\text{ideal } MA} = \frac{1100}{10} = 110\,\text{lb}$$

If the timber were arranged as a second–class lever, with one end on the ground and with the axle supported 1 ft from the end, what effort would be required at the other end to produce a lift of 1100 lb?

$$\text{ideal } MA \text{ of lever} = \frac{EF}{RF} = \frac{11\,\text{ft}}{1\,\text{ft}} = 11$$

$$\text{ideal } E = \frac{R}{\text{ideal } MA} = \frac{1100\,\text{lb}}{11} = 100\,\text{lb}$$

Applications of Levers. The lever is undoubtedly one of the most ancient machines. Even today, it is one of the most useful. Whenever a mechanic uses a pry, he is making use of a lever. In emergencies, if a jack is not available, a heavy plank or a small tree can be used as a lever to lift the wheel of a car or truck out of the mud. Familiar examples of levers are: sugar tongs; a hammer when pulling a nail; a shovel; scissors and shears; the oars of a rowboat; and the steering mechanism of an automobile. The linkage systems for controlling the rudder, tail-wheel, ailerons, and elevators of an airplane are constructed of levers which transmit motion and force by means of cables and single fixed pulleys. The muscles and bones of the human body form a series of levers, most of which are of the third class; the forearm is an example.

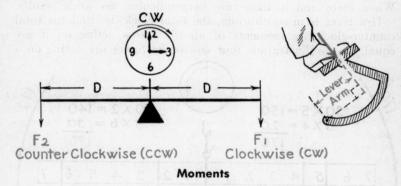

CW

F₂
Counter Clockwise (CCW)   F₁
                     Clockwise (CW)

Moments

Levers and the Principle of Moments. Consider a balanced lever, such as the see-saw, with arms of equal length and with equal forces acting on each arm. Each force, acting on its lever arm, *tends* to make the bar turn or rotate about the fulcrum. F_1 tends to produce *clockwise*, or positive, rotation; and F_2 tends to produce *counter-clockwise*, or negative, rotation. These two opposing tendencies must be equal, for there is no rotation in either direction; that is, the lever is balanced, or in equilibrium. If a larger force were substituted for one of the forces, or if either force were moved nearer to the fulcrum, the lever would begin to turn. Whether it turned clockwise or counter-clockwise would depend on which force produced the greater turning effect.

The *moment* of a force about a point is the measure of the turning effect of that force about that point. Numerically, the moment of a force is equal to the product of the force and the *perpendicular distance* from the point to the line of action (or direction) of the force. This perpendicular distance is called the *lever arm* of the force.

A force of 10 lb acting at the end of a lever arm 5 ft long has a moment of $10 \times 5 = 50$ *lb-ft*. A force of 10 g with a lever arm of 5 cm would have a moment of 50 *g-cm*. Thus a moment *appears* to have the units of work—force × distance. *Actually a moment is **not** equivalent to work.* In a moment, the force is multiplied by a distance *at right angles* to the direction of the force; we have already seen (p. 49) that work results only when a force is multiplied by a distance *in the direction* of the force. When force and distance are perpendicular, no work results.

If a lever is in equilibrium, the total clockwise and the total counter-clockwise moments of all the forces acting on it are equal. In the illustration, four downward forces are acting on a

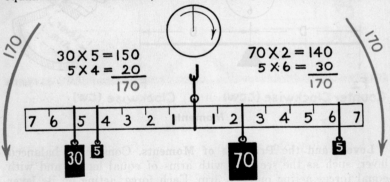

bar which is in equilibrium. The total clockwise and the total counter-clockwise moments are calculated as follows:

COUNTER-CLOCKWISE	CLOCKWISE
Force $\times \dfrac{\text{Lever}}{\text{Arm}}$ = Moment	Force $\times \dfrac{\text{Lever}}{\text{Arm}}$ = Moment
30 (lb) $\times$ 5 (ft) = 150 lb-ft	70 (lb) $\times$ 2 (ft) = 140 lb-ft
5 (lb) $\times$ 4 (ft) = 20 lb-ft	5 (lb) $\times$ 6 (ft) = 30 lb-ft
CCW Moments = 170 lb-ft	*CW Moments* = 170 lb-ft

The *law of moments* states that in a body in equilibrium *the sum of the clockwise moments is equal to the sum of the counterclockwise moments* about any point. This law can be used in solving all lever problems. When you apply the law of moments to a problem, draw a diagram to represent the situation, and indicate clearly on the diagram: (1) the magnitude and location of each force; (2) the perpendicular distance from each force to the fulcrum; and (3) any unknowns to be calculated. Remember, also, that the sum of the upward forces equals the sum of the downward forces, for any body in equilibrium.

TYPICAL PROBLEMS

A balanced plank rests on a fulcrum at its center. A 75-lb boy is seated 5 ft from the fulcrum. (*a*) To maintain balance, how far from the fulcrum, on the other end of the plank, should a 125-lb boy sit?

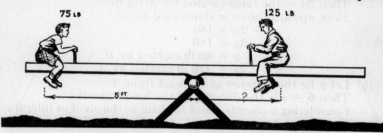

$$CCW \text{ moments} = CW \text{ moments}$$
$$75 \text{ lb} \times 5 \text{ ft} = 125 \text{ lb} \times x \text{ ft}$$
$$x = 3 \text{ ft}$$

(*b*) A 50-lb boy joins the 75-lb boy and sits 4 ft from the fulcrum. To maintain balance, what should be the new distance from the 125-lb boy to the fulcrum?

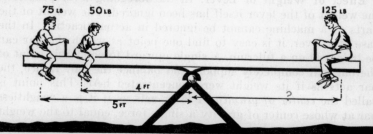

$$CCW \text{ moments} = CW \text{ moments}$$
$$(75\,\text{lb} \times 5\,\text{ft}) + (50\,\text{lb} \times 4\,\text{ft}) = 125\,\text{lb} \times x\,\text{ft}$$
$$x = \frac{375 + 200}{125} = 4.6\,\text{ft}$$

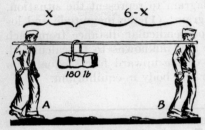

Two soldiers (A and B) carry a 180-lb case of ammunition between them supported from a 6-ft pole. A holds one end of the pole, while B holds the other end. A carries twice as much load as B. (a) What is the force exerted by each? (b) What is the distance of the load from A?

(a) Let y be the force exerted by B (in lb)
Then $2y$ = the force exerted by A (in lb)
Since upward forces = downward forces,
$$y + 2y = 180$$
$$3y = 180$$
$$y = 60\,\text{lb exerted by } B$$
$$2y = 120\,\text{lb exerted by } A$$

(b) Let x be the distance of the load from A
Then $6 - x$ is the distance of the load from B
Considering moments about the load as the pivot or fulcrum:
Force of A × lever arm of A = force of B × lever arm of B
$$120x = 60(6 - x)$$
$$120x = 360 - 60x$$
$$180x = 360$$
$$x = 2\,\text{ft, distance of load from } A$$
$$6 - x = 4\,\text{ft, distance of load from } B$$

Effect of Weight of Lever. In the foregoing lever problems, the weight of the lever itself has been ignored. The weight of the parts of a machine cannot be ignored in actual practice. In the case of a lever, it is easy to find one point at which the bar can be balanced on a fulcrum. A single upward force at this point of the bar will completely support and balance the bar. Hence, the bar acts as if its weight were concentrated here. This point is called the *center of gravity*. A lever acts as if it is a weightless bar at whose center of gravity a single force, equal to the weight of the lever, is exerted downward. This force exerts moments just as though it were an actual weight suspended on the lever.

TYPICAL PROBLEM

A 6-ft shovel weighs 20 lb and balances when supported on a fulcrum placed $1\frac{3}{4}$ ft from the shovel end. An unknown weight is hung 6 in from the handle end, so that to keep the shovel balanced the fulcrum must be moved 30 in farther from the shovel end. What is the unknown weight?

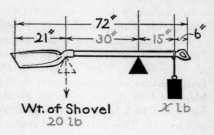

Wt. of Shovel
20 lb

x lb

(*Note:* In solving this problem, change all lengths into inches to avoid small decimal fractions of a foot.)

$$CCW \text{ moments} = CW \text{ moments}$$
$$20 \text{ lb} \times 30 \text{ in} = x \text{ lb} \times 15 \text{ in}$$

$$x = \frac{20 \times 30}{15} = 40 \text{ lb}$$

A meter stick balances at the 50-cm mark. When a 20-g weight is suspended at the 80-cm mark, the stick balances at 57.5 cm. What is the weight of the meter stick?

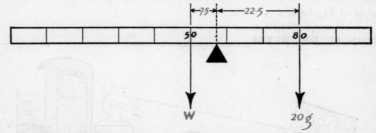

Let W be the unknown weight.
$$CCW \text{ moments} = CW \text{ moments}$$
$$W \times 7.5 = 20 \times 22.5$$

$$W = \frac{20 \times 22.5}{7.5} = 60 \text{ g}$$

Compound Machines. Two or more simple machines used in combination in such a way that each of them acts on another form a compound machine. The chief reasons for using compound machines are convenience of arrangement and greater mechanical advantage. The inclined plane is frequently used in combination with a windlass (wheel-and-axle) or with a block and tackle. Compound lever systems are common.

The ideal mechanical advantage of a compound machine is equal to the product of the separate mechanical advantages of the simple machines composing the compound machine. In the combination of levers shown in the illustration, a lever with an ideal *MA* of 5, one with an ideal *MA* of 1.5, and one with an ideal *MA* of 2 form a lever system with an ideal *MA* of (5 × 1.5 × 2) = 15. This principle of compound machines can be verified,

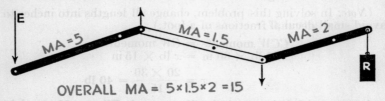

OVERALL MA = 5×1.5×2 =15

as in the case of any simple machine, by comparing D_E with D_R; the actual *MA* can be determined by dividing *R* by *E*. In many cases, the ideal *MA* is most easily calculated by means of the ratio of D_E to D_R.

TYPICAL PROBLEM

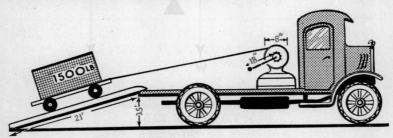

In the illustration, an inclined plane and a wheel-and-axle are being used to load a 1500-lb case onto a truck. Rollers are placed under the case. The truck bed is 3.5 ft high, and the inclined plane is 21 ft long. The wheel of the windlass is 8 in in diameter, and the crank is 18 in long. (*a*) What is the ideal *M A* of the combination of inclined plane and wheel-and-axle? (*b*) What theoretical effort is needed to pull the case up the incline? (*c*) If the effort actually used is 87 lb, what is the actual MA? (d) What is the efficiency of the combination? (e) How many revolutions must the crank move to pull the case up the incline onto the truck?

(a) ideal MA = ideal MA (plane) $\times$ ideal MA (windlass)

$$= \frac{\text{length of plane}}{\text{height of plane}} \times \frac{\text{length of crank}}{\text{radius of wheel}}$$

$$= \frac{21}{3.5} \times \frac{18}{4} = 27$$

(b) theoretical $E = \frac{R}{\text{ideal } MA} = \frac{1500 \text{ lb}}{27} = 55.5 \text{ lb}$

(c) actual $MA = \frac{R}{E} = \frac{1500}{87} = 17.2$

(d) efficiency $= \frac{\text{actual } MA}{\text{ideal } MA} = \frac{17.2}{27} \times 100 = 63.7\%$

(e) $D_E = D_R \times$ ideal MA = 21 ft $\times$ 27 = 567 ft

$D_E = 2\pi L \times$ no. of revolutions

$$567 \text{ ft} = \frac{2 \times 3.14 \times 18 \text{ in}}{12 \frac{\text{in}}{\text{ft}}} \times N \text{ revolutions}$$

$$N = \frac{567 \times 12}{2 \times 3.14 \times 18} = \textbf{60.3 revolutions}$$

Gears. The toothed wheels a and B in the diagram are called *spur gears*. Spur gears, as well as other kinds of gears, are compound machines consisting of wheels-and-axles arranged so that the output of one wheel-and-axle becomes the input of the next. If effort, E, is applied to the rim of wheel A, the force will be magnified at the axle, a. This magnified force will be applied to gear B by the meshing teeth, and will be further magnified at the axle b. The ideal MA of this compound machine is given by the following formula:

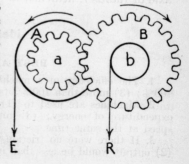

$$\text{ideal } MA = \frac{\text{diameter of } A}{\text{diameter of } b} \times \frac{\text{no. of teeth on } B}{\text{no. of teeth on } a}$$

The ratio between the numbers of teeth on B and a may be called the *gear ratio Ba*.

If the axle b is provided with teeth, it can drive a third gear C, which may have an axle c driving still another gear D, and so on indefinitely. The overall ideal MA of such a gear train can be expressed as follows:

$$\text{ideal } MA = \frac{\text{diam. of first wheel}}{\text{diam. of last axle}} \times \text{ratio } Ba \times \text{ratio } Cb \times \text{ratio } Dc, \text{etc.}$$

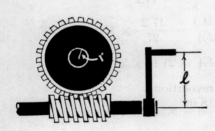

A *worm gear* is a combination of a screw (called a *worm*) and a spur gear. It is often employed to increase force and decrease speed, in such machines as the worm-driven rear axle of automotive vehicles, the worm-reduction gears of some electric motors, and some types of winches. One revolution of the worm turns the gear through an angle equal to one tooth of the gear, or $\frac{1}{n}$ revolutions, where n is the number of teeth on the gear.

The ideal MA, when the effort is applied to a crank of length l (which turns the worm), and the resistance is applied to an axle of radius r, attached to the spur gear, is:

$$\text{ideal } MA = \frac{nl}{r}$$

BEST ANSWER TEST

1. The efficiency of a machine is never (1) 100%; (2) less than 100%; (3) more than 100%; (4) affected by the coefficient of friction.

2. Machines are used to (1) create energy; (2) do work with less expenditure of energy; (3) multiply force; (4) multiply force and speed at the same time.

3. If there were no friction, (1) input would be less than output; (2) output would be less than input; (3) output would equal input.

4. A uniform meter stick will balance at the (1) fulcrum; (2) 50 cm point; (3) end; (4) moment of force.

5. Increasing the effort arm of a lever (1) requires an increase in the resistance arm; (2) decreases the velocity ratio of the lever; (3) increases the efficiency of the lever; (4) increases the moment of the effort force.

6. A single movable pulley (1) has an *MA* of 1; (2) has an *MA* of 2; (3) has an *MA* of ½; (4) has no practical applications.

7. The moment of a force (1) is the time the force acts; (2) is equivalent to work; (3) is the product of force and force arm; (4) is the sum of the force and the force arm.

8. The *MA* of a compound machine (1) is less than the *MA* of any of the simple machines composing it; (2) equals the sum of the *MA*s of the simple machines composing it; (3) equals the product of the *MA*s of the simple machines composing it.

9. A perpetual motion machine is impossible because (1) the U. S. patent office no longer accepts patent applications for them; (2) energy can be destroyed, but not created; (3) friction cannot be eliminated.

10. When 2 weights are hung from a uniform beam, one on either side of the fulcrum, and the beam is balanced, we know that (1) the weights are equal; (2) the weight arms are equal; (3) the moments are equal (4) the fulcrum is directly beneath the center of gravity of the beam.

The _____(11)_____ of a force is increased by increasing the lever arm of the force. Six foot-pounds is (slightly more than, slightly less than, exactly the same as) _____(12)_____ one kilogram-meter. A single fixed pulley and a single rope support a weight of 150 lb; the effort is _____(13)_____; the *MA* is _____(14)_____. A windlass is an example of the simple machine called _____(15)_____. A force of 100 lb 5 ft from the fulcrum of a lever is just as effective as a force of 50 lb _____(16)_____ ft from the fulcrum. A painter's scaffold weighing 200 lb is supported by 2 ropes 12 ft apart; a tension on each rope is _____(17)_____ lb. Small pieces of carborundum embedded in the treads of stairs reduce accidents by increasing _____(18)_____. The simple machine having the largest ideal *MA* and the largest amount of friction is the _____(19)_____. Idea' *MA* for any machine is found by dividing _____(20)_____. by _____. Actual *MA* for any machine is found by dividing _____(21)_____ by _____. Coefficient of friction is found by dividing _____(22)_____ by _____. Mountain roads generally have a gradual ascent in order to increase the _____(23)_____.

PROBLEMS

1. *(a)* What force is needed to lift a 500 lb weight by means of an inclined plane 10 ft long and 2.5 ft high? *(b)* How much work is done?

Ans. (a) 125 lb (b) 1250 ft-lb

2. If it requires a force of 125 lb to slide a 250 lb cake of ice up an incline 12 ft long and 5 ft high, how much work is done *(a)* against gravity? *(b)* against friction? *(c)* What is the efficiency of the incline?

Ans. (a) 1250 ft-lb (b) 250 ft-lb (c) 83.3%

3. What force, neglecting friction, is needed to lift 100 lb by means of a wheel and axle, whose diameters are 1 ft and 4 in respectively?
Ans. 33.3 lb

4. Draw a diagram of a set of pulleys with a mechanical advantage of 5. (*a*) What force would be needed to lift a 640 lb weight with this set? (*b*) How much work must be supplied to lift the weight 10 ft if the efficiency of the set of pulleys is 80%? Ans. (a) 128 lb (b) 8000 ft-lb

5. The crank of a windlass is one foot long, the diameter of the axle about which the rope is wound, is 8 inches. (*a*) What force on the crank will support a 90 lb weight? (*b*) How much work is done when the weight is lifted 24 feet? (Neglect friction.) Ans. (a) 30 lb (b) 2160 ft-lb

6. A 10 lb weight is carried at the end of a 2 ft stick slung over a boy's shoulder. (*a*) How much force must the boy's hand exert at the other end of the stick, 10 inches from his shoulder, in order to balance this weight? (*b*) What force is exerted on his shoulder? (Neglect the weight of the stick.) Ans. (a) 14 lb (b) 24 lb

7. A 10 ft board is pivoted in the middle. A 120 lb boy sits on one end, and an 80 lb boy on the other. Where can a 50 lb child be placed to balance the board? Ans. 4 ft from fulcrum on 80 lb side

8. A uniform beam 12 ft long weighing 150 lb is placed on a pivot 3 feet from one end. How heavy a weight at this end will balance a 250 lb man standing at the other end of the beam? Ans. 900 lb

9. Where is the center of gravity of a 4 ft bar weighing 25 lb, if it can be balanced at its midpoint with a 30 lb weight at one end and a 15 lb weight at the other? Ans. 0.8 ft from 15 lb end

10. The length of an inclined plane is 13 ft and its height is 5 ft. Find what weight will be supported on the plane by a force of 300 lb which is acting parallel to the plane. Ans. 780 lb

11. A uniform bar, 15 lb in weight and 6 feet long, is supported at both ends, *A* and *B*. A weight of 20 lb is hung 1 ft from *A*; a weight of 10 lb is hung 2 feet from *B*. (*a*) Make a careful diagram of the above and compute the supporting forces at *A* and *B*, neglecting the weight of the bar. (*b*) Compute the total supporting forces at *A* and *B* when the weight of the bar is considered.
Ans. (a) A: 20 lb; B: 10 lb (b) A: 27.5 lb; B: 17.5 lb

12. A weight of 150 lb is supported between two boys, *A* and *B*, on a stick 12 ft long. *A* supports 70 lb. Using the principle of moments, find how far from *B* the weight is located. (Neglect the weight of the stick.) Ans. 5.6 ft

13. A jackscrew has a pitch of 0.25 in and the effort is applied 6 in from the end of a bar 30 in long. (*a*) What theoretical resistance should be overcome by 80 lb of effort? (*b*) If the machine is 30% efficient, what actual resistance would be overcome?
Ans. (a) 48,300 lb (b) 14,500 lb

14. An inclined plane and a single movable pulley are used to load an 840-lb case onto a truck. The bed of the truck is 45 in high and the inclined plane is 22½ ft long. (*a*) What is the ideal *MA?* (*b*) If the effort required to slide the box up the inclined plane is 105 lb, what is the actual *MA?* (*c*) What is the efficiency? Ans. (a) 12 (b) 8 (c) 66.7%

SIX— HYDRAULIC AND PNEUMATIC MACHINES

Transmission of Force. We have seen how a force applied at one point of a pulley is carried to other points by means of a connecting link, the flexible rope of the pulley. One of the main reasons for using machines is to transmit force. We use the machine to transmit the force from its point of application to other points. During transmission, the force may remain the same, or it may be increased or decreased. In the simple machines we have so far considered, the force is transmitted by matter which is solid and, in many cases, rigid. Examples of these connecting links are: the rigid bar of a lever; the flexible rope of a block and tackle; and a rigid inclined plane. But the medium for transmitting force does not have to be solid or rigid; it may be, and very often is, a gas (usu-

ally air) or a liquid. Machines which transmit force by means of liquids are called *hydraulic machines*. Examples are the hydraulic jack and the hydraulic brakes of automotive vehicles. *Pneumatic machines* are those which operate by use of air or other gas. Examples are the air brake systems of trucks, buses, and trains. The operation of both hydraulic and pneumatic machines is based on Pascal's law.

Pascal's Law. Pressure applied to any part of a confined liquid or gas is transmitted with undiminished intensity to every other part. The pressure acts with equal force on all equal areas (of the surfaces confining the liquid or gas) and at right angles to them. Insert a stopper into the neck of a glass bottle filled with water. Hit the stopper a sharp blow, and the bottom of the bottle will fall out. Suppose the area of the stopper is 1 sq in and

the force of the blow is 18 lb. The pressure added by the force
of the blow is 18 lb per sq in. This additional pressure, being
transmitted throughout the water, acts with undiminished intensity against each square inch of the area of the bottle. If the
bottom has an area of 25 sq in, the total new force acting on it
is 450 lb, calculated as follows:

$$F = P \times A = 18\frac{lb}{in^2} \times 25 \ in^2 = \textbf{450 lb}$$

No wonder the bottom will fall out!

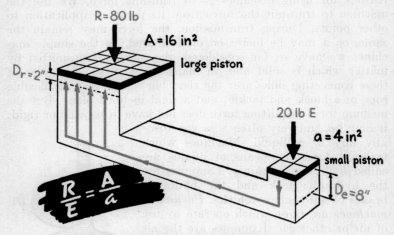

Principle of the Hydraulic Press

The Hydraulic Press. The hydraulic press supplies a good
example of the way a fluid can be used to transmit and multiply
force. In a hydraulic press (see the illustration) there are two
connected cylinders, one much larger than the other, each of
which contains a tight-fitting piston. The liquid generally used
in a press is water or oil. In the drawing, note that the force of
20 lb applied to the small piston, whose area is 4 sq in, provides
a pressure of 5 lb per sq in. This pressure is transmitted equally
throughout the liquid, and thus exerts a force of 5 lb on each
square inch of the large piston. If the area of the large piston is
16 sq in, the total force is 80 lb.

$$F = P \times A = 5\frac{\text{lb}}{\text{in}^2} \times 16 \text{ in}^2 = \textbf{80 lb}$$

An applied (input) force of 20 lb has been multiplied to produce an output force of 80 lb; hence, the mechanical advantage is 4. The ratio of the area of the large piston to the area of the small piston is also 4 (16 in² ÷ 4 in²). Thus the ideal *MA* of this machine is:

$$\text{ideal } MA = \frac{\text{area of large piston}}{\text{area of small piston}} = \frac{A}{a}$$

To find the actual *MA*, of course, we compare the resistance overcome with the effort applied:

$$\textbf{actual } MA = \frac{R}{E} = \frac{\textbf{force on large piston}}{\textbf{force on small piston}} = \frac{F}{f}$$

Because there must be some friction, the actual *MA* is always less than the ideal *MA*, so that the efficiency is necessarily less than 100%.

When we use the hydraulic press, any gain in force is obtained at the expense of distance or speed. If the small piston moves downward 8 in, it will force 32 cu in of liquid into the large cylinder (4 in² × 8 in = 32 in³). The 32 cu in of additional liquid will push up against the large piston and raise the piston 2 in (32 in³ ÷ 16 in² = 2 in). Thus,

$$\text{ideal } MA = \frac{D_E}{D_R} = \frac{8}{2} = \textbf{4}$$

Applications of the Hydraulic Principle. Because the hydraulic principle makes possible a very large mechanical advantage of force, hydraulic machines of tremendous size are used for operations requiring great force, such as: bending or shaping steel plates; punching holes in sheet metal; and lifting very heavy weights. Many service stations are equipped with hydraulic hoists used for raising an automobile so that a mechanic can work more conveniently on its lower structure. Other familiar uses of the hydraulic principle are found in the hydraulic chairs of barbers and dentists; hydraulic jacks and elevators; and presses for baling cotton and paper, compressing books, and extracting the oil from seeds. Automobile brake systems are nearly all of the hydraulic type.

The area of a circle is proportional to the square of the radius (and the square of the diameter). In all formulas for the hydraulic principle, **radius²** or **diameter²** can be substituted for area, if the pistons are circular in shape.

TYPICAL PROBLEMS

The cross-section areas of the cylinders in a hydraulic press are **3 sq in and 60 sq in**. If a force of 75 lb is applied to the smaller piston, how much weight will the larger piston support?

$$\frac{F}{f} = \frac{A}{a}; \frac{F}{75} = \frac{60}{3}; F = \frac{75 \times 60}{3} = 1500 \text{ lb}$$

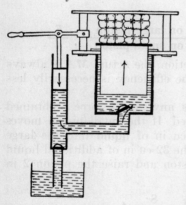

A hydraulic press is being used to bale cotton. The diameter of the small piston is $\frac{3}{4}$ in; the diameter of the large piston is 15 in. The lever operating the small piston is 20 in long. The fulcrum is at the other end of the lever (class 2). The small piston is attached between the fulcrum and the handle at a point 4 in from the fulcrum. The effort is applied at the handle. (*a*) What is the ideal *MA* of this hydraulic press? (*b*) What resistance should be overcome by an effort of 30 lb? (*c*) Through what distance will the effort move if it compresses the resistance 8 in?

(*a*) ideal MA_{overall} = ideal $MA_{\text{lever}} \times$ ideal MA_{press}

$$= \frac{\text{effort arm}}{\text{resistance arm}} \times \frac{D^2}{d^2}$$

$$= \frac{20}{4} \times \frac{(15)^2}{(0.75)^2} = 2000$$

(*b*) theoretical $R = E \times$ ideal $MA = 30 \times 2000 = 60{,}000 \text{ lb}$

(*c*) ideal $MA = \frac{D_E}{D_R}$

$$D_E = \text{ideal } MA \times D_R = 2000 \times 8 = 16{,}000 \text{ in} = 1333 \text{ ft}$$

Note: This is accomplished, of course, by means of many strokes of the handle.

Pneumatic Machines. An airbrake system operates on the hydraulic principle, but uses air as the medium for transmitting the force. When pressure is applied to air or other gases, the gases are readily compressed into less space; liquids, on the contrary, are practically incompressible. If a bottle is filled with air instead of water, a sharp blow on the stopper will merely drive the stopper farther down the neck of the bottle. The bottom will not fall out, as it would in the case of a bottle filled with water. The force of the blow is used up partly in compressing the air, but largely by friction between the stopper and the neck of the bottle.

The large volume of air that can be crowded into a pneumatic tire indicates the compressible nature of gases. When an inflated tire is punctured, however, or when the valve is opened, the rush of air demonstrates the tendency of compressed gas to expand again to its normal volume. Pressure of the compressed gas explains the firmness of an inflated tire.

The more the volume of a gas is reduced, the greater is the pressure exerted by the gas. Compressed air is a valuable means of exerting large forces. It is used in some hydraulic lifts and in such machines as the pneumatic hammer, pneumatic drill, and pneumatic riveter. Compressed air operates pneumatic carriers (used in department stores) and air brakes. It keeps water out of caissons, diving bells, and tunnels being drilled under rivers. It is used in sand-blasting and in obtaining sulfur by the Frasch process. A gas transmits the pressure which operates a steam- or air-gauge of the Bourdon type.

The atmosphere exerts a pressure of nearly 15 lb per sq in at sea level. Some pneumatic devices are operated by this atmospheric pressure. If a region of less pressure can be maintained, the greater force of the atmosphere can be used to accomplish work. Devices operating on this principle include the siphon, the lift pump, a soda straw, the filling mechanism of a fountain pen, and the hydrometer syringe.

In the siphon, for example, the upward pressure at point A is equal to the atmospheric pressure minus the downward pressure of the column of liquid, AC. At point B the upward pressure is atmospheric pressure minus the downward pressure of the column BC. As a result, the net pressure at A is greater than at B, and the liquid flows through the tube from A to B. This continues as long as the level of *B* is lower than that of *A*. In the case of water, *AC* must not exceed 34 ft (the maximum height of a column of water supported by normal atmospheric pressure);

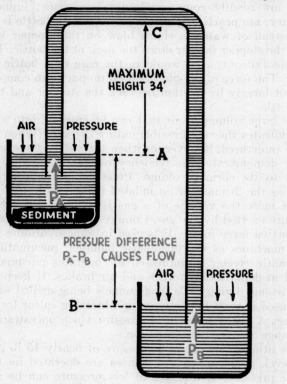

Principle of the Siphon

if *AC* were greater than 34 ft, the columns in both tubes would both stand at 34 ft, the bend of the tube would be empty, and there would be no pressure difference to produce flow. This maximum height depends, of course, on the density of the liquid used. A mercury siphon could not be more than about 30 in high.

Boyle's Law. Suppose a gas is confined in a cylinder with a movable piston and the temperature is kept constant. If the pressure of the piston is doubled, the volume of gas is reduced by one-half. If the piston pressure had been halved, the volume would have doubled. In other words, if the temperature remains unchanged, the product of the pressure and the volume (of a given weight of gas) is a constant.

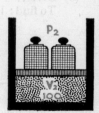

$$P_1 V_1 = P_2 V_2$$

This formula expresses Boyle's law, first discovered (in about 1662) by the Irish scientist, Robert Boyle. Boyle's law states that *when the temperature remains constant, the volume of a confined gas varies inversely as its pressure.* In the formula, P_1 and V_1 represent the original pressure and volume of the gas, while P_2 and V_2 represent the changed pressure and volume. P and V may be stated in any units of pressure and volume, but the formula applies only to the absolute pressure of the gas.

Most pressure gauges read the so-called gauge pressure of a gas—that is the difference between the pressure of the gas and atmospheric pressure. A gas at atmospheric pressure has a gauge pressure of zero. If the atmospheric pressure is 14.5 lb per sq in, and the pressure gauge reads 20 lb per sq in, the absolute pressure of the gas is 14.5 + 20 = 34.5 lb per sq in.

absolute pressure = gauge pressure + atmospheric pressure

gauge pressure = absolute pressure − atmospheric pressure

TYPICAL PROBLEM

(*a*) If 500 cu in of a gas under a pressure of 15 lb per sq in absolute are compressed into 20 cu in, what will the pressure then be? (*b*) If the gas were compressed to 1050 lb per sq in, what would its volume be?

(*a*) **Given:** $P_1 = 15$ lb/in^2; $V_1 = 500$ in^3; $V_2 = 20$ in^3;
   To find: P_2

$$P_1 V_1 = P_2 V_2$$
$$15 \times 500 = P_2 \times 20$$
$$P_2 = \frac{15 \times 500}{20} = \textbf{375 lb/in}^2$$

(b) **Given:** $P_1 = 15$ lb/in^2; $V_1 = 500$ in^3; $P_2 = 1050$ lb/in^2;
   To find: V_2

$$P_1 V_1 = P_2 V_2$$
$$15 \times 500 = 1050 \times V_2$$
$$V_2 = \frac{15 \times 500}{1050} = 7.14 \text{ in}^3$$

Applications of Boyle's Law. Cylinders of highly compressed helium are used to inflate blimps and observation and barrage balloons. When the gas enters the cells of balloons, its pressure decreases but its volume increases. Life preservers for aviators, and rubber life rafts are inflated by highly-compressed carbon dioxide contained in a small iron cylinder.

Relation of Gas Pressure to Density. Changing the pressure of a gas does not affect its weight but merely crowds the molecules closer together. Clearly, then, *the density of a gas varies directly as its pressure.*

$$\frac{D_1}{D_2} = \frac{P_1}{P_2}$$

TYPICAL PROBLEM

10,000 cu ft of air under normal sea level pressure (29.92 in of mercury) are lifted to an altitude of 18,000 ft where the pressure is 14.96 in of mercury. The temperature remains constant. (a) What will the volume of air be? (b) What will its density be (normal density = 1.2 oz per cu ft)?

(a) $P_1 V_1 = P_2 V_2$
   $29.92 \times 10,000 = 14.96 \times V_2$
$$V_2 = \frac{29.92 \times 10,000}{14.96} = 20,000 \text{ ft}^3$$

(b) $\dfrac{D_1}{D_2} = \dfrac{P_1}{P_2}$
$$\frac{1.2}{D_2} = \frac{29.92}{14.96}$$
$$D_2 = \frac{1.2 \times 14.96}{29.92} = 0.60 \text{ oz/ft}^3$$

Molecular Explanation of Boyle's Law. A confined gas always exerts pressure against the walls of its container. This pressure is caused by the bombardment of the rapidly moving molecules which make up the gas. The higher the rate at which the gas molecules strike the molecules composing the walls of the container, the greater is the pressure. When a gas is compressed, its molecules must act within a smaller space; hence, a greater number of molecules per second strike against the confining surfaces. In other words, the pressure increases. When the volume of a gas is increased, a smaller number of molecules strike against each part of the container, and the gas pressure is decreased.

EXCLUSION TEST

Give the number of the term in each of the following groups which has little or no relation to the others.

1. (1) hydraulic jack; (2) Pascal's law; (3) lift pump; (4) barber's chair; (5) air brakes.

2. (1) Boyle's law; (2) siphon; (3) compressed carbon dioxide; (4) airplane de-icing equipment; (5) gas density.

3. (1) small piston; (2) large piston; (3) *MA;* (4) hydraulic press; (5) efficiency.

4. (1) gas pressure; (2) molecular motion; (3) Boyle's law; (4) Pascal's law.

COMPLETION TEST

A balloon *(is, is not)* _____(5)_____ fully inflated at the start of an ascent because _____(6)_____. Boyle's law states that the volume of a confined gas at constant temperature varies _____(7)_____ as the pressure. As the pressure on a gas is increased, the density of the gas _____(8)_____. Pascal's law states that _____(9)_____ in a liquid is transmitted with undiminished _____(9)_____. Pascal's law *(does, does not)* _____(10)_____ apply to gases. The increase in force obtained at the large piston of a hydraulic press is obtained at the expense of _____(11)_____. On the two pistons of different diameters in a hydraulic press, the pressure on each is *(the same, directly proportional to the area, inversely proportional to the area)* _____(12)_____; the force on each is *(the same, directly proportional to the area, inversely proportional to the area)* ___(13)___. Liquids, and not gases, are generally used in the hydraulic press because gases are _____(14)_____. To use the hydraulic principle in order to gain speed, the effort force should be applied to the ___(15)___ piston.

QUESTIONS

1. Compressed air is elastic. Give the molecular explanation of this.

2. A beaker is inverted and pushed downward into water until the volume of air is one-third the volume of the beaker. How does the air pressure within the beaker compare with normal atmospheric pressure?

3. Explain why oil, not water, is used in a hydraulic press.

4. In the automobile service station hydraulic hoist, where is the small piston?

5. Describe how atmospheric pressure may be used in the accomplishment of work.

6. The temperature of 5 cu ft of air is kept constant while the pressure on it is increased five-fold. Explain what happens to (a) the volume; (b) the density, of the gas.

7. Explain the meaning of: "$P_1 \times V_1 = k$."

8. A hole is carefully made in a vacuum-bulb incandescent lamp held under water. Explain what occurs.

PROBLEMS

1. In a hydraulic press a force of 10 lb is applied to the small piston whose area is 2 sq in. What load will be supported by the large piston whose area is 100 sq in?
Ans. 500 lb

2. The diameters of the small and large pistons of a hydraulic press are 1 in and 10 in respectively. How will the force on the large piston compare with the force on the small piston?   Ans. 100 times as great

3. How will the distances moved in problem 2 compare?

$$\text{Ans. } \frac{D_E}{D_R} = 100$$

4. What force is needed on the small piston of a hydraulic press ½ in in diameter to produce a force of 200 tons on the large piston 8 in in diameter?
Ans. 1560 lb

5. What should be the area of the piston on a hydraulic elevator to permit it to lift 5 tons, if the available water pressure is 100 lbs per square inch?
Ans. 100 sq in

6. The pistons of a hydraulic press are 0.8 in and 12 in in diameter, and the small piston is attached 6 in from the fulcrum of a 2nd class lever 2 ft long. (a) What is the ideal MA of this press? (b) What effort should be sufficient to overcome a resistance of 1½ tons at the large piston? (c) What is the efficiency of the press if the actual effort required is 6.25 lb? (d) If the resistance is overcome through a distance of 4 in, what is the effort distance?
Ans. (a) 900 (b) 3.33 lb (c) 53.3% (d) 3600 in

7. How much space would 100 cc of hydrogen under a pressure 76 cm of mercury, occupy if the pressure were reduced to 40 cm of mercury?
Ans. 190 cc

8. To what volume would the oxygen in a 4 cu ft tank under pressure of 1500 lb/in² expand if released? (Assume atmospheric pressure equal to 15 lb/sq in.)
Ans. 400 cu ft

9. An iron cylinder has a volume of 6 cu ft and is filled with air at atmospheric pressure. How much more air must be pumped into it to raise the pressure to 100 lb/in²?
Ans. 34 cu ft

10. Calculate the density of the compressed air in the cylinder in problem 9. (Air under normal pressure weighs 1.22 oz per cu ft.)
Ans. 8.13 oz per cu ft

SEVEN— WORK, ENERGY, AND POWER

Work and Energy. In our study of machines we have really been considering one kind of energy, namely, the energy of mechanical work. When work is done on a machine, energy is actually being put into the machine; when the machine does work against the resistance, this energy comes out of the machine. This energy—measured by the work done in overcoming a resistance—is called *mechanical energy*. All machines transfer mechanical energy from their input to their output.

There are several other forms in which energy may appear, and mechanical energy can be converted into any of them. For example, the energy of work done against friction is always converted into *heat* energy. The mechanical energy used to turn the shaft of an electric generator becomes *electrical* energy at the output of the generator. When a force is exerted against a body free to move without friction, the body acquires speed; the work or mechanical energy of moving the body is turned into *kinetic* energy of the body (energy of motion).

Mechanical energy can also be stored. For example, the mechanical energy involved in winding a clock becomes stored in the mainspring. As the mainspring uncoils, this energy is released and does work on the gears of the clock. Such stored energy is called *potential energy*—in this case, *mechanical* potential energy. When a weight is lifted against gravity, the energy becomes stored in the body as *gravitational* potential energy. This potential energy may be converted into kinetic energy when the body is allowed to fall, or may be converted into mechanical energy as in the case of clocks operated by falling weights. *Chemical* potential energy is stored in every substance; this energy is often converted into heat energy and light energy when chemical reactions occur; it may also be changed into electrical energy, as in dry cells and storage batteries. *Electrical* potential energy can be stored in condensers, and *magnetic* potential energy exists everywhere in the space around a magnet.

87

In the remaining chapters of this book, we shall study, in turn, each of these various forms of energy, and the methods of converting one to the other. We shall find that whenever such a conversion occurs, a definite amount of one kind of energy is always changed into a definite amount of the other kind. Energy is never created, and is never destroyed; the total amount in the universe is constant, and all that ever happens to it is that it changes its form. This important generalization is called the *law of conservation of energy*.

Power. Suppose an excavation can be dug by one worker in 60 days, or by two workers in 30 days, or by a steam shovel in 1 day. In each case, the same amount of work is done. *Time* does not enter into calculation of the *amount* of work done.

Power is the term which takes into account the time element or the *rate* at which work is done. *Power is the rate of doing work, or the rate of transforming or transferring energy.* Power is expressed as the amount of work done per unit of time (usually 1 second or 1 minute).

$$\text{power} = \frac{\text{work}}{\text{time}} = \frac{\text{force} \times \text{distance}}{\text{time}}$$

$$P = \frac{W}{t} = \frac{FD}{t}$$

If we say that an electric hoist did 20,000 ft-lb of work in lifting a 2000-lb load to a height of 10 ft, we are stating only how much work was accomplished. But if we add that the time required was 16 sec, we can compute the power of the machine:

$$P = \frac{W}{t} = \frac{20,000 \text{ ft-lb}}{16 \text{ sec}} = 1250\frac{\text{ft-lb}}{\text{sec}}$$

When comparing machines, then, we need a unit that will indicate how fast they can perform the tasks for which they were designed. If one machine does the same amount of work in less time than another, the faster machine is said to develop more power; if it completes the task in one-half the time needed by the second machine, it develops twice as much power. The power a given machine develops is not a constant, but varies somewhat with the various tasks performed by the machine.

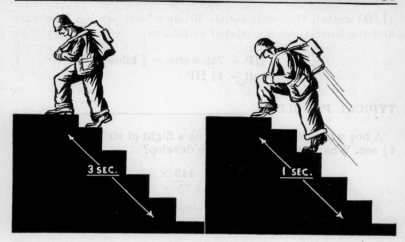

Power. At the left the soldier climbs the stairs in 3 seconds; at the right, he climbs them in 1 second. In each case he does the same amount of work; on the right, however, he develops three times as much power as on the left, because the work is performed in one third the time.

Units of Power. The horsepower (HP) is the unit commonly used to express the power ratings of most types of machinery, including steam engines, gas engines, and some electric motors. *One horsepower is equal to 33,000 ft-lb of work per minute, or 550 ft-lb per second.* To calculate the HP rating of a machine, divide the power developed in ft-lb per min by 33,000, or the power in ft-lb per sec by 550.

$$\text{HP} = \frac{\text{ft-lb per minute}}{33,000} = \frac{\text{ft-lb per sec}}{550}$$

Steam engines may develop several hundred horsepower. The horsepower of modern automobile engines may reach 100 or more. The type of engine used in the Flying Fortress develops 125 HP per cylinder; each 18-cylinder engine develops about 2200 HP, and the four engines give a total of 8800 HP.

For describing electric motors and other electrical appliances, the power units commonly used are the *watt* and the *kilowatt*

(1,000 watts). One watt equals 10^7 dyne*-cm per sec. The watt
and the horsepower are related as follows:

$$1 \text{ HP} = 746 \text{ watts} = \tfrac{3}{4} \text{ kilowatt}$$
$$1 \text{ kilowatt} = 1\tfrac{1}{3} \text{ HP}$$

TYPICAL PROBLEMS

**A boy who weighs 145 lb runs up a flight of stairs 13 ft high, in
$4\tfrac{3}{4}$ sec. What horsepower does he develop?**

$$\text{HP} = \frac{\text{ft-lb per sec}}{550} = \frac{145 \times 13}{4.75 \times 550} = 0.72 \text{ HP}$$

Note: A human being can develop 1 HP or more, for a short
time. For continued work, the horsepower of most people ranges
from about $\tfrac{1}{7}$ to $\tfrac{1}{5}$ HP.

**What is the horsepower of an engine that hoists 15 tons of coal
up a mine shaft 120 ft deep, in $4\tfrac{1}{2}$ min?**

$$\text{HP} = \frac{\text{ft-lb per min}}{33,000} = \frac{15 \times 2000 \times 120}{4.5 \times 33,000} = 24.2 \text{ HP}$$

Torque and Power. Torque is the turning effect produced at the
shaft of an engine or motor. Thus an electric motor or a steam
engine may be at rest or turning very slowly, and still be developing a tremendous torque. Power on the other hand measures
the *rate* at which the torque performs work. Thus *power is proportional to torque times speed of rotation.* If an engine develops
the same torque at all speeds, its power increases as it gains
speed. This is approximately the case in gasoline engines. The
torque produced depends on the pressure developed by the explosion in the cylinder, and is fairly constant for all speeds.
Therefore, a gasoline engine develops its maximum power at a
fairly high speed of rotation.

This torque is not sufficient to start the car from rest, or carry
it up steep hills, or through mud, sand, etc. Therefore gears are
used to change the torque-speed ratio at the wheels of the car.

* The dyne is a unit of force equal to $\tfrac{1}{980}$ gram. See page 115.

The gears allow the engine to operate at its normal speed, but reduce the speed of the wheels; since the power being developed is the same (depends only on engine speed), the torque is increased (since torque = power ÷ speed). Shifting gears in a car is simply a method of allowing the engine to run at high speed (thereby developing great power) while having the wheels turn slowly (thereby developing great torque).

The torque of gasoline and steam engines is fairly constant; the torque of electric motors, however, is usually largest at low speeds.

Determination of Horsepower. The *brake horsepower* (BHP) is the power delivered at the engine flywheel or propeller. Brake horsepower is determined by coupling the engine to a power-absorbing device which enables the power output to be measured accurately. A simple way to measure the power output is to use a brake that is in contact with a revolving drum attached to the crankshaft of the engine or the armature shaft of an electric motor whose power is to be measured. This arrangement is known as a Prony brake.

In using a Prony brake to determine the horsepower of an electric motor, note that the difference between the readings of the two scales equals the turning force of the motor. This force acts through the circumference of the drum

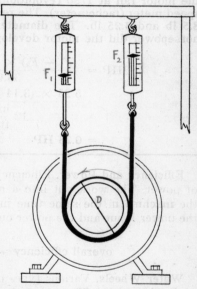

The Prony Brake. The difference between the scale readings measures the torque at the rim of the pulley. The work output of the motor is being converted to heat by the friction of the belt.

during each revolution. The work done per minute is therefore equal to force × circumference × rpm. The horsepower is obtained by dividing this product by 33,000:

$$BHP = \frac{force \times circumference \times rpm}{33,000}$$

$$BHP = \frac{(F_1 - F_2) \times \pi D \times rpm}{33,000}$$

where F_1 and F_2 are in lb, and D is in ft.

TYPICAL PROBLEM

During a test to determine the horsepower of an electric motor, the motor ran at 1780 revolutions per minute as indicated by a speed meter (tachometer). The readings of the spring scales were 8.5 lb and 3.25 lb. The diameter of the drum was $3\frac{1}{8}$ in. What horsepower did the motor develop?

$$\begin{aligned} BHP &= \frac{(F_1 - F_2) \times (\pi D) \times rpm}{33,000} \\ &= \frac{5.25 \times (3.14 \times 3.125 \text{ in}) \times 1780}{12\frac{\text{in}}{\text{ft}} \times 33,000} \\ &= \textbf{0.23 HP} \end{aligned}$$

Efficiency and Power. Efficiency can be computed on the basis of power. The work put into a machine and the work done by the machine in the same time interval, determine, respectively, the power input and the power output of the machine. Hence,

$$\text{overall efficiency} = \frac{\text{power output}}{\text{power input}}$$

Water Wheels. Various types of water wheels have been used to develop power. The water of a waterfall can, theoretically, do as much work on a water wheel as would be needed to lift the same water to the top of the fall. Niagara Falls are about 160 ft high. To lift 1 cu ft of water to the top of this fall would require 10,000 ft-lb of work:

$$\text{Work} = F \times D = 62.5 \times 160 = \textbf{10,000 ft-lb}$$

Each cu ft of water plunging over the precipice can give back this much energy by doing work on a water turbine located in the power house at the foot of the fall.

The horsepower a waterfall can develop depends on its height and on the weight of the water flowing over it per second.

$$HP = \frac{\text{pounds per second} \times \text{height in feet}}{550}$$

For example, if 12,500 cu ft of water per second flow over a waterfall 120 ft high,

$$HP = \frac{12,500 \times 62.5 \times 120}{550} = 170,400 \text{ HP}$$

QUESTIONS

1. A man walks up a flight of stairs in 15 seconds and later runs up the same stairs in 5 seconds. Compare in each case (a) the amount of work done; (b) the power developed.

2. A strong man is often described as being very powerful. Why is such a description technically inaccurate? What is really meant by it?

3. Explain why an automobile has a 3-speed transmission.

4. What is the ultimate source of the energy which an electrical generator driven by a water wheel transforms into electrical energy? Explain.

PROBLEMS

1. How much work can an 8 HP engine do in 2 minutes?

Ans. 528,000 ft-lb

2. A hoisting engine lifts a 1 ton rock a distance of 11 feet in 10 seconds. (a) How much work does it do? (b) What horsepower is expended?

Ans. (a) 22,000 ft-lb (b) 4 HP

3. How long will it take a 10 HP engine to lift an 1100 lb weight a distance of 50 ft?

Ans. 10 sec

4. (a) How much work does a 25 HP motor do in lifting an elevator weighing 2 tons, a distance of 44 ft? (b) How long does it take?

Ans. (a) 176,000 ft-lb (b) 12.8 sec

5. In testing the horsepower of an electric motor, the motor made 860 revolutions in 30 seconds. Two spring scales attached to the Prony brake gave readings of 10¼ lb and 4½ lb. The diameter of the brake wheel was 3¾ in. What horsepower did the motor develop?

Ans. 0.295 HP

6. The volume of water per second flowing over a waterfall 80 ft high is 5,400 cu ft. What horsepower does the waterfall develop?

Ans. 49,000 HP

7. A waterfall is 60 ft high and 2200 cu ft of water flow over it per second, driving a turbine connected to an electrical generator. If the overall efficiency is 30%, how many kilowatts does the generator develop?

Ans. 3360 KW

EIGHT—   COMPOSITION AND
RESOLUTION OF FORCES

General. Force has been defined as that which *changes,* or *tends* to change, the motion of a body. There are several kinds of forces, the most common being mechanical pushes and pulls, gravitational attraction, and electrical and magnetic attraction and repulsion. In the study of moments (p. 67), we learned that (1) several forces may act upon a body at the same time; (2) *balanced* forces produce a condition of equilibrium—if the body is at rest, no motion is produced.

In this chapter, we shall consider the effect of several forces acting at the same point of a body (*concurrent forces*) but in different directions. As before, if these concurrent forces are balanced, equilibrium is produced; if they are unbalanced, a change in motion is produced. The effect of force to produce motion is discussed in the next chapter.

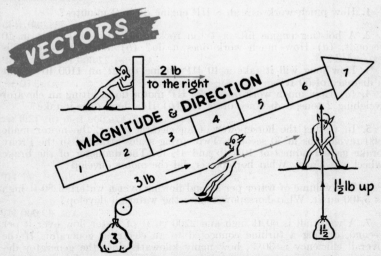

The vector representation of each force is in red.

Vector Representation of Forces. To describe a force adequately, we must indicate both its *magnitude* and the *direction* in which it is acting. A force may be represented by a straight line drawn to scale (say, 1 in = 80 lb) with an arrow point at one end to show the direction, the tail of the arrow representing the point at which the force acts. This representation of a force is known as a *vector,* and any quantity which has both magnitude and direction is a *vector* quantity. Examples of vector quantities are *force, velocity,* and *acceleration.*

Resultant of Concurrent Forces. The *resultant* of two or more forces acting simultaneously upon the same point of a body is the single force which would produce the same effect if it replaced all the original forces. The determination of the resultant of concurrent forces is termed the *composition* (addition) of forces.

Two Forces in the Same Direction. *The resultant of two concurrent forces in the same direction (0° apart) is their arithmetical sum.* The resultant of 10 lb and 7 lb acting in the same direction is 17 lb; that is, a force of 17 lb will produce the same effect as the two forces combined. (See diagrams, next page.)

Two Forces in Opposite Directions. *The resultant of two concurrent forces in opposite directions (180° apart) is their arithmetical difference, and its direction is in the direction of the greater force.* The resultant of 10 lb to the left and 7 lb to the right is a force of 3 lb to the left; that is, a single force of 3 lb to the left would produce the same effect as forces of 10 lb to the left and 7 lb to the right combined.

Two Forces at an Angle. *The resultant of two concurrent forces acting at an angle between 0° and 180° is represented by the diagonal of a parallelogram drawn to scale with the two forces at the given angle as the sides.*

Let *OA* and *OB* represent two forces, 100 lb and 80 lb respectively, drawn to scale and at a given angle. Complete the parallelogram, *OARB,* and construct the diagonal, *OR,* which represents both the magnitude and the direction of the resultant of *OA* and *OB.* The value of *OR* may be determined by measurement, and in this case is equal to 115 lb; that is, a single force of 115 lb in the direction *OR* will have the same effect as the combined forces of 80 lb and 100 lb in the directions *OA* and *OB* respectively. Note that the resultant of two forces may be less than either of them (parallelogram *OA'R'B'*).

COMPOSITION of VECTORS

$F_1=7$ $F_2=10$ $F_R=17$

SAME DIRECTION

$F_1=10$ $F_R=3$ $F_2=7$

OPPOSITE DIRECTIONS

$F_1=100$ $F_R=60$ $F_2=80$

$F_1=100$ $F_R=115$ $F_2=80$

AT ANY ANGLE

$F_1=30$ $F_2=50$ $F_R=\sqrt{F_1^2+F_2^2}$ $F_2=40$

AT RIGHT ANGLES

F_3 F_2 F_1 = F_3 F_2 $F_{R(1,2)}$ F_1 = F_3 $F_{R(1,2,3)}$ $F_{R(1,2)}$ F_2 F_1

SEVERAL CONCURRENT FORCES

Two Forces at Right Angles. *In the case of two concurrent forces at right angles, the resultant is the square root of the sum of the squares of the two forces.* That is, the resultant force (F_R) may be computed by the Pythagoras theorem, giving a more rapid and more accurate result.

$$F_R = \sqrt{F_1^2 + F_2^2}$$

TYPICAL PROBLEM

What is the resultant of two concurrent forces of 60 lb and 80 lb acting at right angles?

$$F_R = \sqrt{F_1^2 + F_2^2}; \quad F_R = \sqrt{60^2 + 80^2} = \sqrt{3600 + 6400} =$$

$$\sqrt{10,000} = 100 \text{ lb}$$

Resultant of Several Forces. Any set of concurrent forces, no matter how many, may always be represented by a single resultant force. The method is illustrated in the bottom diagram on page 96. As shown, first find the resultant of two of the forces by the parallelogram law; in the diagram, $F_R(1, 2)$ is the resultant of F_1 and F_2. Then find the resultant of this force and one of the remaining forces; $F_R(1, 2, 3)$ is the resultant of $F_R(1, 2)$ and F_3. This procedure is continued until all the forces have been used.

As the diagram shows, the same result may be obtained by the *polygon method*: add the vectors head to tail, maintaining the proper direction of each. The resultant is the vector drawn from the tail of the first vector to the head of the last, thus forming a polygon.

When the forces themselves form a closed polygon, the last vector ending at the tail of the first, there is no resultant—the forces are in equilibrium.

Equilibrant. *The equilibrant of two or more concur*

F_R is the resultant of F_1 and F_2; F_E is the equilibrant of the two forces.

rent forces is the single force which is equal to, but opposite in direction to, the resultant. It is sometimes called the *anti-resultant.* The equilibrant is thus the single force which just prevents the motion of the body upon which the other forces act. In any set of balanced forces, the removal of any one of the forces destroys equilibrium. Thus, *each force in a set of balanced forces is the equilibrant of all the others.*

Summary of Rules for Solving Problems. 1. Let a point represent the body upon which the forces are acting.

2. Choosing a suitable scale, from this point draw lines at the correct angle and of the proper length, to represent the forces. (The larger the scale, the more accurate is the answer.)

3. Always represent the forces (as well as the resultant and the equilibrant) as arrows pointing *away from* the point. That is, always indicate pushes as pulls. (Two arrow heads should never touch.)

4. Complete the parallelogram by drawing from the extremity of each line correctly representing one force, a line parallel to the line correctly representing the other force.

5. From the point upon which the two forces act, draw the diagonal which represents the resultant.

6. The equilibrant would be a line equal in length to, but opposite in direction from, the resultant.

7. If two original forces are at right angles, remember that in a right triangle, (hypotenuse) $^2 =$ (one side) $^2 +$ (other side) ^{2}, or $F_R^2 = F_1^2 + F_2^2$.

Vector Addition of Velocities. A velocity, as well as a force, may be represented by a vector (1) whose length represents the velocity, (2) whose direction is in the direction of motion, (3) whose point of origin represents the moving body. The resultant of two or more concurrent velocities can be found by the same methods used for finding the resultant of concurrent forces. For example, the motion of a body in a northeasterly direction may be the resultant of a velocity due north and a velocity due east.

TYPICAL PROBLEMS

An airplane capable of cruising at 240 mph when there is no wind is headed due east. A wind is blowing from the northeast (45°) at 30 mph. Find: (*a*) the actual velocity of the plane (ground speed); (*b*) the direction of travel of the plane (true course).

(*a*) actual velocity = scale length of OR = **220 mph**
(*b*) direction of travel = direction of OR = **96° E of N**

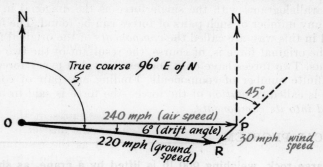

Find the resultant of a force of 6 lb N. E. and a force of 10 lb S. E.

Draw OA and OB to represent the two forces. Complete the parallelogram $OARB$. The resultant is the force represented by the diagonal OR.

Since triangle OAR is a right triangle,

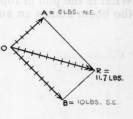

$$OR = \sqrt{OA^2 + AR^2}; \ OR = \sqrt{6^2 + 10^2}$$
$$= \sqrt{136} = 11.7 \text{ lb}$$

Note: A force of 11.7 lb in the direction OR will have the same effect on a body as the forces OA and OB acting together.

How large a weight can be supported by two ropes each making an angle of 60° with the horizontal, if each rope is pulled with a force of 100 lb?

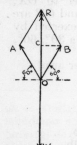

Forces OA and OB support the weight OW.
Therefore, the weight $OW = OR$, the resultant of OA and OB.
Draw BC perpendicular to OR.
Triangle OBC is a 30°, 60°, 90° triangle.

$BC = 50$ lb (short leg = $\frac{1}{2}$ hypotenuse); $OC =$

$$\sqrt{100^2 - 50^2} = 50\sqrt{3} \text{ lb}$$

$$\therefore OR = 2 \times OC = 100\sqrt{3} \text{ lb} = 173.2 \text{ lb}$$

Resolution of a Force. Every *single* force can be considered to be the resultant of some *pair* of concurrent forces. By constructing parallelograms with the single force as the diagonal in each case, any number of such pairs of forces can be found. The forces found in this way are called the *components* of the original force, and the original force is, of course, the resultant of the two components. Two forces have only one resultant, but every force has an infinite number of components. Finding any pair of components is called *resolution* of the force—the force is said to be *resolved into its components*.

TYPICAL PROBLEM

A large rock, weighing 900 lb is lifted by a crane, as shown. What is the pull of rope OA, and the push of the boom BO, when the boom makes an angle of 30° with the vertical?

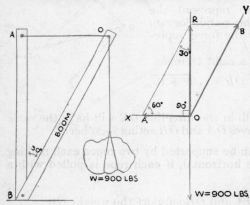

Draw force $OW = 900$ lb, vertically downward. Draw OX in the direction of rope OA. Draw OY in the direction of boom BO. Draw OR equal and opposite to OW. Since rope OA and boom OB support the weight, their resultant is OR. From R draw RA parallel to OY and RB parallel to OX. Then OA and OB are the forces exerted by the rope and the boom, respectively. Triangle OAR is a 30°, 60°, 90° triangle.

Let $OA = x$; then $AR = 2x$ [hypotenuse = 2 × shorter arm]
$$OA^2 + OR^2 = AR^2$$
$$x^2 + 900^2 = 4x^2$$
$$3x^2 = 900^2$$
$$x = 300 \sqrt{3} = \textbf{519.6 lb}$$
$$\therefore \text{Pull of the rope} = \textbf{519.6 lb}$$
$$\text{Push of the boom } (2 \times 519.6) = \textbf{1039.2 lb}$$

Most problems involving forces, velocities, and other vector quantities can be simplified by resolving the vectors into components *at right angles* to one another. When this is done we obtain what is usually meant by the phrase "component of a force in a given direction." It is understood that the second component is in a direction at right angles to the one under consideration. Each component is the total effective value of the original force in that direction.

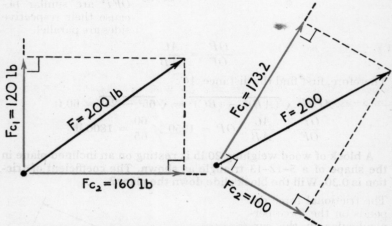

Resolution of the Same Force in Two Different Ways

Components may be found for any pair of directions—the illustration shows the same force resolved in two ways, the components in each case being shown in red. The components selected in any case will depend on the conditions of the particular problem being solved. Note that a force has no component in a direction at right angles to itself.

Velocities, and other vector quantities, may be resolved into components.

TYPICAL PROBLEMS

A barge and a tug boat pulling it, move in parallel paths 25 feet apart. The tow rope is 65 ft long and the pull along the rope is 1950 lb. Find the effective component of this force in the direction of motion of the barge.

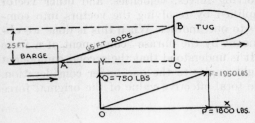

Draw force $OF = 1950$ lb parallel to rope AB. Drop FP perpendicular to horizontal line OX.

OP represents the component of OF in this direction.

Triangles ABC and OFP are similar because their respective sides are parallel.

$$\frac{OP}{OF} = \frac{AC}{AB}$$

Therefore, first find the distance AC:

$$AC = \sqrt{(AB)^2 - (BC)^2} = \sqrt{65^2 - 25^2} = 60 \text{ ft}$$

$$\frac{OP}{OF} = \frac{AC}{AB}; \quad OP = 1950 \times \frac{60}{65} = \textbf{1800 lb}$$

A block of wood weighing 20 lb is resting on an inclined plane in the shape of a 5–12–13 triangle as shown. The coefficient of friction is 0.30. Will the block slide down the plane?

The frictional force depends on the force perpendicular to the surfaces in contact (p. 55). Hence first find the component of the weight perpendicular to the plane.

From the diagram we see that triangle OWP is similar to triangle ABC; hence:

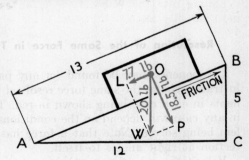

$$\frac{OP}{OW} = \frac{AC}{AB} = \frac{12}{13}$$

$$OP = 20 \times \frac{12}{13} = \textbf{18.5 lb}$$

Force of friction = coeff. of friction $\times$ normal force

$$= 0.30 \times 18.5 = \textbf{5.55 lb}$$

But component of weight along the plane is:

$$OL = OW \times \frac{5}{13} = 20 \times \frac{5}{13} = \textbf{7.7 lb,} \text{ which is greater than } \textbf{5.55 lb}$$

Hence, the block will slide down the inclined plane.

Note: It can be shown that a body will always slide down an incline when the tangent of the angle ($BC \div AC$) exceeds the coefficient of friction. The tangent in this case is $\frac{5}{12} = 0.416$ (which is greater than 0.30).

The Inclined Plane. In the chapter on simple machines (p. 61), we saw that the mechanical advantage of an inclined plane is length divided by height. From the preceding typical problem, we can see that the *component of the weight along the inclined plane* is proportional to the ratio of height to length. In other words, the force needed to push a weight up the plane (assuming no friction) is this component—$W \times \frac{h}{l}$. Thus by means of components we see why the mechanical advantage of an inclined plane is length divided by height.

Sailing into the Wind. It is quite possible to sail a boat almost directly against the wind. This is the result of two facts:

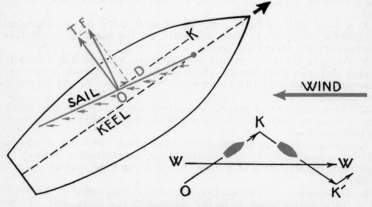

Forces on a Sailboat Tacking Against the Wind

(1) a fluid such as air always exerts pressure at right angles to a surface even when the fluid is moving past the surface at some other angle; (2) this force of the air perpendicular to a sail has a component in the direction of the prow which moves the boat forward.

As shown in the diagram, the wind blowing against the slanting sail produces the air reaction force *OF* perpendicular to the surface of the sail. This force is resolved into two components 90° apart, as shown. The component *OD* is the useful force that drives the boat forward parallel to the keel. The component *OT* only tends to tip the boat and move it sidewise; the deep keel largely prevents this force from acting. Therefore, the boat moves in the direction *OK*. After a while, the boat is turned so that the keel takes the direction *KK'*. Later, the direction *OK* is resumed, and so on. Consequently, the net effect of the wind is to propel the boat in the direction *WW* along a zig-zag course.

BEST ANSWER TEST

1. The single force that can replace two or more forces and produce the same effect is called the (1) resultant; (2) equilibrant; (3) moment of the force; (4) magnitude.

2. Which of the following is *not* a vector quantity? (1) force; (2) acceleration; (3) velocity; (4) volume.

3. The magnitude of the resultant of two concurrent forces may be increased by (1) decreasing the angle between them; (2) increasing the angle between them; (3) drawing a larger parallelogram to represent them.

4. A force that combines with two or more other forces to produce equilibrium is called (1) their resultant; (2) the magnitude; (3) their component; (4) their equilibrant.

5. To make the force exerted more effective when pulling a heavily-loaded sled over level ground, the rope should be (1) nearly vertical; (2) nearly horizontal; (3) 45 degrees to the ground; (4) 60 degrees to the ground.

6. The equilibrant of several concurrent forces (1) acts due north; (2) is equal to their sum; (3) is equal to their product; (4) is equal to their resultant.

7. Sailing a boat in the direction from which the wind is blowing (1) is an impossibility; (2) illustrates the composition of forces; (3) illustrates the resolution of a force; (4) illustrates the multiplication of a force.

8. As an incline is made steeper, the parallel component of the weight of a body resting upon it is (1) increased; (2) decreased; (3) not affected; (4) changed to a perpendicular component.

PROBLEMS

1. What is the resultant of a 60 lb force and an 80 lb force acting at right angles to each other?   Ans. 100 lb

2. Find the force on the anchor cable of a boat on which the wind acts in an easterly direction with a force of 2000 lb, and the tide in a southerly direction with a force of 3000 lb.   Ans. 3610 lb

3. How large a weight can two ropes support, if each is pulled by a force of 100 lb at an angle of 30° to the horizontal?   Ans. 100 lb

4. What weight can be hung from two ropes making an angle of 60° with each other, if each rope can sustain a tension of 100 lb?
                                                              Ans. 173.2 lb

5. An airplane moving at a speed of 240 miles per hour, due west, meets a wind blowing from the north at a speed of 60 miles per hour. In what direction and with what speed will the airplane move?
                                              Ans. 248 mi/hr 76° W of S

6. A force of 120 lb acts due east, while a concurrent force of 80 lb acts 30° east of north. Find the resultant and its direction. (Solve by construction of a parallelogram.)   Ans. 175 lb 66° 27′ E of N

7. Find the equilibrant of two concurrent forces, one of 600 lb acting southwest and the other 150 lb acting north.   Ans. 50 lb

8. A force of 100 lb directed northwesterly, one of 200 lb directed northward, and one of 150 lb directed due east act concurrently. Find the resultant.   Ans. 282 lb

9. A boy pulling a sled with a 6.5 ft rope, the end of which is 2.5 ft above the sled, exerts a force of 78 lb along the rope. What is the effective component in a horizontal direction?   Ans. 72 lb

10. A 100 lb weight is supported by two ropes making an angle of (a) 120°, (b) 90°, (c) 60°. What is the pull in each rope in each case?
                                      Ans. (a) 100 lb (b) 70.7 lb (c) 57.8 lb

11. A rope holding a barrage balloon to the ground makes an angle of 45° with the horizontal. If the lifting ability of the balloon is 2000 lb find (a) the tension in the rope, (b) the horizontal force of the wind.
                                              Ans. (a) 2828 lb (b) 2000 lb

12. A boat and the engine towing it move in parallel paths which are 50 feet apart. The tow rope is 130 feet long and the force applied to the end of the rope is 1300 lb. Find what component of the 1300 lb acts parallel to the path of the boat.   Ans. 1200 lb

13. A boy draws a cart by exerting a force of 10 lb on the handle, which reaches from his hand to the axle of the cart, a distance of 30 inches. If his hand is held 18 inches higher than the axle of the cart, what part of the force exerted by him is effective in drawing the cart forward?   Ans. 8 lb

14. A motor boat can travel 12 mi/hr in still water. If the current in the stream is 3 mi/hr, how long will it take the boat to travel (a) 2 miles upstream, (b) 2 miles downstream?   Ans. (a) $\frac{2}{9}$hr (b) $\frac{2}{15}$ hr

Uniform Motion. When a body is at different points in space at different times, we say that the body is in motion. In order to describe such motion, we usually select some fixed point and then state how far the body is from that point (and in what direction) for each instant of time. If the distance through which the body moves in a given length of time is always the same, the motion is called *uniform*. For example, a body moving uniformly might be 10 feet from the starting point after 1 second, 20 feet away after 2 seconds, 30 feet away after 3 seconds, etc. In this case, the body moves 10 feet every second—and this is described by saying that the body has a *speed* of 10 feet per second. A body in uniform motion always has a constant speed. These facts can be expressed as a mathematical equation:

$$v = \frac{s}{t}, \text{ or } s = vt$$

where s is the distance moved in the time t, and v is the speed of the body. The units of v depend upon the units in which s and t are measured. For example, v may be in feet per second, miles per hour, centimeters per minute, etc. The above equation is true only for uniform motion.

Speed and Velocity. The *speed* of a body has to do only with the distance through which it moves in a unit of time. *Velocity* is the term used when both speed and direction are to be considered. Thus a body moving uniformly along a circular path has constant speed, but because the direction of its motion is always changing, it does not have a constant velocity. Velocity is a vector quantity, since it has both magnitude (speed) and direction.

The effect of a change in velocity without a change in speed will be considered later in this chapter. For the present, we may disregard the difference between velocity and speed because we are going to consider motion in a straight line only—motion with no change in direction.

106

Non-Uniform or Accelerated Motion. Any motion in which the velocity does not remain constant is called *non-uniform* motion. The *rate* at which velocity changes is called *acceleration*. Acceleration is positive when the velocity is increasing, and negative when it is decreasing.

Uniformly Accelerated Motion. If the velocity of a body changes by the same amount during each unit of time, its acceleration is constant or uniform. The following diagram shows in graph form what happens to a body which is accelerated uni-

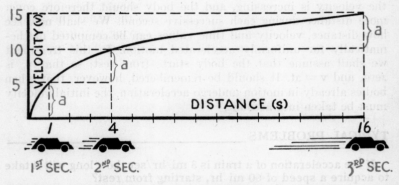

Uniform Acceleration. The velocity changes by the same amount during each successive second.

formly from rest. At the beginning (zero seconds), the velocity is zero. At the end of 1 second, the velocity is 5 (miles per hour); at the end of the second second, the velocity is 10; at the end of the third second, it is 15. The velocity has increased by 5 miles per hour each second, and therefore the body has a uniform acceleration of *5 miles per hour per second.*

If the change in velocity (Δv)* is divided by the time, t, during which the change occurred, we obtain the acceleration, a:

$$a = \frac{\Delta v}{t}, \text{ or, } \Delta v = at$$

* The Greek letter *delta* (Δ) is used to represent a *d*ifference between two measurements. "Δv" is read "delta v," and means "the change in v."

If a body has a velocity v_o at first (zero time), and it accelerates at the rate a, then:

$$v = v_o + \Delta v = v_o + at$$

where v is the final velocity at the end of the time t.

The diagram also shows how the position of the body varies in uniformly accelerated motion. We see that the distance does *not* change uniformly: during the first second the body moves 1 unit distance, during the second second it moves 3 (a total of 4), and during the third second it moves 12. This is to be expected since the velocity is increasing, and the body should therefore cover more distance during each successive second. We shall now see how distance, velocity and time values can be computed mathematically for uniformly accelerated motion. In this treatment we shall assume that the body starts from rest, so that v_o is zero, and $\mathbf{v = at}$. It should be remembered, however, that when bodies already in motion undergo acceleration, the initial velocity must be taken into account.

TYPICAL PROBLEMS

If the acceleration of a train is 3 mi/hr/sec, how long will it take to acquire a speed of 60 mi/hr, starting from rest?

$$a = 3\frac{\text{mi}}{\text{hr}} \div \text{sec} = 3\frac{\text{mi}}{\text{hr} \times \text{sec}}; \quad v = 60\frac{\text{mi}}{\text{hr}}; \quad t = ?$$

$$t = \frac{v}{a}; \quad t = \frac{60\dfrac{\text{mi}}{\text{hr}}}{3\dfrac{\text{mi}}{\text{hr} \times \text{sec}}} = \textbf{20 sec}$$

What speed will the above train have 10 sec after it starts?

$$v = at; \quad v = 3\frac{\text{mi}}{\text{hr} \times \text{sec}} \times 10\,\text{sec} = \mathbf{30\frac{\text{mi}}{\text{hr}}}$$

The brakes of an automobile can reduce its speed from 45 mi/hr to 20 mi/hr in 4 sec. What is the negative acceleration?

$$a = \frac{\Delta v}{t}; \quad a = \frac{(45 - 20)\dfrac{\text{mi}}{\text{hr}}}{4\,\text{sec}} = \textbf{6.25 mi/hr/sec}$$

Average Velocity. The average velocity of a body during a given time interval can be found by dividing the total distance, s, by the time, t:

$$v_{ave} = \frac{s}{t}$$

$$\text{or, } s = v_{ave} \times t$$

Average Velocity in Uniformly Accelerated Motion. In uniformly accelerated motion, the average velocity is the arithmetical average of the initial velocity and the final velocity:

$$v_{ave} = \frac{v_o + v}{2}$$

If $v_o = 0$, the formula becomes:

$$v_{ave} = \frac{v}{2}$$

Since $v = at$:

$$v_{ave} = \frac{at}{2}$$

Distance Traversed. We have seen that distance equals average velocity times time. Expressed mathematically,

$$s = v_{ave} \times t = \frac{at}{2} \times t \text{ or,}$$

$$s = \tfrac{1}{2} at^2$$

for a body starting from rest.

TYPICAL PROBLEMS

A truck starting from rest accelerates at the rate of 6 ft/sec² (6 ft per sec per sec). How far has it travelled after 5 sec?

$$a = 6\frac{\text{ft}}{\text{sec}^2}; \quad t = 5 \text{ sec}; \quad s = ?$$

$$s = \tfrac{1}{2} at^2; \quad s = \tfrac{1}{2} \times 6\frac{\text{ft}}{\text{sec}^2} \times (5 \text{ sec})^2 = \frac{6 \times 25}{2} \times \frac{\text{ft}}{\text{sec}^2} \times \text{sec}^2$$

$$= \textbf{75 ft}$$

If the acceleration of a body starting from rest is 10 ft/sec², how long will it take the body to go 125 ft?

$$a = 10 \text{ ft/sec}^2; \quad s = 125 \text{ ft}; \quad t = ?$$

$$t^2 = \frac{2s}{a}; \quad t^2 = \frac{2 \times 125}{10} = 25; \quad t = 5 \text{ sec}$$

Relation Between Velocity and Distance. Under conditions of uniform acceleration, it is sometimes necessary to know the final velocity at the end of a certain distance traveled, rather than at the end of a given time. The formula to be used can be derived from the others, as follows:

$$(1) \quad v = at, \text{ so that } t = \frac{v}{a}$$

$$(2) \quad s = \tfrac{1}{2} at^2$$

Substituting for t its value obtained in step (1):

$$(3) \quad s = \tfrac{1}{2} a\left(\frac{v}{a}\right)^2$$

Simplifying:

$$(4) \quad s = \frac{v^2}{2a}$$

And solving for v:

$$(5) \quad v = \sqrt{2as}$$

TYPICAL PROBLEMS

A body is moving with a uniform acceleration of 4 ft/sec². What velocity does it have after traversing a distance of 288 ft?

$$a = 4\frac{\text{ft}}{\text{sec}^2}; \quad s = 288 \text{ ft}; \quad v = ?$$

$$v^2 = 2as; \quad v^2 = 2 \times 4 \times 288 = 2304$$

$$v = \sqrt{2304} = 48 \text{ ft/sec}$$

A bomb dropped from a plane is accelerated by gravity at the rate of 32 ft/sec/sec. (*a*) How far must it fall in order to acquire a velocity of 500 ft/sec? (*b*) How long will it take to reach this velocity?

(*a*) $v = 500 \text{ ft/sec}; a = 32 \text{ ft/sec/sec}; s = ?$

$$s = \frac{v^2}{2a} = \frac{500^2}{2 \times 32} = 3910 \text{ ft}$$

(b) $v = 500$ ft/sec; $a = 32$ ft/sec/sec; $t = ?$

$$t = \frac{v}{a} = \frac{500}{32} = 15.6 \text{ sec}$$

ACCELERATION OF FALLING BODIES

Newton's Law of Gravitation. Newton formulated the law of universal gravitation, as follows:

Every body in the universe attracts every other body with a force that is directly proportional to the product of the masses (weights) of the two bodies and inversely proportional to the square of the distance between their centers.

Expressed as a formula,

$$\text{Grav. Force} = G \times \frac{m_1 m_2}{d^2}$$

where G is the *gravitational constant*.

All objects on or near the surface of the earth attract the earth and are attracted by it—that is, they have *weight*. The greater the mass of the body, the greater is its weight. The greater the altitude, the smaller is the weight of a given body, because it is farther from the center of the earth; d^2 increases, thus decreasing the gravitational force. At an infinite distance from the earth, the object has no weight (although its mass is the same any-where). A plumb line supported near the side of a mountain is not parallel to another plumb line at a greater distance from the mountain, because the mass of the mountain attracts the plumb bob which is nearer to it with greater force.

Freely Falling Bodies. All bodies fall at the same rate, re-gardless of their weight, provided the effect of air resistance is neglected. In a vacuum, a light body and a heavy body have the same constant acceleration imparted to them by the pull of the earth. To be sure, the pull of the earth on a 10-lb body is twice what it is on a 5-lb body, but then there is twice as much matter in the 10-lb body to set into motion. Hence the accelerating force *per unit of weight* is the same in both instances. The acceleration due to gravity is approximately **980 cm/sec²** or **32 ft/sec².** (There are some variations with latitude, altitude, and the character of the earth's crust at various localities, but they are slight.)

Air reduces somewhat the acceleration due to gravity, and the resistance offered by the air depends on the size and shape of the falling body. Parachutes largely overcome the acceleration due to gravity; bombs, on the other hand, are streamlined to utilize this acceleration to the fullest extent possible.

Galileo is supposed to have dropped objects of various shapes and weights from the leaning tower of Pisa in 1590. The objects, starting from rest together, struck the ground at the same instant. Thus he disproved the popular belief (dating from the time of Aristotle) that heavy objects fall faster than light ones. He also verified his hypothesis by experiments with bodies rolling down inclined planes.

Formulas Relating to the Acceleration of Falling Bodies. The formulas previously given for uniformly accelerated motion also hold for freely falling bodies. The symbol g and its numerical value, 32 ft/sec² or 980 cm/sec², is simply substituted for a in the same formulas. For example,

$$s = \tfrac{1}{2} g t^2$$

TYPICAL PROBLEM

(a) How far will a body fall in 10 sec? (b) What speed will it acquire? (c) How far will it fall during the last second?

$t = 10$ sec; $a = g = 32$ ft/sec/sec; $s = ?$ $v = ?$

(a) $s = \tfrac{1}{2} g t^2 = \tfrac{1}{2} \times 32 \times (10)^2 =$ **1600 ft**
(b) $v = gt = 32 \times 10 =$ **320 ft/sec**
(c) In 10 sec, body fell **1600 ft**
In 9 sec, the body fell

$$s = \frac{32 \times 9^2}{2} = 1296 \text{ ft}$$

Hence, during 10th sec, body fell

1600 ft − 1296 ft = **304 ft**

The Pendulum. In the physics laboratory, the simple pendulum affords a convenient method for determining the value of g, that is, the acceleration due to gravity. The formula for the period of a pendulum is:

$$t = 2\pi \sqrt{\frac{l}{g}}$$

in which t is the time required for a complete swing of the pendulum; this is termed the *period* of the pendulum; l is the length of the pendulum; and g is the acceleration due to gravity.

If the quantities t and l are measured in an experiment, the value of g can be calculated as follows:

$$g = \frac{4\pi^2 l}{t^2}$$

Since for all ordinary purposes the acceleration due to gravity may be considered a constant, *the period of the pendulum varies directly as the square root of its length.* To double the time for a complete swing, the pendulum must be made four times as long. The period of a pendulum does *not* depend upon the weight or material of the pendulum bob or upon the amplitude of the swing provided that the amplitude is small. (The *amplitude* is the distance the pendulum bob moves on either side of its position of rest.)

MOTION PRODUCED BY FORCE

Newton's Laws of Motion. Sir Isaac Newton made a long series of investigations concerning the motion of bodies, repeating some of Galileo's experiments and making use of numerous astronomical observations. His conclusions are usually presented in the form of *three* laws of motion. Actually, the first two of these laws are the same law, the second being a more precise statement of the first, while the third law is not entirely a law of motion, as we shall see.

Force and Acceleration—Newton's First Two Laws. Newton observed that the motion of a body is accelerated only when an unbalanced force acts upon the body. *If a body is not acted upon by an unbalanced force, it continues at rest if it is at rest, or it continues to move uniformly in a straight line if it is already moving.* This is commonly called Newton's first law.

The property of matter which makes this law true is called *inertia.* Inertia accounts for the fact that a person jumping from a moving car continues to move forward after leaving the car, and for the fact that persons in an accelerating train feel as though they are being pushed in the direction opposite to the acceleration.

Newton then set about determining the exact relationship between the magnitude of the unbalanced force and the acceleration which it produces.

He discovered that *the acceleration of a given body is proportional to the unbalanced force acting upon it*. If a force of 10 grams gives a body an acceleration of 25 cm/sec/sec, then a force of 20 grams produces an acceleration of 50 cm/sec/sec. The harder you push against a body (if it is free to move without friction) the faster it will accelerate.

Newton then found that the *acceleration produced by a given force is inversely proportional to the weight of the body*: a force of 10 grams acting on a 2-gram weight produces twice as great an acceleration as the same force of 10 grams acting on a 4-gram weight.

These facts can be expressed as follows:

$$a \propto \frac{F}{W}, \text{ or, } F \propto Wa$$

where F is the unbalanced force acting on a body, W is its weight, and a is the acceleration produced. *The acceleration is always in the direction of the unbalanced force.* The proportion, $F \propto Wa$, is Newton's second law.

Gravitational Acceleration. Every freely falling body has the same acceleration, $g = 980$ cm/sec/sec, or 32 ft/sec/sec. In other words, since the force of gravity on a body is equal to its weight, a *force* of W grams acting on a *weight* of W grams produces an acceleration of g. Any other force on the body would produce a proportional acceleration, as expressed by the following relation:

$$\frac{a}{g} = \frac{F}{W}$$

where a is the acceleration produced by any force F, and g is the acceleration produced by the force W equal to the weight of the body. From this proportion we obtain the very useful and important equation:

$$F = \frac{W}{g} \times a$$

In order to use the formula F and W must be measured in the same units (pounds, grams, etc.) and a and g must also be in the same units.

The quantity W/g is the *mass* of the body.

In the metric system, a special unit of force is often used—the *dyne*. The dyne is equal to $\frac{1}{980}$ gram. One dyne of force will give a weight of 1 gram an acceleration of 1 cm/sec/sec.

TYPICAL PROBLEMS

(*a*) **What acceleration is produced by a 10-lb force acting on a body weighing 100 lb?** (*b*) **What force would be needed to give this body an acceleration of 8 ft/sec²?**

(*a*) $F = 10$ lb; $W = 100$ lb; $a = ?$

$$F = \frac{W}{g}a; \quad a = \frac{Fg}{W} = \frac{10 \times 32}{100} = \textbf{3.2 ft/sec}^2$$

(*b*) $W = 100$ lb; $a = 8$ ft/sec²; $F = ?$

$$F = \frac{W}{g}a = \frac{100}{32} \times 8 = \textbf{25 lb}$$

What force is required to give an automobile an acceleration of 5 miles per hour per second, if the automobile weighs 1.4 tons, and friction is neglected?

$$W = 1.4 \text{ tons} = 1.4 \text{ tons} \times 2000 \text{ lb/ton} = 2800 \text{ lb}$$

$$a = 5 \text{ mi/hr/sec} = 5 \times \frac{5280\frac{\text{ft}}{\text{mi}}}{3600\frac{\text{sec}}{\text{hr}}} = 7.34 \text{ ft/sec/sec}$$

$$F = ?$$

$$F = \frac{W}{g}a = \frac{2800}{32} \times 7.34 = \textbf{642 lb}$$

Centripetal and Centrifugal Forces. Acceleration means a change in velocity. As explained on page 106, even a change in *direction* constitutes a change in velocity. Hence, a body which has the direction of its motion changed is actually accelerated, even though its *speed* does not change. Since such a change in direction is an acceleration, it follows from Newton's laws that an unbalanced force is required to produce this acceleration. That is why a fireman attempting to make water flow through a curved hose may have to lean on the hose with his entire weight to keep the water in the desired curved path. Similarly, a weight swung in a circle at the end of a string produces a large force in the string which may even break the string. It is this force which is causing the body to change its direction at each instant as it follows the circular path. If the string breaks, so that the force ceases to act on the body, it flies off in *a straight line tangent to the circle* (that is, in whatever direction it happened to be moving at the instant the string broke).

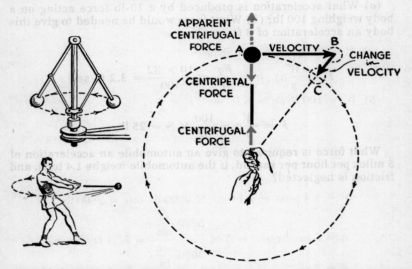

Centripetal and Centrifugal Forces. When the athlete releases the hammer, it flies off along a tangent to the circle.

The diagram shows why the body is accelerating and in what direction. At position *A* it has a velocity represented by the vector *AB;* but the body actually arrives at point *C*. Therefore its velocity has been changed by an amount equal to the vector *BC*. You will notice that *BC* points inward toward the center of the circle, indicating that the force producing acceleration must be acting toward the center (since acceleration is always in the direction of the force producing it). Thus we have a situation in which the body always moves tangent to the circle, is always accelerating toward the center, yet is always at the same distance from the center. It tends to fly off, and the string keeps pulling it back.

The force of the string pulling the body toward the center of the circle is called the *centripetal* force. When a force is exerted on a body, the body always pushes or pulls back on the force in the opposite direction (see "Action and Reaction" below). Thus the body pulls on the string with a *centrifugal* force equal and opposite to the centripetal force. It is this centrifugal force which we feel as a tug in the string.

The centrifugal force acts *as though there were an external force* pulling the body outward away from the center. Actually no such force exists—the only centrifugal force is that produced by the inertia of the body itself. When the centripetal force is removed, the centrifugal one disappears.

Some practical applications of centrifugal force are as follows. (1) Milk and cream are separated by being whirled about rapidly in the cream separator. The milk, being denser, is thrown to the outside; the cream drains off near the center. (2) Clothes are dried in large laundries (and some home washing machines) by being whirled rapidly in perforated cylinders. The water is thrown off by centrifugal force. (3) Governors are used on steam and gas engines to control their speeds. The positions of certain weights are changed by centrifugal force as the speed of the governor changes, operating levers which control the throttle.

MOMENTUM

Action and Reaction—Newton's Third Law. In our study of centrifugal force we have seen an example of two equal and opposite forces—an action resulting in a reaction. This is an illustration of Newton's third law: *Every force is accompanied by an equal and opposite reacting force.* Other illustrations of this law are:

1. When walking, you push your foot against the earth, which exerts an equal and opposite force against the foot, thus enabling you to move forward. If you tried to walk on perfectly smooth ice, you would not be able to push against the earth, the earth consequently would exert no reacting push against you, and you would not be able to move.

2. In the illustration, the boy is attempting to walk from the rowboat to the dock. As in the case of walking on land, the boy's foot is exerting a force on the boat and the boat is exerting an equal and opposite force on the foot. In this case, the boat is free

to move under the action of the force on it, and the boy finds himself in the water instead of on the dock.

Action and Reaction

3. In the garden sprinkler, the wall at the bend in the spout deflects the water. The force exerted by the wall in deflecting the water is matched by an opposite reaction force of the water on the wall. Consequently the spout moves backward as the water spurts forward.

Momentum. The product of the mass (W/g) of a body and its velocity, v, is called the *momentum* of the body:

$$\text{momentum} = \frac{Wv}{g}$$

A small body may have a large momentum if its velocity is large; a heavy body may have a large momentum even if its velocity is small. Note that momentum, like velocity, is a vector quantity.

When a body accelerates, its velocity v changes; therefore *acceleration always produces a change in momentum.* We have already seen that for a body accelerating from rest, $a = \dfrac{v}{t}$.

Therefore,

$$F = \frac{W}{g}a = \frac{W}{g} \times \frac{v}{t} \text{ or,}$$

$$Ft = \frac{W}{g}v = \textbf{momentum.}$$

From this we see that *the product of a force and the time during which it acts is equal to the momentum imparted to a body by the action of that force.*

Ft is termed *impulse* and *Wv/g* is *momentum.* Hence, *impulse equals momentum gained or lost.* This simply means that the longer a force acts, the greater the effect it produces in changing momentum through changing the velocity of the body. A baseball player would express this idea by saying that when a batter "follows through" with his bat, the ball is given a greater velocity than if he does not follow through.

When a moving tank strikes an obstacle, some of the tank's momentum is converted to an impulse which destroys the obstacle.

Equal and Opposite Momentums. If body A acts on body B, the force of body A on body B is exactly equal and opposite to the force of body B on body A (action and reaction). Since this pair of forces acts during the same time interval, the impulse (Ft) is the same for each body, and hence *each body undergoes exactly the same change in momentum, but in opposite directions*. If one body gains momentum to the right, the other body will gain momentum to the left (that is, lose momentum to the right).

This explains the recoil of a gun, and also the action of the garden sprinkler. As the expanding gas in a gun barrel acts on the shell, an equal and opposite force acts against the breech. The breech and gun barrel therefore accelerate backwards while the projectile accelerates forward. Since the gun is much heavier than the projectile, the *velocity* given to the gun is much less than the *velocity* imparted to the projectile—but the total *momentum* gained by each is the same.

If the gun is fastened to the earth, the reaction force acts to move the entire earth—resulting in an infinitesimal but nevertheless real change in the earth's motion in space. When the shell strikes the earth its momentum is returned to the earth and the original change in the earth's motion is offset by an equal change in the opposite direction. Thus the many small changes in the earth's momentum produced by the acceleration of bodies on the earth eventually cancel out. In fact we find that in any system of bodies in which all the forces present are acting between the bodies themselves, and there are no external forces on the system, the total momentum of the bodies will remain constant. For each force increasing the momentum of one body in one direction, there is a reaction force increasing the momentum of some other body in the opposite direction. Since momentum is a vector quantity, adding equal and opposite momentums always gives zero. Thus we see that Newton's third law can be restated as follows:

In any system of bodies not acted upon by an outside force, the total momentum remains constant, regardless of any changes which take place in the motions of the individual bodies.

This is called the Law of Conservation of Momentum, and is actually a summary of Newton's three laws of motion.

TYPICAL PROBLEM

A soldier weighing 160 lb throws himself, with a velocity of 20 ft/sec, at a training dummy weighing 200 lb. How fast are the soldier and dummy moving just after the impact.

Momentum lost by soldier must equal momentum gained by dummy

Let v = velocity of soldier and dummy after impact

Momentum of dummy = $\dfrac{200\,v}{32}$

Momentum of soldier before impact: $\dfrac{160 \times 20}{32}$; after impact: $\dfrac{160\,v}{32}$

Loss of momentum by soldier = gain in momentum by dummy

$$\frac{160 \times 20}{32} - \frac{160\,v}{32} = \frac{200\,v}{32}$$
$$3200 = 360\,v$$
$$v = \textbf{8.9 ft/sec}$$

Independence of Motions. A bullet is dropped at the same time another is fired horizontally. Both strike the ground at the same time; that is, they both fall at the same rate. In the case of the bullet which has been given a horizontal motion, this motion is independent of the downward acceleration due to gravity. That these motions are independent of each other follows from Newton's second law.

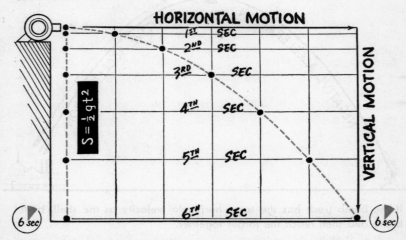

HORIZONTAL MOTION

1ST SEC

2ND SEC

3RD SEC

$S = \frac{1}{2}gt^2$

4TH SEC

5TH SEC

6TH SEC

VERTICAL MOTION

6 sec   6 sec

Under the action of the vertical force of gravity, both bullets have the same vertical acceleration and reach the ground at the same time. The bullet which was fired horizontally continues to move uniformly in the horizontal direction, since there is no horizontal force acting upon it.

When a bombing plane flying horizontally drops a bomb, the bomb tends to continue in horizontal straight-line motion with the speed of the plane at the time it was released. However, gravitational force accelerates it downward at the rate of 32 ft/sec^2. These two motions operate simultaneously but independently of each other, and give the bomb a curved path as shown in the drawing; the path is a *parabola*. If the plane continued flying horizontally at the same speed as when the bomb was released, and if there were no air resistance, the plane would be directly above the bomb when the latter hit the target—no matter from what height the bomb was dropped. Note that the bomb follows the same path as the shell shot from the gun. Therefore bombers are "flying artillery."

Kinetic Energy. When a body is acted upon by a force, the work done by the force is equal to the energy of motion (kinetic

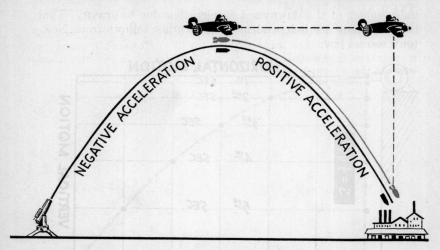

If the bomb (red) has the same horizontal velocity as the shell, both bomb and shell reach the target together.

energy) gained by the body, if there is no friction or other energy loss. Thus we have:

(1) Work done on a body = force × distance = Fs.

But, if the force is constant, the body accelerates uniformly, so that by the formula on page 110,

(2) $$s = \frac{v^2}{2a}$$

Furthermore, we have the formula:

(3) $F = \dfrac{W}{g}\, a$, or, multiplying both sides by s: $Fs = \dfrac{W}{g}\, as$

Substituting for s its value in equation (2):

(5) $$Fs = \left(\frac{W}{g}\, a\right) \times \left(\frac{v^2}{2a}\right) = \frac{Wv^2}{2g} = KE$$

Therefore the kinetic energy of a body is given by equation (5):

$$KE = \frac{Wv^2}{2g}$$

TYPICAL PROBLEM

The head of a hammer weighs 8 oz, and is moving at a velocity of 40 ft/sec as it strikes the head of a nail. (a) How much energy is transferred to the nail? (b) If the nail is driven $\frac{1}{2}$ in into the wood, what is the average resistance offered by the wood?

(a) $W = 8 \text{ oz} = 0.5 \text{ lb}; v = 40 \frac{\text{ft}}{\text{sec}}; g = 32 \frac{\text{ft}}{\text{sec}^2}$

$$KE = \frac{Wv^2}{2g}; KE = \frac{0.5 \times (40)^2}{2 \times 32}$$

$$= \frac{0.5 \times 1600}{2 \times 32} = \textbf{12.5 ft-lb}$$

(b) Work on nail $= 12.5$ ft-lb; $d = \frac{1}{2}$ in $= \frac{1}{24}$ ft; $F = ?$

$$\text{Work} = Fd; F = \frac{\text{Work}}{d}; F = \frac{12.5}{\frac{1}{24}} = \textbf{300 lb}$$

Center of Gravity, Equilibrium, and Stability. The *center of gravity of* a body is the point where all the weight *seems* to be concentrated. At this point the body may be supported and balanced by a single force.

To find the center of gravity of a body, suspend it by means of a cord attached successively at several different points. If all the lines represented by the cord in its various positions are extended inwardly into the body, the point at which they intersect is the center of gravity.

The *stability* of a body is a measure of the difficulty of tipping it, and is increased by making its center of gravity as low as possible and its base as large as possible. The body will tip over

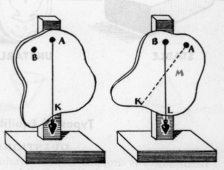

Center of Gravity of an Irregularly Shaped Body. The point M is the center of gravity of the body.

when a line drawn from its center of gravity toward the center of the earth falls outside the area of the base. Tanks, jeeps, low-slung automobiles, and a crouching football linesman are examples of bodies with great stability. An unstable body has a small base and a high center of gravity.

If the center of gravity of a body must be *raised* when it is tipped over, it is in *stable equilibrium*. In this case, the body would tend to return to its original position if the tipping were slight. If the center of gravity of a body is *lowered* by a slight push, the body is in *unstable equilibrium*. In this condition, the body will not return to its original position when pushed, but will go farther from it. If the center of gravity of a body remains at the *same* level after a slight push, the body is in *neutral equilibrium*. In this case, the body comes to rest after the push with its center of gravity neither raised nor lowered from its original position.

A rectangular solid lying on a surface is an example of stable equilibrium. A coin balanced on its edge is in unstable equilibrium. A ball on a horizontal surface is an example of neutral equilibrium.

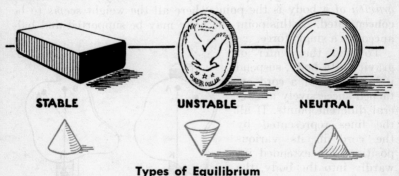

STABLE   UNSTABLE   NEUTRAL

Types of Equilibrium

QUESTIONS

1. An object is dropped from a certain height and at the same time from the same point a bullet is fired horizontally. Explain what occurs.

2. In a tug of war, each team pulls on the rope with a force of 1500 lb. What is the tension in the rope? Explain.

3. State the significance of Galileo's experiment on falling bodies.

4. What is the effect on the gravitational force between two bodies when the distance between them is increased four-fold?

5. What principle is illustrated by the fact that a ball thrown upward does not continue to rise indefinitely?

6. (*a*) Why is it easier to catch a baseball dropped from a height of 50 feet than one dropped from a height of 500 feet? (*b*) Is the latter 10 times as difficult to catch as the former? Explain.

7. What principles are illustrated by the fact that a large-bore cannon has a greater recoil than a small-bore cannon?

MULTIPLE ANSWER TEST

Each of the following groups of introductory words is followed by several completion statements. In the space provided before each one, write a plus sign if the completed statement is true; write a zero if it is false.

I. *By acceleration is meant*

1. _____ the velocity of a body;
2. _____ the change in velocity of a body;
3. _____ the rate of change of velocity of a body;
4. _____ the change in velocity of a body divided by the time required to produce the change.

II. *The final velocity of a uniformly accelerated body starting from rest*

5. _____ depends in part on the weight of the body;
6. _____ depends in part on the acceleration;
7. _____ depends in part on the time during which the body is accelerated;
8. _____ equals the product of acceleration and time.

III. *Neglecting air resistance, a freely falling body*

9. _____ falls 980 cm in the first second;
10. _____ has a velocity of 32 ft/sec at the end of the first second;
11. _____ has an average velocity of 32 ft/sec during the first two seconds;
12. _____ is accelerated by a force equal to its weight.

IV. *The inertia of a body*

13. _____ tends to slow it down if it is in motion;
14. _____ tends to give it uniform motion;
15. _____ tends to speed it up if it is in motion;
16. _____ produces centripetal force if the body moves in a curved path.

PROBLEMS

(*Note:* Neglect air resistance. $g = 32$ ft/sec^2)

1. What is the acceleration of a train that starts from rest and acquires a speed of ·60 miles/hour (88 ft/sec) in 12 sec? Give your answer in (*a*) miles per hour per second, (*b*) feet per second per second.

Ans. (a) 5 mi/hr/sec (b) 7.33 ft/sec/sec

2. An auto traveling with a speed of 15 miles per hour increases its speed to 40 miles per hour in 10 seconds. What is its acceleration?

Ans. 2.5 mi/hr/sec

3. A ball rolls down an incline, acquiring, in 10 seconds, a speed of 40 cm/sec. (*a*) What is the acceleration? (*b*) What speed would be reached in 5 sec?   Ans. (a) 4 cm/sec/sec (b) 20 cm/sec

4. (*a*) How far will a body move from rest in 8 sec if accelerated at the rate of 100 cm/sec^2? (*b*) What speed will it acquire?
                                        Ans. (a) 3200 cm (b) 800 cm/sec

5. An auto can be brought to a stop at the rate of 11 ft/sec^2? In what distance can it be brought to rest from a speed of 30 mi/hr?   Ans. 88 ft

6. A train traveling at a rate of 60 mi/hr is brought to a stop in a distance of 242 ft. (*a*) What is its negative acceleration? (*b*) In what distance could this train be stopped from a speed of 30 mi/hr?
                                        Ans. (a) 16 ft/sec^2 (b) 60.5 ft

7. An auto starting from rest acquires a speed of 30 mi/hr in 10 sec. (*a*) What is its acceleration? (*b*) How far has it traveled from its starting point?   Ans. (a) 4.4 ft/sec^2 (b) 220 ft

8. (*a*) How far will a body fall in 5 sec? (*b*) What speed will it acquire? (*c*) How far does it fall in the last second?
                                        Ans. (a) 400 ft (b) 160 ft/sec (c) 144 ft

9. (*a*) How long must a body fall to acquire a speed of 96 ft/sec? (*b*) How far must the body fall?   Ans. (a) 3 sec (b) 144 ft

10. A ball is thrown upwards into the air with a speed of 96 ft/sec. (*a*) How far does it rise? (*b*) How long is it before it returns to the ground?   Ans. (a) 144 ft (b) 6 sec

11. From what height must a body be dropped so that its velocity upon striking the earth will be 60 mi/hr?   Ans. 121 ft

12. (*a*) How long does it take for a bomb to strike a ground target when dropped from an airplane in level flight at an altitude of 14,400 ft? (*b*) With what downward velocity will it strike the target? (*c*) If the bomber has a speed of 270 mi/hr, how far ahead of the target must the bomb be dropped for a hit?   Ans. (a) 30 sec (b) 960 ft/sec (c) 11,880 ft

13. How long is a "seconds pendulum," that is, one whose period is 1 sec?   Ans. 0.81 ft, or 24.8 cm

14. A force of 200 lb is exerted by the engine in starting a car. If the weight of the car is 3200 lb, what is the acceleration?   Ans. 2 ft/sec^2

15. An automobile weighing 3600 lb, starting from rest, attains a speed of 30 mi/hr in 20 sec. What unbalanced force does the engine exert?   Ans. 247.5 lb

16. An 800-lb gun shoots a 4-lb projectile with a muzzle velocity of 1200 ft/sec. Calculate the recoil velocity of the gun.   Ans. 6 ft/sec

17. If the time required for the projectile (prob. 16) to travel the length of the gun barrel is 0.006 sec, what is the average force exerted by the explosion?   Ans. 25,000 lb

18. What is the kinetic energy of the bomb in problem 12 at the instant of striking, if it is a 2-ton "block-buster"?   Ans. 57,600,000 ft-lb

19. What is the kinetic energy of the projectile in problem 16 as it leaves the muzzle of the gun?   Ans. 90,000 ft-lb

TEN—   HEAT AND ITS TRANSFER

The Nature of Heat. Heat can best be defined as the total kinetic energy possessed by the molecules of a substance. As explained previously, every body is composed of molecules, all of which are in perpetual, but random motion. It is the total kinetic energy of these moving molecules which is called the *heat energy* of a body.

Sources of Heat. Since heat is a form of energy, it is produced only by conversion of other forms of energy into heat.

1. *Chemical Energy.* During many chemical reactions, potential energy stored within the atoms of the reacting substances is released and converted into heat energy of the new substances produced. The burning of wood, coal, oil, or gas is used as a source of heat in our homes and in industry. The explosive effects of TNT, dynamite, and gunpowder are the results of the heat produced during a chemical reaction within the explosive.

2. *Electrical Energy.* The passage of an electric current through any substance produces heat energy in the substance. The electric iron, toaster, furnace, heater of an aviator's suit, are some examples of the conversion of electrical energy into heat.

3. *Mechanical Energy.* Friction, the compression of gases, and the impact of bodies all produce greater motion of the molecules of the bodies involved—in other words they produce heat. Compression of the air in a Diesel engine cylinder heats the air to such an extent that the fuel oil immediately ignites when injected into the cylinder. Hammering of a piece of metal will cause it to become quite hot.

4. *Radiant Energy.* Light rays, ultra-violet and infra-red rays, X-rays, and other radiations produce heat in bodies which they strike. The most obvious example of this is the heating effect of sunlight. The sun is the original source of almost all the energy used by man.

Conversion of Heat. Just as other forms of energy can be turned into heat, heat can also be turned into any other form of energy. The heat energy released by the combustion of fuel in a gasoline engine is changed into mechanical energy of the pistons and crankshaft. The thermocouple is a device in which heat produces a flow of electric current. Moreover, the heat energy of every body in the universe is continuously being converted into radiant energy and lost to outer space. All forms of energy are sooner or later changed to heat, and then radiated out into space.

Heat and Temperature. *Temperature* is a measure of the *average* kinetic energy of *each individual* molecule of a body. Thus two bodies may have the same temperature, but have different quantities of heat. For example, a beaker containing 100 grams of water will have twice as much heat energy as a beaker of 50 grams of water, if both are at the same temperature. Temperature tells you what is happening to the individual molecule; heat depends on all the molecules taken together.

Heat cannot be measured directly, but temperature can be measured. Since temperature (the average energy of each molecule) increases when heat is added to a body, and decreases when heat is removed from the body, changes in temperature can be used to detect and measure changes in total heat content of a body. Measurement of heat and temperature changes will be considered later.

Temperature and Heat Transfer. Heat energy can be transferred from one body to another, if the first body is at a *higher temperature* than the second. Touch a hot radiator with your finger, and the sensation is the result of heat being transferred from the metal to the nerve endings in your skin. Touch a window pane on a cold day, and you feel the heat leaving your warm skin and entering the glass.

Problems of Heat Transfer. Because heat will flow from one body to another when, *but only when,* one is at a higher temperature than the other, we frequently face problems concerned with (1) keeping heat where we want it, (2) keeping heat away from where we don't want it, and (3) getting heat to where we do want it. In winter, heat constantly escapes from our homes to the cold air outside; in summer, heat flows irresistibly from the outside to the interiors of our homes. Preventing heat loss from ovens, steam pipes, boilers, and incubators, and preventing entrance of heat into refrigerators and cold storage rooms are major engineering problems.

On the other hand, heat transfer is often desirable, and the problem then is to facilitate the process. We make special efforts to transfer a maximum of heat to boilers and cooking utensils, to transfer a maximum of heat from radiators to the air in our homes, and to remove a maximum of heat from the cylinder walls of our automobile and aircraft engines.

It is important, therefore, to study the methods by which heat transfer can occur.

Conduction. Conduction is direct transference of heat by molecular impact. When one part of a metal bar, for example, is heated in a fire, molecules at the point being heated move more rapidly, collide more vigorously with their neighbors, and transmit some of their energy to them. In this way, heat is transmitted throughout the body. This heat conduction continues until all portions have the same average molecular activity, or temperature. Solids, liquids, and gases differ considerably in their ability to conduct heat.

Solids as Conductors. Some solids are good conductors; others are poor conductors. In general, metals are good conductors, while non-metals, such as glass, paper, wood, asbestos, etc., are poor conductors. Radiators, cooking utensils, soldering irons, and other devices for transferring heat are therefore usually made of metals. Very poor conductors may serve to prevent the loss of heat from a body; thus rock wool, paper, sawdust, glass wool, and asbestos are used as *insulators*.

Metals vary among themselves in their ability to conduct heat. Silver, copper, and aluminum are among the best; iron, brass, and mercury are less effective. The exhaust valves of some airplane engines are made hollow, and the space is then filled with sodium; this metal is one of the best heat conductors known, and by carrying the heat away rapidly prevents the exhaust valve from "burning."

Feeling is an unreliable indication of temperature because of the dissimilar conductivities of different materials. A tile bathroom floor feels colder to the bare feet than a carpet (though both are at the same temperature), because the tile conducts heat away from the body more rapidly than the carpet does. Similarly, a wet finger will freeze to a cold bar of metal, but not to a piece of wood at the same temperature, because the metal is a better conductor than the wood.

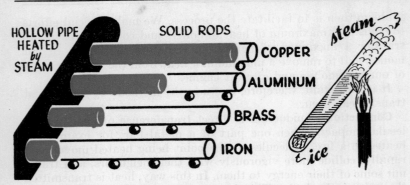

Conductivity in Different Metals. The diagram on the left shows that, as heat (shown in red) passes along the rods from the heated ends (left to right), the wax pellets drop off. The end of the red portion marks points on the rods which have reached the same temperature, showing that copper is the fastest conductor, iron the slowest, of the four metals.

Water Is a Poor Conductor. The diagram at the right shows that water at the top of a test tube can be boiled while ice at the bottom remains unmelted. The portion of the water in red has been heated by the flame.

Liquids and Gases as Conductors. Liquids are poor conductors of heat; gases are extremely poor conductors of heat. The water at the top of a test tube can be boiled, while the water at the bottom remains cold. A piece of ice kept at the bottom of the test tube (by means of a wire mesh to prevent the ice from floating) will not be melted, though the water at the top is boiling.

Furs, woolen clothing, feathers, snow, etc., are poor conductors of heat because they contain so much air space. Since the air is trapped in small cells or pockets and thus cannot circulate, it is commonly called "dead air." Glass wool, ground cork, etc., are effective insulators for heat largely because they contain much "dead air" space.

Convection. When a gas or a liquid is heated, the heated portion expands and becomes less dense, and is forced upward by the surrounding cooler and denser fluid. Colder portions sink, and when heated, rise in their turn. This process continues until the entire liquid or gas has the same temperature throughout. Thus convection is heat transference in fluids by currents resulting from unequal temperature and the resulting unequal densities. Convection cannot take place in solids.

There are many common applications and examples of convection in liquids and gases.

1. In heating liquids, heat is supplied at the bottom of the vessel. In cooling a liquid, the top portions should be cooled so that they can sink and bring about circulation.

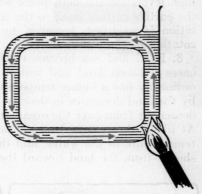

2. The warmest air in a room is usually found near the ceiling and the coolest air near the floor.

Convection Currents

3. Dwellings are frequently heated by hot-air or hot-water radiator systems in which the air or water, heated in the cellar, rises to radiators throughout the house. That is, it is forced upward by cooler and denser air or water in another part of the system.

4. Heat from a stove or "radiator" is distributed throughout a room largely by convection, although, to a lesser extent, by radiation also (discussed in the next section). "Radiators" are more correctly called convectors. Heat passes through the metal by conduction and heats the air in contact with it. The heated air rises and circulates by convection.

5. Ventilation is secured by convection, if windows are opened at the top and bottom. The cold air enters at the bottom, while the warm air is forced out the top. Dwellings may be kept cooler in summer by opening the windows at the highest and lowest parts of the house at night and closing them during the day. A large fan in the attic forcing out hot air may reduce the temperature as much as ten degrees.

6. The refrigerating unit is placed at the top of a refrigerator. The cold air sinks and forces warmer air up to the unit to be cooled.

7. The sun heats the air and oceans of the earth unequally, and thus brings about winds and ocean currents. Equatorial regions are warmer than polar regions, hence the earth's atmosphere tends to circulate by rising at the equator and moving at high levels toward both poles where it descends and flows over the earth's surface back to the equatorial zone. This ideal circulation is modified, however, by other factors, principally the rotation of the earth.

8. Land and sea breezes result from the temperature differences between land and water. During the daytime, the land ordinarily has a higher temperature than the water. Air warmed by the land decreases in density and winds are caused as cooler, denser air from over the ocean (or lake) moves in to displace it. At night, the reverse is true; that is, the land cools below the temperature of the water, and the winds consequently blow off-shore—from the land toward the water.

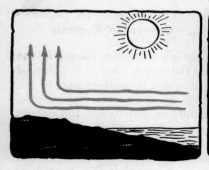

Air rises over the heated land during the day.

At night, air rises over the water, which remains warm.

Radiation. In the two types of heat transfer just considered, conduction and convection, the two bodies had to be in actual contact, since the transfer in each case was by molecular impact. The only difference between convection and conduction is that in convection, circulation of one body constantly brings fresh molecules into the region of heat transfer. Heat, however, can also pass from one body to another through an intervening space by means of *electromagnetic radiations*.

The nature of these radiations will be discussed in Chapter 14. It is sufficient to state here that the vibrations of the particles of a body always result in the emission of radiations. When these radiations strike another body, corresponding vibrations are produced in the particles of this "receiving" body. Thus heat energy of a body is constantly being changed into radiant energy, and this energy is partly changed back into heat energy when it enters another body.

Radiant energy travels through empty space at 186,000 miles per second, in straight lines. Examples of radiations are light, X-rays, ultra-violet rays, infra-red rays, and radio waves. The majority of radiations emitted by hot bodies are infra-red rays, which can be considered to be invisible "light" waves.

Reflection, Transmission, and Absorption of Radiation. Radiation passes freely through empty space. When it impinges on matter, it is affected in three ways:

1. Some of the radiant energy is *reflected* from the surface of the body, that is, the direction of travel of the wave is changed.

2. Some of the radiant energy enters the body and *passes through* it.

3. The remainder of the energy is *absorbed* and converted into heat.

The way in which radiation divides when it strikes a body depends of course on the material of the body. Gases, for example, transmit almost all the sun's radiations, absorbing very little, and reflecting practically none. A black fur coat, on the other hand, transmits none of the energy, reflects very little, and absorbs almost all. A silver mirror reflects almost all the radiant energy which strikes it.

In general, dark, rough surfaces absorb heat radiations, and smooth, bright surfaces reflect them. The former are consequently warmed more rapidly by radiation than are the latter. In summer we wear light-colored clothing; in winter we wear dark clothing. Blimps and dirigibles are painted silver to reflect the sun's heat. Highly polished sheet metal in the walls of a building keep radiant heat out in summer and reflect radiant heat back into the house in winter.

Relation Between Absorption and Radiation Rates. A body which absorbs radiation readily, also radiates it readily. This means that a dark, rough body will radiate more energy than a

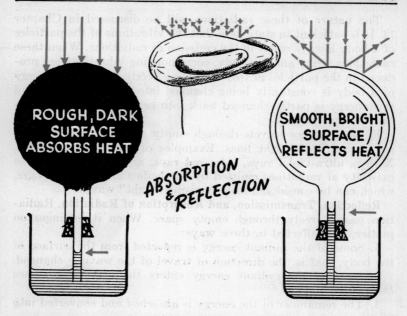

ROUGH, DARK
SURFACE
ABSORBS HEAT

SMOOTH, BRIGHT
SURFACE
REFLECTS HEAT

*ABSORPTION
& REFLECTION*

The balloon is not heated by the sun's rays because the rays are reflected by the bright surface of the balloon.

bright body at the same temperature. Stoves are painted black for that reason.

Other Factors Affecting Rate of Radiation. Rate of radiation depends also on the *amount of surface area* from which radiation can leave, and on the *temperature* of the radiating body.

The cooling fins on an air-cooled engine offer a large surface for the radiation of heat. Some radio tubes have cylindrical plates with metal extensions running lengthwise. These fins promote the dissipation of heat by radiation (remember that the tube contains a vacuum).

An increase in temperature will also increase the rate of radiation from a body. The radiation rate rises sharply with temperature, being proportional to the fourth power of the absolute (Kelvin) temperature (see p. 146). Doubling the absolute temperature of a body multiplies its radiation rate by sixteen!

Radiant heat can be focused, as shown by the use of a "burning" lens, and the use of parabolic reflectors on electric heaters.

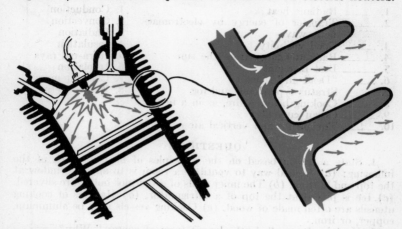

Principle of Cooling Fins. Heat produced inside the engine cylinder enters the cylinder wall and escapes by conduction within the wall and by radiation through the large surface area provided by the fins.

Solar Radiation and the Atmosphere. Heat radiation from the sun (*insolation*) is the most important factor in determining weather. Insolation is partly reflected, partly absorbed, and partly transmitted by the atmosphere, the bodies of water, and the bodies of land on the earth. The following table describes what happens to insolation.

Effect on Insolation	By Air	By Water	By Land
Reflection	Very little	Very much	Some
Absorption	Very little	Some	Very much
Transmission	Very much	Some	Almost none

The absorption of insolation by land areas heats the earth's surface, and raises its temperature. This heating effect is greatest when the sun's rays are perpendicular to the surface, thus explaining the high temperatures of the tropics.

ASSOCIATION TEST

I	II
1. _____ Radiant heat	1. Conduction
2. _____ Transfer of energy by electromagnetic waves	2. Convection
	3. Radiation
3. _____ Good visibility	4. Insulation
4. _____ Radiant energy from the sun	5. Infra-red rays
5. _____ Best in metals	6. Insolation
6. _____ "Dead air" space	7. Cold air mass
7. _____ Stratus-type clouds and fog	8. Warm air mass
8. _____ Cooking below a fire, as in a broiler	
9. _____ Ocean currents	
10. _____ Turbulence and vertical air currents	

QUESTIONS

1. State a reason based on the principles of heat for each of the following: (a) A good way to ventilate a room is to open a window at the top and bottom. (b) The inner walls of a thermos bottle are silvered. (c) Ice is placed at the top of a refrigerator. (d) Handles of cooking utensils are often made of wood. (e) Cooking vessels may be aluminum, copper, or iron.

2. Heat is often called "the lowest form of energy." Why?

3. Deserts are intensely hot during the day but very cold at night. Explain.

4. Give a complete explanation for land breezes and sea breezes.

5. It is claimed that snow melting rapidly on the roof of a dwelling indicates a wastage of fuel. Explain.

6. Give an example not mentioned in the text to illustrate that radiant heat can be reflected and focused.

7. Explain why objects made of metal in a room feel colder than objects made of other materials, although they have the same temperature.

8. Account for the warmth of woolen clothing and woolen blankets.

9. After a radio vacuum tube has been in operation for some time the glass bulb becomes hot. How is the heat transferred from filament to bulb?

10. Explain how all three methods of heat transference are involved in the heating of a schoolroom by a steam heating system.

11. Why is it advisable to defrost an electric refrigerator when the cooling coil becomes coated with ice?

12. Explain how a room can be heated by a fireplace.

ELEVEN

EXPANSION AND THERMOMETRY

Expansion in General. In most instances, raising the temperature of a substance (solid, liquid, or gas) tends to make it expand, that is, increase in volume. Decreasing the temperature causes it to contract. On the basis of the molecular theory, this is not difficult to explain: the rise in temperature causes each molecule to move faster, thus bombarding its neighbors with greater force and pushing them farther away. The net effect is that each molecule acquires more space in which to move, and the total volume occupied by all the molecules increases. When the substance is cooled, the opposite effect takes place.

Expansion of Solids. The fact that solids do expand when heated can be demonstrated in many ways. Applications and examples of this general behavior are numerous. **(1)** Space is left between the ends of railroad rails to allow for their expansion in summer. **(2)** Pipes for carrying steam or hot liquids (as in the Frasch sulfur extraction process and in petroleum refineries) are fitted with expansion joints, or contain large loops, to take care of expansion and contraction caused by changes of temperature in the material carried by the pipes. **(3)** The cylinder head and the cylinder barrel of the Wright Cyclone engine are securely fastened together by first heating the head and chilling the barrel in dry ice and then inserting the latter into the former. When both come to the same temperature, they are tightly joined due to the contraction of the head as it cools and the expansion of the barrel as it warms. **(4)** A cold glass tumbler cracks when hot water is put into it. The inside expands while the outside is still cold, since glass is a poor conductor of heat. Thick glass is more likely to crack than thin glass. **(5)** Concrete pavements sometimes buckle in very hot weather because of expansion. **(6)** When an automobile or airplane engine which is very hot is allowed to cool, the noises it makes are caused by contraction—it is not falling apart.

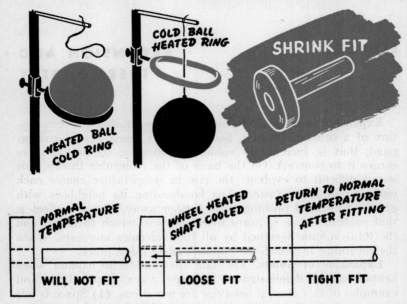

Principle of the Shrink Fit. The ball when heated does not pass through the cold ring; when the ring is heated, and the ball is cold, expansion of the ring and contraction of the ball permits the ball to fall through the ring. At room temperature, the shaft is slightly too large to fit into the wheel. By heating the wheel and cooling the shaft, the expanded diameter of the wheel (red) is larger than the contracted diameter of the shaft (red). At room temperature, the wheel contracts tightly around the expanding shaft.

Coefficient of Linear Expansion. Suppose a rod of iron is one centimeter long at a temperature of 20°C. If the temperature is increased one degree to 21°C, the length of the rod will increase a certain fraction of a centimeter. If the rod had been 10 cm long, the expansion would have been ten times as great; if the temperature increase had been 10 degrees instead of one degree, the expansion would also have been ten times as great.

Thus linear expansion of a given substance is proportional to the *original length* and proportional to the *temperature change*. The change in length for each unit of length for each degree change in temperature is called the *coefficient of linear expansion* of a substance.

From this definition of coefficient of linear expansion, we can write the following formula:

change in length =
original length × temperature change × coefficient of lin. exp.

Or,

$$\text{coefficient of lin. exp.} = \frac{\text{change in length}}{\text{original length} \times \text{temperature change}}$$

This gives us the experimental method of measuring coefficient of linear expansion: measure the length of a rod, heat it through a measured temperature change, and measure the change in length; then substitute in the formula.

TYPICAL PROBLEM

A rod of brass exactly 20 in long at 0°C is heated to 100°C and found to be 20.036 in long. What is the coefficient of expansion of brass?

$$\text{coefficient of lin. exp.} = \frac{\text{change in length}}{\text{original length} \times \text{temperature change}}$$

$$= \frac{(20.036 - 20)}{20 \times 100} = 0.000018 \text{ per } °C$$

If we let k_l represent the coefficient of expansion, l_o the original length of the body, and use Δl * and Δt for *changes* in length and temperature, respectively, the expression given above becomes:

$$k_l = \frac{\Delta l}{l_o \Delta t}$$

Unequal Expansion of Solids. All solids do not expand at the same rate, i.e., they do not have the same coefficient of expansion. Tables giving the coefficients of expansion of various solids are readily available in reference handbooks of physics.

* See footnote on page 107.

Whenever two unlike solids are to be joined together by a direct seal, their coefficients of expansion must agree or the seal will not hold. For example, wire sealed into glass, as in electric lamps and radio tubes, must have the same coefficient of expansion as the glass, otherwise either the seal will not be tight or it will be too tight and the glass will crack with changes in temperature. Special alloy wire is generally used for this purpose. The enamel of bath tubs, stoves, etc., must have the same coefficient of expansion as the sheet iron underneath it.

Principle of the Compound Bar. A thin strip of brass and a thin strip of steel firmly fastened together along their length constitute a *compound bar* or *bi-metallic strip*. When this compound bar is heated, one metal expands more than the other. The bar bends to permit one metal to become longer and still be attached to the other. The metal with the greater coefficient of expansion will be on the outside of such a bend. For a compound bar of brass and steel, the brass will be on the outside of the bend when the bar is heated. If the bar is cooled, as by surrounding it with dry ice, the bending will be in the opposite direction.

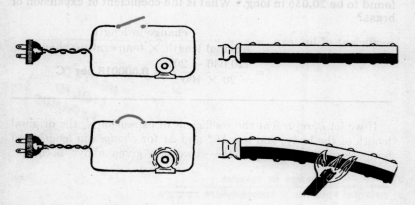

The Compound Bar. The diagram shows the use of a compound bar for controlling the motor of an electric refrigerator. The compound bar is inside the refrigerator. If the temperature rises too high, the bar bends, closes the motor circuit, and starts the refrigerator. When the temperature has been lowered to the proper temperature, the compound bar straightens out and disconnects the motor.

Compound bars are widely used in *thermostats* to open or close electric circuits and thus control heat and temperature automatically. The bending of the bar in one direction when a room, for example, becomes warmer, opens an electric circuit and thus turns off the stoker, oil burner, or blower. When the room cools to a predetermined temperature, the bar straightens out and again closes the circuit, thereby turning on the heat. Incubators, refrigerators, electric ovens, and numerous other devices are regulated as to temperature in this way. (See diagram, page 140.)

In electric switches which turn lights off and on, or operate flashing signals intermittently, a small compound bar bends back and forth with temperature changes caused by a little heater coil wound around it.

Compound bars are used to operate fire alarms or signals; they control the entrance of steam into steam radiators; and they are used in some dial-type and recording thermometers.

Coefficient of Volume Expansion. When dealing with liquids or gases, the change in *volume* must be considered rather than the change in length, since fluids do not have any fixed shape. In the illustration, heating the flask results in an increase in the volume of the liquid; since the liquid is free to change its shape in any direction, the excess liquid expands up the capillary tube.*

As in the case of linear expansion, the coefficient of volume expansion, K_v, is given by the formula:

The liquid shown in red represents the expansion which occurs when heat is applied.

$$K_v =$$

$$\frac{\text{change in volume}}{\text{original volume} \times \text{temperature change}}$$

$$= \frac{\Delta v}{v_o \Delta t}.$$

Relation Between Volume Expansion and Linear Expansion. For all practical purposes, the coefficient of volume expansion of

---

* The flask expands also, but its coefficient of volume expansion is less than that of water, so that there is a net expansion of the liquid.

any substance is three times its coefficient of linear expansion (a fact which can be shown mathematically). For example, K_l for glass is .000009, so that K_v for glass is .000027. K_v for mercury, however, is .00018, several times that of glass, thus explaining why mercury rises and falls in a glass thermometer tube.

In general, liquids have much higher coefficients of expansion than do solids. An automobile radiator filled with water when cold, will overflow when the engine warms up.

Measurement of Temperature. Since expansion and contraction result from temperature changes, it is possible to measure temperature with a substance of practically constant coefficient of expansion, attached to a scale which will measure its volume as the temperature changes. Mercury, alcohol, and such gases as helium, hydrogen, and nitrogen are used in thermometers.

The Mercury Thermometer. The *mercury thermometer* consists of a capillary tube with a bulb blown at one end. The bulb and capillary tube are filled with mercury and heated until the mercury overflows, driving all the air out of the capillary tube. The end of the capillary is then sealed.

The *fixed points* on the thermometer are taken as the melting point of pure ice and the boiling point of pure water under a pressure of 760 mm of mercury. The fixed points are located and marked on the stem of the thermometer. The freezing point is called 0° on the Centigrade thermometer and 32° on the Fahrenheit thermometer; the boiling point is called 100° on the Centigrade and 212° on the Fahrenheit. The space between the fixed points is then divided into 100 equal parts (or degrees) on the Centigrade and 180 equal parts on the Fahrenheit thermometer.

Relation of Centigrade to Fahrenheit Scale. 100 Centigrade degrees equal 180 Fahrenheit degrees. Hence, a change of 1 degree on a Centigrade thermometer would mean a change of 1.8, or 9/5, degrees on a Fahrenheit thermometer. Conversely, a change of 1 degree Fahrenheit would mean a change of 5/9 of a degree Centigrade. A rise of 90° on a Fahrenheit thermometer would be a rise of 5/9 × 90°, or 50°, on a Centigrade thermometer. A drop of 45° Centigrade would be 9/5 × 45, or 81°, Fahrenheit.

When a Centigrade thermometer reads 0°, the Fahrenheit temperature is 32°. Hence, to change temperature readings from one scale to the other, the following formulas may be used.

To change to °C: °C = (°F − 32) × 5/9 (*Subtract 32 first*)

To change to °F: °F = (°C × 9/5) + 32 (*Add 32 last*)

Since a Fahrenheit degree is 5/9 of a Centigrade degree, a temperature rise of 1°F produces only 5/9 the expansion resulting from a rise of 1°C. *Hence the coefficient of expansion per °F is 5/9 of its value per °C.*

Other Types of Thermometers. Mercury freezes at about − 40°C, and boils at about 357°C so that a mercury thermometer cannot be used outside this range. Alcohol is commonly used in thermometers for measuring lower temperatures because its freezing point is about − 130°C; however, alcohol boils at 78°C. The *alcohol*

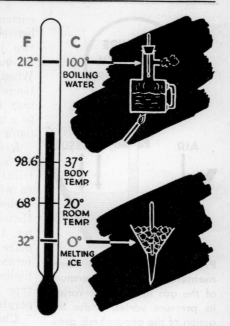

The fixed points of the thermometer are based on the temperature of boiling water (100°C or 212°F) and melting ice (0°C or 32°F).

thermometer is made in the same way as the mercury thermometer.

The *gas thermometer* may be used to measure extremely low and also very high temperatures (up to about 1500°C.) In practice the volume generally remains constant and changes in pressure are used to indicate changes in temperature. (See Charles' Law, p. 146.)

The *thermoelectric thermometer* consists of two dissimilar metallic wires joined at both ends and having a sensitive electric meter in the circuit. If one junction of the wires is heated, an electric current flows through the wires. The strength of the

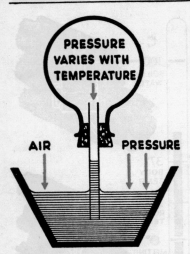

PRESSURE
VARIES WITH
TEMPERATURE

AIR   PRESSURE

Principle of the Gas Thermometer. As the temperature of the gas in the flask varies, its pressure varies; under the action of the atmospheric pressure, the liquid in the tube rises when the temperature drops, falls when the temperature rises.

current depends on the *difference* between the temperatures of the two junctions. The temperature of one junction must be known. When the current is measured, the temperature of the other junction may be determined by reference to a graph or table which accompanies the instrument.

Resistance thermometers operate upon the fact that the electrical resistance of a conductor (a wire which carries a current) varies with the temperature. Hence, in this type of thermometer, the temperature of a given place (such as the interior of a furnace or oven) can be found by finding the resistance of a special type of wire exposed to the temperature being measured.

Changes in the Coefficient of Expansion. For most substances the coefficient of expansion changes with the temperature. It is usually slightly greater at higher temperatures, although for most solids the change is so small that it can be neglected in the ordinary temperature range. In the case of water, however, the change is quite marked, and results in important physical effects.

Unusual Expansion of Water. *Water at 4° Centigrade always expands when its temperature changes,* no matter in which direction the change occurs. It expands continuously if heated to 100°C; if cooled to 0°C, it expands slightly instead of contracting as do most liquids. Notice that this means that the coefficient of expansion of water below 4°C is *negative.* There is a further expansion when the water freezes at 0°C and forms ice. The ice, however, behaves like any other solid and contracts as the temperature drops below 0°C. Note that water has its smallest volume (maximum density) at 4°C.

In the winter, water near the top of a pond or lake is cooled by contact with the cold air, contracts, becomes denser, and sinks to the bottom. This continues until the entire pond has a temperature of 4°C. If the top layer is now cooled further, it expands, and therefore remains on top. The only way the lower layers can be cooled below 4° is by the slow processes of conduction and radiation up through the water (a poor conductor). The result is that the top layer will be cooled down to 0°, and may even freeze, while below it are successively warmer layers ranging up to 4°. Once the ice forms on the top of a pond, it becomes an excellent insulator, and the water beneath it seldom freezes all the way down. As a result, aquatic life in the pond is able to continue through the winter.

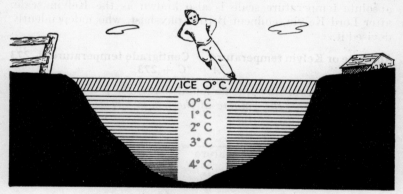

Temperature Variations in a Frozen Pond

Expansion of Gases and Absolute Zero. It is fairly common knowledge that gases expand in volume when heated and contract when cooled. As compared to solids and liquids, gases are unique in that *the coefficient of volume expansion is the same for all gases.* Any gas expands or contracts at the same rate as all other gases when the temperature changes. The coefficient of volume expansion of gases is usually expressed as a fraction, 1/273 per degree C, where the original volume of the gas is measured at 0°C.

If the volume of a given weight of gas is 273 cu ft at 0°C and the temperature is raised 1°, the volume increases by $\frac{1}{273}$ to

274 cu ft. If cooled 1°, the volume decreases by $\frac{1}{273}$ to 272 cu ft. If cooled to −10°, the volume decreases by $\frac{10}{273}$ to 263 cu ft. If this rate of contraction continued, a gas cooled to −273°C would occupy no volume at all. This is a theoretical consideration and impossible in fact; but it does indicate the impossibility of any temperature lower than −273°C. This temperature is called *absolute zero.*

If absolute zero is assigned the value of 0 (instead of −273) and the value for each degree is the same as for the Centigrade temperature scale, then a temperature of 0°C becomes 273° absolute, 100°C becomes 373° absolute, 560°C becomes 833° absolute, −20°C becomes 253° absolute, etc. *To change Centigrade temperature readings to the absolute scale, add 273.* The absolute temperature scale is also known as the Kelvin scale, after Lord Kelvin, eminent British physicist, who independently devised it.

Absolute or Kelvin temperature = Centigrade temperature + 273
$$°A = °C + 273$$

The Gas Laws. Gay-Lussac found that *if the pressure on a gas remains constant, the volume of the gas is directly proportional to its absolute temperature*:

$$\frac{\text{original volume}}{\text{original absolute temperature}} = \frac{\text{new volume}}{\text{new absolute temperature}}$$

$$\frac{V_1}{T_1} = \frac{V_2}{T_2}$$

Charles found that *if the volume of a gas remains constant, the pressure exerted by the gas is directly proportional to the absolute temperature*:

$$\frac{\text{original pressure}}{\text{original absolute temperature}} = \frac{\text{new pressure}}{\text{new absolute temperature}}$$

$$\frac{P_1}{T_1} = \frac{P_2}{T_2}$$

Since gas pressure is caused by molecular bombardment, this law indicates that molecular motion decreases as the temperature decreases. Absolute zero, then, is the condition of no molecular motion.

Boyles' Law (previously given, p. 82) says that *if the temperature of a gas remains constant, the product of the volume of the gas and the pressure exerted upon it is a constant*:

original volume $\times$ original pressure =

new volume $\times$ new pressure

$$V_1 P_1 = V_2 P_2$$

These three gas laws may be combined to give the following *general gas law formula*:

$$\frac{V_1 P_1}{V_2 P_2} = \frac{T_1}{T_2}$$

All types of problems involving changes in the volume, temperature, or pressure of gases may be solved by the use of this formula. *Remember that absolute temperatures must be used.* Volume may be measured in any units, such as liters, cu ft, or cc; pressure in any units, such as lb per sq in, mm or in of mercury, or millibars.

TYPICAL PROBLEM

An automobile tire was inflated to 30 lb gauge pressure when the atmospheric pressure was 14.4 lb per sq in and the temperature was 19°C. What pressure did the air in the tire exert when, after driving, the temperature of the air in the tire became 37°C?

Assume constant atmospheric pressure, and no material change in the tire volume. Remember that *gauge pressure + atmospheric pressure = absolute pressure.*

Given: $P_1 = 30 + 14.4 = 44.4$ lb/in²; $T_1 = 19 + 273 = 292°A$; $T_2 = 37 + 273 = 310°A$

To find: P_2

$$\frac{P_1}{T_1} = \frac{P_2}{T_2}; \quad \frac{44.4}{292} = \frac{P_2}{310}$$

$$P_2 = \frac{310 \times 44.4}{292} = 47.1 \text{ lb/in}^2 \text{ absolute pressure}$$

$$47.1 - 14.4 = 32.7 \text{ lb/in}^2 \text{ gauge pressure}$$

MULTIPLE ANSWER TEST

I. *Coefficient of linear expansion means*

    1. _____ the amount of expansion a 100-cm rod undergoes during a temperature change of 100 degrees;

    2. _____ the increase in length of a unit length during a 1-degree temperature rise;

    3. _____ the actual decrease in length of a 3-ft rod of metal, divided by 3, divided by the decrease in temperature.

II. *The behavior of water when its temperature changes from 10°C to 0°C is unusual, in that*

    4. _____ the higher the temperature, the smaller the volume;

    5. _____ it changes to a solid at 4°C;

    6. _____ it first contracts and then expands;

    7. _____ it reaches its maximum density at a temperature above its freezing point.

III. *By "absolute zero" is meant*

    8. _____ the condition of no molecular motion;

    9. _____ a temperature of −273°C;

    10. _____ the temperature at which matter has no volume.

COMPLETION TEST

The number of Fahrenheit degrees corresponding to 100 Centigrade degrees is _____(11)_____. The expansion rate for all gases is _____(12)_____. When a parcel of air rises upward over a mountain, it undergoes adiabatic _____(13)_____. The dry adiabatic lapse rate is _____(14)_____. The wet adiabatic lapse rate is _____(15)_____. Descending air undergoes adiabatic heating according to the _____(16)_____ lapse rate. At constant pressure, the volume of a given weight of gas is directly proportional to _____(17)_____. When a shallow puddle of water freezes solid, it ordinarily freezes from the _____(18)_____. In general, the coefficient of volume expansion of liquids is _____(19)_____ than that for solids. In solving problems based on the gas laws, ____(20)____ temperatures must be used.

QUESTIONS

1. A compound bar is constructed of silver and platinum at room temperature. When cooled to the freezing point of mercury (−39°C), which metal will be found on the outside of the curve? Explain. (Coefficient of linear expansion: *silver*—17×10^{-6}; *platinum*—9.0×10^{-6})

2. State whether each of the following statements is true or false and give a reason for your answer. (*a*) The bore of a thermometer need not be uniform in diameter. (*b*) The temperature of a body is a reliable indication of the amount of heat it contains. (*c*) In order to increase the sensitivity of a mercury thermometer, it is advisable to use a tube of smaller bore. (*d*) The volume of 1 lb of water at 4°C is less than the volume of 1 lb of water at 0°C. (*e*) The expansion of a metal when heated is explained by assuming that the individual molecules expand.

3. Why would water be an unsatisfactory material for use in a thermometer? Why is mercury considered a good material for this purpose?

4. Why is it impossible to seal a brass wire into a glass rod?

5. How do you think the height of a suspension bridge across a river would compare in summer and in winter? Explain.

PROBLEMS

1. Which of the following would have the greatest length at 20°C when cooled from 100°C? (*a*) a 100-cm rod of copper, $k = 0.000014$; (*b*) a 99-cm rod of invar, $k = 0.0000009$; (*c*) a 101-cm rod of zinc, $k = 0.000026$.   **Ans. Zinc**

2. Which of the following would have the smaller volume at 60°C if warmed from 10°C? (*a*) 500 cc of mercury, $k = 0.000182$; (*b*) 490 cc of alcohol, $k = 0.00104$.   **Ans. Mercury**

3. Which of the following is (*a*) the highest temperature, (*b*) the lowest temperature? (*a*) 1500°F; (*b*) 1000°C; (*c*) 500°K; (*d*) 150°K; (*e*) 75°C; (*f*) 25°F.   **Ans. (a) 1000°C (b) 150°K**

4. The steel cables of a suspension bridge are 5280 ft long when the temperature is 30°. How long will they be at 0°C? ($k = 0.000013$)
                                                                    Ans. 5278 ft

5. A brass water pipe is 12 ft long when water at 45°F flows through it. How much longer would it be when water at 180°F flows through it? ($k = 0.000019$)   **Ans. 0.03 ft**

6. A 10-gal container is completely filled with alcohol. How much will overflow if the temperature rises 25°C, $k = 0.00104$? (Neglect expansion of container.)   **Ans. 0.26 gal**

7. On a certain day when the temperature was 21°C, the volume of a gas was 250 cc. Find the new volume if the temperature changes to 10°C.   **Ans. 240.6 cc**

8. A gas measures 150 cc at 20°C, under a pressure of 740 mm. What will it measure at 10°C and 750 mm pressure?   **Ans. 143 cc**

9. A gas in a steel container under pressure of 15 lb/sq in absolute is heated from 20°C to 1192°C. Find the pressure developed. (Neglect expansion of the container.)   **Ans. 75.2 lb/sq in**

10. Air at 68°F rises 1500 ft over a mountain and then drops 800 ft into a valley. What is the temperature of the air (*a*) at the top of the mountain? (*b*) at the bottom of the valley?   **Ans. (a) 59.8°F (b) 64.2°F**

11. Moist air at sea level has a temperature of 58°F and its saturation temperature is 36°F. If a parcel of this air rises over a 6000-ft mountain and then descends to an 1800-ft level, (*a*) at what altitude will condensation begin? (*b*) What will be the temperature of the air at the 6000-ft level? (*c*) What will be the temperature of the air after descent?   **Ans. (a) 4000 ft (b) 30°F (c) 53.1°F**

TWELVE— MEASUREMENT OF HEAT AND CHANGES OF STATE

How Heat Can Be Measured. As stated on page 128, heat cannot be measured directly, but experiments have shown that the temperature of a given body will increase the same number of degrees every time the same amount of heat is added to it. Therefore by measuring the temperature rise in a body, we can determine how much heat has been added to it. Just how this is done will now be explained.

The Units of Heat Measurement. In order to raise the temperature of 1 gram of water 1°C, a certain definite amount of heat is required. This quantity of heat has been called *1 calorie.*

The amount of heat needed to raise 1 lb of water 1°F has been called *1 British thermal unit* (*1 B.T.U.*). The B.T.U. is thus another unit of heat measurement. It is used frequently in mechanical engineering in this country and in Great Britain.

Since there are 454 grams in 1 pound, and $1°F = \frac{5}{9}°C$,

$$1 \text{ B.T.U.} = 252.2 \text{ calories}$$

Specific Heat. By definition, every gram of water absorbs 1 calorie of heat for every 1°C increase in temperature. To raise the temperature of 15 grams of water 22°C, for example, would require $15 \times 22 = 330$ calories. If 1 gram of *aluminum*, however, is heated through 1°C, it absorbs only 0.217 calories—that is, 0.217 times as much as an equal weight of water. To raise the temperature of 15 grams of aluminum 22°C requires only $15 \times 22 \times 0.217 = 71.6$ calories. This ratio (0.217 to 1) between the heat absorbed by aluminum and the heat absorbed by water, for the same weight and same temperature rise, is called the *specific heat* of aluminum. It is equal numerically to the number of calories required to raise the temperature of 1 gram of the substance 1°C.

The specific heat of water is, of course, 1. All other common substances have specific heats less than 1. As examples, the specific heat of iron is 0.113; of lead, 0.031; of ice, 0.5; of steam, 0.5; of alcohol, 0.65.

Specific heat has been described in terms of heat absorbed during a temperature rise. It should be remembered that the same quantities of heat are given off (liberated) when the temperature of a substance falls. In the illustration above, 15 grams of aluminum would *give off* 71.6 calories if the temperature *dropped* 22°C.

Application of Specific Heat to Heat Calculations. Suppose now that we have a weighed quantity of a substance whose specific heat is known. During an experiment it is found that the temperature of the substance rises a certain number of degrees. How much heat did the substance absorb?

To find out, simply multiply the weight of the substance (grams) by the temperature change (°C), and multiply this product by the specific heat. As a formula, this can be written as follows:

heat gained or lost = weight × temperature change × specific heat

$$\Delta H \qquad = \quad W \quad \times \qquad \Delta t \qquad \times \quad \text{sp. ht.}$$

TYPICAL PROBLEM

100 g of aluminum cool from 650°C to 25°C. The specific heat of aluminum is 0.22. How much heat is given out?

Given: $W = 100 \text{ g}; \Delta t = 650°C - 25°C = 625°C$; sp. ht. $= 0.22$ cal/g/°C

To find: ΔH

$\Delta H = W \times \Delta t \times \text{sp. ht.};$ $\qquad \Delta H = 100 \times 625 \times 0.22 = \textbf{13,750 calories lost}$

Heat Exchanges. If two bodies at different temperatures are mixed, heat will flow from the one at higher temperature to the one at lower temperature, until both bodies have the same temperature. It is clear that the quantity of heat given up by the warmer body is exactly equal to the heat absorbed by the colder body. Thus,

heat lost by Body A = heat gained by Body B

$$W_A \times \Delta t_A \times \text{sp. ht.}_A = W_B \times \Delta t_B \times \text{sp. ht.}_B$$

This equation is called the *law of heat exchange*. It is true only when neither substance, *A* or *B*, passes through a change of state (such as melting, boiling, etc.). The equation may be used to find any one of the six quantities, if the other five are known.

Determination of Specific Heat. The law of heat exchange may be used to determine specific heat of a substance. The method (called the method of mixtures) is as follows:

1. Place a weighed quantity of cold water, at a known temperature, in an insulated container (calorimeter), whose weight and specific heat are also known.

2. Heat a weighed sample of the substance to a known temperature.

3. Transfer the hot substance to the cold water, stir thoroughly, and note the final temperature reached by the mixture.

4. Substitute the known quantities in the equation of heat exchange, and solve for the specific heat of the substance.

TYPICAL PROBLEM_____

100 g of aluminum shot are heated in a steam bath until the temperature reaches 90°C. A calorimeter (sp. ht. = 0.09) weighs 70 g and contains 300 g of water at a temperature of 15°C. When the aluminum shot is mixed with the cold water, the final temperature becomes 20°C. What is the specific heat of the aluminum?

In this heat exchange, heat is lost by the aluminum, and the total heat lost is gained partly by the cold water and partly by the cold calorimeter. All three materials have the same final temperature. Hence:

heat lost by aluminum = heat gained by water + heat gained by calorimeter

$$W_{Al} \times \Delta t \times \text{sp. ht.} = (W_{H_2O} \times \Delta t \times \text{sp. ht.}) +$$
$$(W_{Cal} \times \Delta t \times \text{sp. ht.})$$
$$100 \text{ g} \times (90° - 20°) \times x = (300 \times (20° - 15°) \times 1) +$$
$$(70 \text{ g} \times (20° - 15°) \times .09)$$
$$7000 \, x = 1500 + 31.5$$
$$x = 0.22$$

CHANGE OF STATE

Physical State. We are all familiar with the three physical states of matter—*solid, liquid,* and *gaseous.* We also know that many substances can exist in all three states, the particular state at any time depending chiefly on temperature. Below 0°C, for example, water is usually in the solid state. The distinguishing feature of this state is that the body has a definite, rigid shape. Modern researches have shown that in solids, the molecules are arranged in a regular pattern, with relatively little freedom of motion.

If the temperature of a piece of ice is increased, the molecules move more rapidly (that is with greater energy) within the small region allotted to each. If the temperature is increased still further, a point is reached at which the energy of motion of the molecules is so great that they break out of their rigid pattern, and the substance enters the liquid state. The chief characteristics of a liquid are flexible shape but constant volume and a definite surface.

If the temperature of a liquid is raised, a point is reached at which the energy of the molecules is so great that they break away from each other altogether, the surface of the body disappears, and the substance enters the gaseous state. A gas has indefinite shape and volume, filling any container completely; in a gas the molecules move freely in all directions, limited only by the walls of the container and collisions with other molecules.

Melting and Freezing. The change of state from solid to liquid is called *melting;* the *melting point* is the temperature at which this occurs. A change from liquid to solid is called *freezing,* and the temperature at which it occurs is the *freezing point.*

In the case of pure, crystalline substances, melting and freezing occur at the same temperature; thus, ice melts at 0°C, and pure water freezes at 0°C; the melting point of pure, solid lead is 327°C, and the freezing point of pure, liquid lead is also 327°C. Non-crystalline and impure materials do not melt at a definite temperature; instead, they soften and gradually melt to a liquid. Glass, tar, butter, paraffin, and solder (an alloy of lead and tin) are examples.

Most sustances contract upon solidifying, and expand upon melting. Water, as we have seen, is a notable exception; when it freezes, the ice takes up more space than the water from which it formed. Water pipes, engine blocks, etc. are often broken or cracked by the freezing of water in them. Type metal (an alloy of lead, tin, antimony, and copper) also expands upon solidifying, thus permitting the formation of sharp letters for printing.

For most substances, an increase of pressure raises the temperature at which the solid melts. For water and type metal, and other substances which expand when they solidify, an increase of pressure *lowers* the melting point. Fresh snow on a heavily-travelled highway soon changes to ice. It is melted by the pressure of cars driving over it, and ice is formed by the freezing that follows the release of pressure. This process, called *regelation,* accounts for the packing of a snowball, and, probably, for the movement of a glacier down its valley.

When a substance is dissolved in a liquid, the freezing point of the liquid is always lowered; that is, the freezing point of the solution is lower than the freezing point of the pure solvent.

Heat of Fusion. If a beaker of cracked ice is placed on a wire gauze and heated moderately, and the melting ice constantly stirred with a thermometer, it will be observed that the temperature remains constant at 0°C until all the ice has changed to water. In other words, melting ice absorbs heat, but its temperature does not change. All solid substances with a definite melting point act in this way—they absorb heat, without any change in temperature, during a change of state from solid to liquid; in the reverse process—freezing from liquid to solid—an equivalent amount of heat is given off without a change in temperature.

The amount of heat absorbed or liberated by 1 gram of a substance during a change of state at its melting point is called its *heat of fusion* (fusion means melting). Because this transfer of heat occurs with no change in temperature, heat of fusion is sometimes called *latent heat* ("hidden" heat). Actually the heat of fusion is used to break up the crystalline structure during melting.

The heat of fusion of ice is 80 calories per gram. This means that 1 gram of ice will absorb 80 calories from its surroundings when it melts. A gram of *water* at 0°C would have to rise to 80° in order to absorb the same amount of heat. This indicates the relatively large cooling effect of melting ice. However, ice has no cooling action if it is kept from melting; it must melt in order to cool its surroundings.

Heat Exchange Accompanied by Change of State. The equation of heat exchange, when a change of state occurs, must be modified to take into account the heat gained or lost during the change of state. If, for example, ice changes to water during a heat exchange, 80 calories for each gram must be added, apart from the heat gained because of temperature changes.

TYPICAL PROBLEM

20 g of ice at −6°C are placed in a calorimeter containing hot water; a final temperature of 8°C is reached by the mixture. Specific heat of ice is 0.5; heat of fusion is 80 cal/g. How much heat was absorbed by the ice and ice water formed?

Heat gained in going from −6° to 0°: $20 \times 6 \times 0.5 =$ 60 cal.
Heat gained in melting at 0°: 20×80 $= 1600$
Heat gained in going from 0° to 8°: $20 \times 8 \times 1$ $= \underline{160}$

Total $= \overline{1820}$ calories

Determining Heat of Fusion. The method of mixtures can be used to determine the heat of fusion of any substance. The procedure, with typical experimental values, is as follows:

1. Weigh a calorimeter (sp. ht. 0.09):   *70 g*
2. Add hot water and weigh again: 270 g
3. Record temperature of water: 75°C
4. Add dry cracked ice, at 0°C.
5. Stir until temperature is constant, and record: 15°C
6. Weigh calorimeter and contents: 400 g
7. Compute weight of hot water: $270 \text{ g} - 70 \text{ g} = 200 \ g$
8. Compute weight of ice added: $400 \text{ g} - 270 \text{ g} = 130 \ g$
9. Compute Δt of hot water (and calorimeter): $75° - 15° = 60°C$
10. Compute Δt of ice water: $15° - 0° = 15°C$
11. Equate heat lost to heat gained, and solve for heat of fusion of ice:

Heat Lost		Heat Gained	
By hot water	*By calorimeter*	*By melting ice*	*By ice water*
$(200 \text{ g} \times 60° \times 1) +$	$(70 \text{ g} \times 60° \times 0.09)$	$= (130 \text{ g} \times x \text{ cal/g}) +$	$(130 \text{ g} \times 15° \times 1)$
12,000	$+$ 378	$=$ $130x$	$+$ 1950
	$10,428 =$	$130x$	
	$x = $ **80.2 calories per gram**		

EVAPORATION

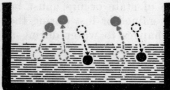

High-speed molecules constantly escape through the surface of a liquid (red molecules). Those shown in black are molecules returning to the liquid from the air.

Evaporation. The molecules in a liquid, such as water, are traveling at various speeds and in many directions. Near the surface some of the molecules will have sufficient speed to break away from the cohesive forces of the liquid and escape into the surrounding space. If the liquid is exposed to the air, these escaping molecules will generally be carried away by air currents or by molecular bombardment from the air itself. This change of a liquid into a gas or "vapor" by the escape of molecules at its surface is called *evaporation*. Objects "dry out" as a result of evaporation.

Evaporation occurs continuously from the surface of all liquids at any temperature. To some extent it occurs from the surfaces of solids as well. Ice, even though kept below its melting point, will evaporate slowly.

From the foregoing explanation of evaporation it is clear that the following factors will affect the rate of evaporation:

1. *Temperature.* A higher temperature means greater molecular energy, and therefore a greater number of molecules escaping each second.

2. *Exposed surface area.* Evaporation rate is proportional to the amount of surface through which molecules can escape.

3. *Concentration of vapor molecules above the liquid.* If molecules of the liquid are present above the liquid, they will tend to fall into the liquid just as those inside the liquid tend to escape. If the liquid is in a closed container, a point will be reached at which just as many molecules are returning to the liquid as are leaving it. Evaporation will then appear to cease, since the amount of liquid will remain constant. Under these conditions, the space above the liquid is said to be *saturated*. The rate of evaporation depends on the degree of saturation of the space above the liquid. As the concentration of vapor increases, the rate of evaporation falls off, until it becomes zero at complete saturation.

4. *Circulation of the air above the liquid.* Circulation of the air removes evaporated molecules and replaces saturated layers with drier air, thus speeding up the rate of evaporation.

5. *Nature of the liquid.* Some liquids evaporate more rapidly (are more *volatile*) than others under the same conditions. Ether and gasoline are more volatile than water; water is much more volatile than mercury.

Cooling by Evaporation. It is well known that a few drops of alcohol evaporating from the back of the hand will produce a cooling sensation. All evaporation results in a cooling of both the liquid and its surroundings. This occurs because the evaporating molecules are the high-speed molecules; those left behind have a lower average speed, hence a lower temperature. As soon as this happens, heat flows from the surroundings into the cooler liquid. In other words, the surroundings are cooled.

Normal body temperature is maintained in part by the evaporation of perspiration from the skin. On a warm day we attempt to increase the rate of evaporation by fanning the air to produce circulation. When the concentration of water vapor in the air is high, evaporation is considerably slowed, and drops of perspiration may even accumulate on the body. On the other hand, a chill is felt when the wet body is exposed to a draft of air or to fairly dry air.

Vapor Pressure. In a sealed bottle containing water, some evaporated liquid is always present in the space above the liquid. These molecules exist in the form of a gas, and as such exert a definite *vapor pressure.* This vapor pressure is exerted independently of the pressure which may be produced by other gases present in the bottle. When the space is saturated with vapor, the pressure produced by the vapor is called the *saturated vapor pressure.* Saturated vapor pressure increases with temperature.

If a liquid is exposed to air in which the existing vapor pressure is less than the saturated vapor pressure for that temperature, the liquid will evaporate until that pressure is reached. If the vapor pressure is higher, liquid will condense out of the air until the pressure is reduced to the saturation value.

Whenever the pressure of a gas confined over water is measured, the saturated vapor pressure of water must be subtracted from the reading, since part of the pressure being read is produced by water vapor mixed with the gas.

ATMOSPHERIC PRESSURE

When the vapor pressure of a liquid is equal to the atmospheric pressure, bubbles of vapor form inside the liquid (the liquid boils).

BOILING

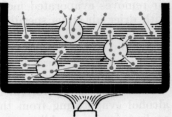

When a liquid boils, high-speed molecules form bubbles inside the liquid; these bubbles rise to the surface, where the molecules are released. Other molecules escape directly through the surface (ordinary evaporation).

Boiling. When bubbles of vapor form inside a liquid, the liquid is said to be *boiling*. *A liquid will always boil when its saturated vapor pressure exceeds the atmospheric pressure upon the liquid.* The reason is as follows: in order for a bubble of gas to exist inside a liquid, the pressure inside the bubble must be at least as great as the pressure of the surrounding liquid. The pressure of the liquid is equal to the atmospheric pressure above it (plus any pressure due to depth in the liquid). Since the space within a bubble in a liquid is always saturated, the pressure in a bubble is equal to the saturated vapor pressure. Therefore no bubble can exist inside a liquid unless the saturated vapor pressure (the pressure inside the bubble) is greater than the atmospheric pressure (the pressure outside the bubble).

The saturated vapor pressure increases as the temperature rises. Therefore, for a given atmospheric pressure, there is a definite temperature at which the liquid will begin to boil, that is, at which vapor bubbles will form throughout the liquid. This temperature is called the *boiling point* of the liquid. Evaporation from the surface, however, continues at all temperatures.

Boiling Point and Pressure. From the preceding discussion it is clear that an increase in atmospheric pressure will increase the boiling point of water (since a higher vapor pressure is needed to produce bubbles). A decrease in pressure lowers the boiling point. The boiling point of pure water, under standard atmospheric pressure of 76 cm of mercury, is 100°C or 212°F. A table of vapor pressures will show that the saturated vapor pressure of water at 100°C is 76 cm, as would be expected.

Near standard pressure, a change of 1 cm in pressure changes the boiling point by as much as 0.37°C. At half atmospheric pressure, 38 cm of mercury, water boils at about 82°C. If the pressure is reduced to 2 cm, water will boil at room temperature. Low pressure (and consequently low temperature) boiling is used to remove water from a substance without charring the product. The manufacture of sugar and evaporated milk are examples of this procedure.

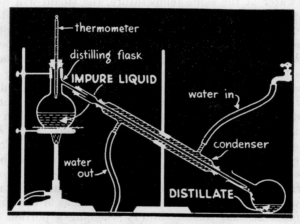

thermometer

distilling flask

IMPURE LIQUID

water in

condenser

water out

DISTILLATE

Water Being Purified by Distillation

On the other hand, increased pressure raises the boiling point, so that at 2 atmospheres water boils at 120°C. The *pressure cooker* is a device for raising the temperature of boiling water, in order to cook foods more rapidly. At high altitudes, where atmospheric pressure is low, a pressure cooker is needed to raise the boiling point of the water to a satisfactory value. The pressure cooker is simply a sealed pot in which pressure is produced by the steam from the boiling water. A valve allows the escape of steam whenever the pressure rises above a safe value.

Distillation is the process of vaporizing a liquid and condensing its vapor back to a liquid. Water and other substances may be purified of non-volatile impurities in this way. Distillation may be carried on under atmospheric pressure, or under increased or reduced pressure.

Heat of Vaporization. No change in temperature occurs during the process of boiling. Boiling water will remain at 100°C, under normal pressure, no matter how strongly it is heated. Additional heat only changes water to steam more rapidly. *The amount of heat required to change 1 g of liquid into vapor at the same temperature is called the heat of vaporization of the substance.*

If 10 g.of *steam* at 100°C are added to a given amount of cold water, and 10 g of *water* at 100° C are added to the same amount of cold water at the same temperature, the steam will heat the cold water to a much higher temperature than will the hot water. This indicates that the steam contains more heat (latent heat) than the hot water, though both are at the same temperature.

The heat of vaporization of water is 540 calories; that is, it requires the addition of 540 calories of heat to change 1 g of water at 100°C into steam at 100°C. When 1 g of a substance in the vapor state condenses to form a liquid, just as much heat (heat of condensation) is given off as is absorbed when 1 g of the liquid is evaporated (heat of vaporization). Thus, *heat of vaporization = heat of condensation.* When 1 g of steam at 100°C condenses, it liberates 540 calories of heat and becomes 1 g of water still at 100°C.

Determination of Heat of Condensation of Water. The method of mixtures is commonly used to determine heat of condensation. The general method consists of (1) weighing a portion of cold water at known temperature in a calorimeter of known weight; (2) passing steam of known temperature into the water in the calorimeter until the temperature rises to the desired degree; (3) weighing the calorimeter and contents to determine weight of steam used.

Heat is gained by the cold water and the cold calorimeter. This heat comes from two sources: (1) the condensation of the steam to water at the same temperature; (2) the cooling of the resulting water to the temperature of the final mixture. Hence, in heat exchanges involving condensation or vaporization and change of temperature,

$$\text{Heat lost} = \text{Heat gained}$$

$$(\text{Wt}_{\text{Steam}} \times \text{heat of condensation}) + (\text{Wt}_{\text{Hot water}} \times \Delta t \times \text{sp. ht.}) =$$

$$(\text{Wt}_{\text{Cold water}} \times \Delta t \times \text{sp. ht.}) + (\text{Wt}_{\text{Calorimeter}} \times \Delta t \times \text{sp. ht.})$$

TYPICAL PROBLEM

A calorimeter (sp. ht. = 0.09) weighs 70 g. Cold water is added and the total weight is found to be 440 g. The temperature is 15°C. Steam at 100°C is passed in, and the final temperature of the mixture is 75°C. The total weight is then 480 g. What is the experimental value of the heat of condensation of steam?

Analysis of the problem for the values of the terms in the formula reveals that:

Wt of cold water is 440 g − 70 g =		370 g
Δt of cold water is 75° − 15°	=	60°C
Δt of the calorimeter is 75° − 15° =		60°C
Wt of steam used is 480 g − 440 g =		40 g
Δt of the hot water (condensed steam) is 100° − 75° = 25°C		

$$\text{Heat lost} = \text{Heat gained}$$

$$(\text{Wt}_{\text{Steam}} \times \text{ht. cond.}) + (\text{Wt}_{\text{Hot water}} \times \Delta t \times \text{sp. ht.}) =$$

$$(\text{Wt}_{\text{Cold water}} \times \Delta t \times \text{sp. ht.}) + (\text{Wt}_{\text{Calorimeter}} \times \Delta t \times \text{sp. ht.})$$

$$(40 \text{ g} \times x) + (40 \text{ g} \times 25° \times 1) =$$

$$(370 \text{ g} \times 60° \times 1) + (70 \text{ g} \times 60° \times 0.09)$$

$$40x + 1000 = 22{,}200 + 378$$

$$40x = 21{,}578$$

$$x = \textbf{539.5 calories/gram}$$

WEATHER

Electrical Refrigeration. Commercial manufacture of ice and electrical refrigeration in the home operate on the same basic science principles. A gas which is easily liquefied, such as sulfur dioxide, ammonia, or dichloro-difluoromethane ("Freon"), is compressed by a pump run by an electric motor. The compressed gas is sent through a coil of tubing, where it is cooled by a fan or a stream of water. This cooled gas, under sufficient pressure, becomes a liquid. After liquefaction, the refrigerant flows into another coil of tubing where the pressure is sufficiently reduced to permit the liquid to boil at low temperature. The heat of vaporization needed to promote the change from liquid to gas comes from the surroundings.

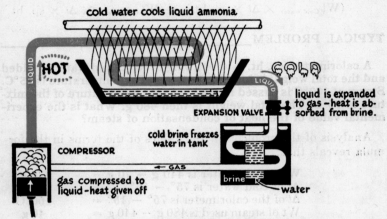

Diagram of an Electrical Refrigerator

In the case of the home refrigerator, the "surroundings" consist of the air within the refrigerator, the walls of the compartments, and the stored food and its containers. In the manufacture of ice, the cooling coils are surrounded by brine (solution of salt) in which containers of pure water are lowered. When the temperature of the brine is lowered below 0°C, the pure water freezes. The brine itself does not freeze because its freezing point has been lowered by the addition of the salt.

Gas Refrigeration. A gas (or kerosene) flame expels ammonia gas from a strong solution of ammonia in water. The resulting pressure, along with cooling by water, cause the ammonia to liquefy. Later, evaporation of the liquid in the cooling compartment removes heat from the interior of the refrigerator. The gaseous ammonia flows through a tube of water, in which it dissolves and returns to the heating unit. The cooling is less rapid than in electric refrigerators, but there are no motors, moving parts, or noise.

Air Conditioning. Complete air conditioning consists of regulating the temperature and moisture content of the air, removing dust and impurities, and assuring its circulation. Heating systems heat the air in winter, and refrigerating units may cool it in summer. Air may circulate by convection, or with the aid of fans or blowers capable of moving a large volume of air at a slow rate. During circulation, dust and impurities are removed by causing the air to pass through filters or sprays of water. A common type of filter contains glass wool coated with oil or other sticky material to collect the dust.

The moisture content of the air is important in relation to personal health and comfort. It must also be carefully regulated in certain stages of the manufacture of textiles and tobacco products, and in paper making and printing. Moisture is generally *added* to air by passing it through sprays of water, over pans of water which expose a large surface area, or past ceramic fins which dip into a trough of water (the water rises through them by capillary action). Moisture is generally *removed* from air by passing it through a spray of cold water or over a cold surface.

Humidity. Whether air is properly conditioned with respect to moisture content really depends upon the *degree of saturation*.

The actual amount of moisture in a unit volume of air is termed *absolute humidity*. It is commonly expressed in *grains* of water vapor per *cubic foot* of air. Air is saturated when, at a given temperature, it holds all the water vapor which it can hold. The higher the temperature, the greater is the amount of water vapor necessary to saturate the air.

The per cent of saturation of air with water vapor is called *relative humidity*:

$$\text{relative humidity} \atop \text{(in \%)} = \frac{\text{absolute humidity}}{\text{quantity of water when saturated} \atop \text{(at existing temperature)}} \times 100$$

Hence, if there is no change in the amount of moisture actually present in the air, a rise in temperature reduces the relative humidity, while a drop in temperature results in increased relative humidity.

For personal comfort, relative humidity of 45–55% is preferable. On hot, "muggy" summer days the relative humidity may reach 90% or more. When relative humidity is too low, as is unfortunately the usual thing in most homes in winter, evaporation takes place too readily; the nose and throat tend to become dry and a higher than necessary temperature is needed for comfort.

Measurement of Relative Humidity. The relative humidity can be found by the use of a *hygrometer,* which consists of a wet- and a dry-bulb thermometer. The bulb of the wet-bulb thermometer is surrounded by a wick, which dips into a reservoir of water. Unless the air is saturated, evaporation occurs from the wick around the bulb. Evaporation is a cooling process. Hence, the wet-bulb thermometer registers a lower temperature than the dry-bulb thermometer. The rate of evaporation depends upon the per cent of saturation of the air, and the difference between the two temperature readings is an indication of the relative humidity, which may be found by reference to a table. The readings of the two thermometers would be the same at 100% relative humidity. If the two thermometers are attached to a board and are whirled through the air, a more accurate measure of relative humidity is obtained. This instrument is called a *sling psychrometer.*

Dew Point. Air always contains some moisture, even over the most arid deserts. The sources of atmospheric moisture include lakes, streams, plant life, and, most important of all, the oceans. If such air is slowly cooled, the relative humidity will rise, as explained previously. Eventually a temperature will be reached at which the air is saturated—that is, the relative humidity is 100%. Any further cooling will result in the condensation of some of the water vapor in the air. This temperature at which the relative humidity reaches 100% is called the *dew point.* The dew point depends only on the *absolute* humidity. The drier the air, the lower its dew point.

To find the dew point experimentally, a highly polished container, such as a calorimeter cup, is cooled by the gradual addition of cracked ice. The ice-water is continually stirred by a thermometer. The temperature of the water when a film of moisture (dew) just forms on the outside of the container gives the dew point.

The "sweating" of pitchers of ice water, the clouding and frosting of windows in the winter, etc., are due to the cooling of a layer of air to a temperature below the dew point. When the earth cools at night through loss of heat by radiation, the air as a whole does not cool as rapidly as blades of grass, roofs, etc. The moist air in contact with these surfaces is cooled and its vapor capacity reduced; hence it becomes more nearly saturated.

When the dew point is reached, moisture condenses out as dew (note that dew does *not* fall). If the dew point (saturation temperature) is below 0°C, *frost* instead of dew is formed.

Cloud Formation. When a mass of air is lifted, the pressure on it decreases and its temperature drops due to expansion. As long as the air is unsaturated, the rate of cooling by expansion is about 5.5°F for each 1000 ft of lift; this is the *dry adiabatic*

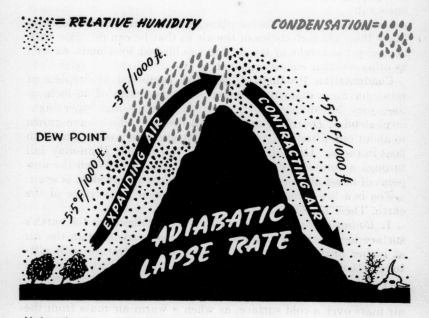

Moist air rising over mountains expands and cools, its temperature dropping 5.5°F for each 1000 ft of ascent. When the temperature drops to the dew point, condensation of moisture in the air begins, and the rising air cools more slowly (3°F per 1000 ft). Upon descending the opposite slope, the air (which has lost much of its moisture) contracts and rises in temperature 5.5°F for each 1000 ft of descent. This warm, relatively dry air produces desert conditions on the far side of the mountain. Such conditions exist to the east of the mountain ranges along the west coast of the U. S., where the prevailing winds are from the west.

lapse rate. At a certain altitude, rising air will reach its saturation temperature (dew point), and moisture will condense. The condensation of water vapor, as a mass of moist air cools to the dew point, produces clouds, fog, and possibly other forms of solid or liquid water which may fall through the air. The condensing moisture gives up its heat of condensation (540 calories per gram) to the surrounding air. This decreases the adiabatic cooling rate to approximately 3°F per 1000 ft; this is the *moist adiabatic* rate.

It is important for the airplane pilot or his meteorologist to know these characteristics of the air so that he can estimate with accuracy the height of the ceiling established by clouds, as well as other weather conditions, such as fog.

Condensation Products. *Clouds* are composed of droplets of water having a diameter of about one thousandth of an inch, or they may be composed of ice crystals (cirrus and other high-level clouds). *Drizzle* is composed of droplets which have grown to about one-fiftieth of an inch in diameter; they seem almost to float in the air. Drops larger than this fall as *rain*. Rain may fall through a colder region and freeze, forming *sleet*. When the dew point of moist air is below 0°C, the condensation product is *snow*.

Fog is a low-lying cloud formed at or near the surface of the earth. There are several types.

1. *Radiation fog* forms on clear, windless nights as the earth's surface loses heat by radiation and becomes cooler than the air at higher altitudes. Since an *increase* in temperature with altitude is the reverse of normal conditions, this is called a *temperature inversion*.

2. *Advection fog* is caused by the movement of a warm moist air mass over a cold surface, as when a warm air mass from the Gulf of Mexico moves over snow-covered land in, say, Ohio or Indiana.

3. *Sea fog* is produced by warm moist air flowing over a relatively colder part of the ocean. A cold stream of water parallels the California coast; hence sea fog is common in this region.

4. *Upslope fogs* form mostly over the western plains when east winds carry moisture-laden air to gradually higher levels. Cooling by expansion produces the fog.

5. *Frontal fogs* form along the boundary between a cold air and a warm air mass. Rain falling into the cold air ahead of the warm front increases its moisture content to the saturation point.

Fog is one of the severest hazards to aviation, and the pilot should be familiar with the various conditions likely to produce fog. Even with instrument flying, radio aids, etc., fog is still a hazard. Pilots, in the interest of safety, should try to avoid the necessity of landing where ceiling and visibility are very low or zero.

Icing Conditions. Ice formation on aircraft is one of the chief hazards of aviation. Ice on the plane adds to its weight, changes the shape of the airfoil (wing), increases "drag," and may interfere with the functioning of the propeller, carburetor, radio antenna, retractable landing gear, etc. Icing conditions are produced in a number of ways.

1. When rain forms at levels of higher temperature and falls into layers of air where the temperature is at or below freezing, the raindrops freeze instantly upon striking the plane. This situation is most likely to be encountered along a warm front, where warm air masses are rising up over colder air.

2. Icing may occur at temperatures 2 or 3 degrees above freezing, as the rain drops striking the moving plane cool by evaporation and then freeze.

3. Most cases of icing occur when planes fly through clouds composed of droplets of *supercooled* water. If water is carefully cooled without being disturbed, it can be cooled several degrees below its freezing point without the formation of ice. Then the slightest agitation causes the supercooled water to freeze almost instantly throughout. Temperatures just below the freezing point favor the formation of clouds composed of supercooled water droplets. A plane flying into such a cloud disturbs the supercooled water, and it freezes immediately all over the plane.

Temperatures of $-15°C$ or lower favor the formation of clouds composed of ice crystals, in which atmospheric moisture changes directly from vapor to solid ice (this type of change of state, in which a solid changes to a gas, or a gas to a solid, without passing through the liquid state, is called *sublimation*). The highest type of clouds (*cirrus*) are composed of ice crystals. There is no danger of icing if a plane flies through clouds composed entirely of ice crystals.

Icing may be avoided generally by following this rule:

*When flying through air whose temperature is between 28° and 34°F, **rise** until the air temperature is outside that range. The higher air will be either colder and drier or warmer and drier.*

BEST ANSWER TEST

1. The effect of an increase in pressure on the boiling point of a liquid is (1) to lower it; (2) to raise it; (3) negligible.

2. The freezing point of a solution is (1) lower than; (2) higher than; (3) the same as—the freezing point of the pure solvent.

3. By relative humidity is meant (1) the weight of moisture in the air; (2) the volume of water in the air; (3) the per cent of moisture in the air; (4) the per cent of saturation of the air.

4. The heat of vaporization for water is (1) less than for any other substance; (2) 80 cal/g; (3) 540 cal/g; (4) the same as the heat of fusion.

5. Clouds begin to form when (1) moisture evaporates into the air; (2) the dew point is reached; (3) moist air rises above 6000 feet; (4) the sun goes down.

6. Fog is really (1) a cloud at or near the ground; (2) composed of ice crystals; (3) a different form of frost; (4) not as hazardous to aviation as commonly thought.

7. Severe icing of aircraft may occur when (1) the plane flies into supersaturated air; (2) a cloud of supercooled water droplets; (3) a hail storm; (4) ice clouds.

8. One calorie is enough heat to (1) melt 1 g of ice; (2) warm 1 g of ice from −2° to 0°C; (3) vaporize 1 g of water; (4) cool 1 g of steam from 102° to 101°C.

9. Which of the following is usually *not* necessary in complete air conditioning? (1) warming the air in winter; (2) cooling the air in summer; (3) adding moisture in winter; (4) adding moisture in summer.

10. Refrigeration by mechanical devices operates on the principle that (1) evaporation is a cooling process; (2) compression of a gas liberates heat; (3) cold air is denser than warm air; (4) the heat of fusion for ice is 80 cal/g.

QUESTIONS

1. The radiators of hot-water heating systems are usually longer than those of steam heating systems. Why?

2. Standing in front of a revolving fan in summer makes you feel cooler. Why?

3. Why are heated dwellings likely to be very "dry" in winter?

4. State a reason, based on the principles of heat, for each of the following: (*a*) Ice is used in a refrigerator. (*b*) Water may be cooled by keeping it in porous canvas bags. (*c*) Water has a moderating influence on climate. (*d*) Ice floats.

5. (*a*) Give an example of two equal quantities of matter that have the same temperature but different quantities of heat. (*b*) Give an example of two quantities of matter one of which, although hotter, has less heat. (c) Mention 4 ways of increasing the rate of evaporation.

6. State with reference to the manufacturing of ice: (a) The use of the compressor. (b) The change in the temperature of the refrigerant brought about by its evaporation. (c) One means employed to hasten the evaporation of the refrigerant. (d) The means used to liquefy the compressed refrigerant.

PROBLEMS

1. How many calories of heat are required to warm (a) 450 g of water from 15°C to 75°C? (b) the same weight of iron (sp ht = 0.11) through the same temperature change?   Ans. (a) 27,000 cal (b) 2970 cal

2. (a) How much heat will 500 grams of water lose in cooling from 100°C to 0°C? (b) How much heat is lost by a copper soldering iron weighing 300 grams, cooling from 400°C to 20°C? (Specific heat = .09).
Ans. (a) 50,000 cal (b) 10,260 cal

3. If 500 grams of water at 10°C are mixed with 200 grams of water at 90°C, what will be the temperature of the mixture?   Ans. 32.9°C

4. How much water at 80°C must be mixed with 2 kgm of water at 5°C to raise its temperature to 70°C?   Ans. 13 kg

5. A 500 gram block of lead (specific heat = .03) is heated and then dropped into 400 grams of water at 15°C raising the temperature to 25°C. What was the original temperature of the lead?   Ans. 292°C

6. A copper can (specific heat = .09) weighs 200 grams and contains 420 grams of water at 15°C. When 350 grams of lead at 220°C are dropped into the water, the temperature of the mixture becomes 20°C. What is the specific heat of the lead?   Ans. 0.031

7. How much heat is required to melt 1 kilogram of ice at 0°C and raise the temperature of the melted ice to 70°C?   Ans. 150,000 cal

8. How much heat must be taken out of 600 grams of water at 90°C to change it to ice at 0°C?   Ans. 102,000 cal

9. What temperature will result if 50 grams of ice at 0°C are put into 350 grams of water at 60°C?   Ans. 42.5°C

10. How much ice at 0°C must be put into 200 grams of water at 90°C to reduce its temperature to 10°C?   Ans. 178 g

11. How much heat is needed to change 200 grams of ice at 0°C into steam at 100°C? (Assume heat of vaporization of water = 540 calories).
Ans. 144,000 cal

12. What temperature will result from the mixture of 10 grams steam at 100°C with 1000 grams of water at 10°C?   Ans. 16.2°C

13. How much steam at 100°C will be needed to raise the temperature of 2000 grams of water from 10°C to 90°C?   Ans. 291 g

14. How much ice will be melted by a 2 kilogram bar of iron (specific heat = .11) at a temperature of 250°C?   Ans. 687.5 g

15. A copper can (specific heat = .09) weighing 200 grams contains 2000 grams of water, and 100 grams of ice at 0°C. If 20 grams of steam at 100°C are put into the can, what will be the resulting temperature?
Ans. 2.24°C

Converting Work to Heat. Whenever work is performed (a force moved through a distance), the work is converted into some form of energy. In lifting a weight, the work done is changed into potential energy; the work done in ejecting a shell from the muzzle of a gun is converted to kinetic energy of the shell; the work of turning an electric generator is changed into electrical energy. Similarly, work can be converted into heat energy.

Work is converted to heat whenever *resistance of friction* is overcome. Count Rumford (Benjamin Thompson) observed that large amounts of heat were generated during the boring of cannon. In one experiment he amazed his watchers by using the heat from friction to boil water in a jacket surrounding a cannon which was being bored with a blunt drill. He demonstrated that unlimited quantities of heat could be obtained from continuous overcoming of friction.

The work of *compressing a gas* is also changed into heat in the gas. The molecules which collide with the moving piston of a compression pump receive some of the kinetic energy of the piston, thus increasing the total kinetic energy of the gas molecules —in other words, their heat content. Conversely, the molecules of an expanding gas lose kinetic energy and are cooled.

The work of *stopping a moving body* suddenly, as in any impact, is converted largely into heat. Flattening a lead ball by hammering it will make the lead quite hot.

Mechanical Equivalent of Heat. There is an exact quantitative relation between heat and work—a certain amount of work is equivalent to a definite amount of heat energy. James Prescott Joule (1818–1889) was the first to make an accurate determination of this quantitative relation. He used an apparatus in which the work of falling weights was changed to heat in water by means of rotating paddles operated by the falling weights. The work done was calculated from the height through which the weights fell; the heat produced was calculated from the weight of water and its temperature rise. Joule found that the mechanical equivalent of heat was given by the following equation:

$$42,700 \text{ gram-centimeters of work} = 1 \text{ calorie}$$

or,

$$778 \text{ foot-pounds} = 1 \text{ B. T. U.}$$

Converting Heat to Work. Heat energy can be converted into mechanical energy by means of a suitable machine called a *heat engine*. All heat engines operate on the same principle—allow a hot gas at high pressure to expand, thereby converting the heat energy of the gas to mechanical energy of some moving part.

In all heat engines, the hot gas is obtained as the result of burning a fuel. If the fuel is burned *inside* the expansion chamber, the engine is called an *internal combustion engine;* if the fuel is burned *outside,* it is an *external combustion engine.* The gasoline and Diesel engines are examples of the former; the steam engine and steam turbine are examples of the latter.

Two Simple Heat Engines. In the simple steam engine on the left, a fire outside the boiler causes the water to boil; the steam formed expands through the nozzles and turns the boiler by reaction. In the simple internal combustion engine (Fourth of July pinwheel), burning occurs inside the engine; the gases formed expand and escape through a hole in the cylinder, turning the pinwheel by reaction.

The Reciprocating Steam Engine. To operate a steam engine, water is first boiled in a boiler heated by fuel burned in a fur-

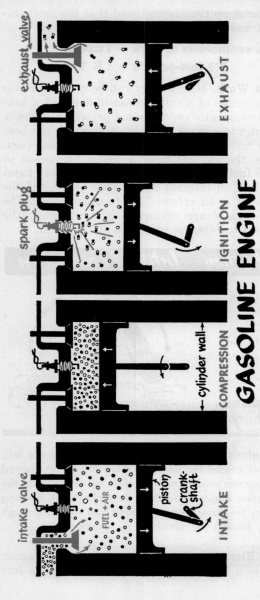

GASOLINE ENGINE

INTAKE

The intake valve opens and the descending piston draws in a mixture of gasoline vapor and air.

COMPRESSION

With both valves closed, the piston ascends and compresses the gas mixture. A moderate rise in temperature occurs.

IGNITION

A spark now ignites the mixture, producing an explosion which drives the piston down. The molecules of gasoline and air are shown combining.

EXHAUST

The exhaust valve opens and the waste gases are driven out by the ascending piston.

DIESEL ENGINE

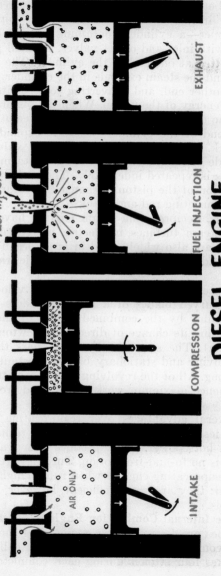

fuel injector

INTAKE

During the intake stroke only air is drawn into the cylinder.

COMPRESSION

The ascending piston compresses the air into a much smaller volume, producing a high temperature.

FUEL INJECTION

A fuel pump or injector now forces a fine spray of fuel oil into the cylinder. The oil immediately ignites, producing an explosion.

EXHAUST

The waste gases are expelled by the ascending piston.

nace. The fuel may be coal, oil, natural or manufactured gas. The steam produced in the boiler is conducted by pipes to the steam engine proper—a cylinder containing a tight-fitting piston and equipped with inlet and outlet valves. A small parcel of steam is first admitted at one end of the cylinder. The steam inlet is then shut off and the steam expands in the cylinder, pushing the piston to the other end, and converting some of its heat energy to mechanical energy of the piston. When the piston completes its travel in one direction, another parcel of steam is admitted at the other end of the cylinder, where it expands and pushes the piston back. In the meantime, an exhaust valve has opened on the first side of the piston, and the spent steam there is ejected. The process is repeated indefinitely. The *reciprocating* (back-and-forth) motion of the piston is changed to rotary motion of a shaft by a connecting rod and crank.

The Steam Turbine. Reciprocating steam engines have been largely replaced by steam turbines in electric power generating stations. Turbines are also widely used in large ocean liners and naval vessels, and increasingly in turboelectric railroad locomotives.

In operation, high-pressure steam traveling at high velocity is directed against the curved blades of a kind of paddle-wheel. The wheel is set spinning by the combined effects of the high velocity of the steam and its change of direction (Newton's law of action and reaction). The steam continues to pass through alternate sets of revolving and stationary blades constantly expanding as it goes along. All of the revolving blades are attached to the same shaft; hence maximum work is obtained from the expanding steam.

Turbines have several advantages over reciprocating steam engines. They weigh less and occupy less space than reciprocating engines of equal horsepower. They produce practically no vibration since there is no to-and-fro motion. Turbines are much more efficient than reciprocating engines when run at high speed and under heavy load; they are not so efficient, however, at low speed with small loads.

The 4-Stroke Cycle Internal Combustion Engines. Most gasoline and Diesel engines are 4-stroke cycle (sometimes shortened to 4-cycle) internal combustion engines. They are so called because the piston makes four strokes during each complete cycle of operation. The gasoline and Diesel engines are shown diagrammatically, and explained, on pages 172–173.

Gasoline and Diesel Engines Compared. There are two important differences between these engines:

1. *Charge.* The gasoline engine cylinder takes in a charge of gasoline vapor and air mixed in the carburetor. This is a device, like an atomizer, in which the stream of air on its way to the cylinder passes over a nozzle connected to a reservoir of gasoline, and draws off the proper amount of gasoline vapor. The Diesel engine takes in a charge of pure air.

2. *Ignition.* Ignition in the gasoline engine is produced by a spark provided by a high-voltage source connected to the terminals of a spark plug. Ignition in the Diesel engine occurs when the fuel is sprayed into the cylinder by a pump; the fuel ignites because of the high temperature produced during compression of the air.

Efficiency of Heat Engines. If all the heat released by the combustion of a fuel could be converted to useful work, 42,700 g-cm of work could be obtained from each calorie, or 778 ft-lb from each B.T.U. A heat engine that did this would be 100% efficient. Unfortunately, heat engines are among the least efficient of mechanical devices because they are subject to certain heat losses about which very little can be done. Typical over-all efficiencies (*brake thermal efficiency*) of several engines, based on work output compared with heat input, are as follows:

Non-condensing steam engine (locomotive)	8%
Condensing steam engines and turbines	15%
Gasoline engines	28%
Diesel engines	35%

The heat value of a pound of coal is about 14,000 B.T.U., equivalent to 10,892,000 ft-lb; a steam locomotive, however, would produce only about 870,000 ft-lb of useful work for each pound of coal burned in its furnace.

The chief reason for this low efficiency is that much of the heat imparted to the steam in the boiler is carried off by the exhaust steam without being converted to work. The same is true of the exhaust gases of the internal combustion engine. In the steam engine, most of the heat in the steam is latent heat of vaporization; when the steam exhausts it is still a vapor, and hence this latent heat of vaporization is not given up in the engine.

Improving the Efficiency of Heat Engines. *Steam Engines.*
The efficiency of a steam engine can be increased if the steam is
allowed to expand further, and thus do more work, before being
exhausted. In ordinary engines, the steam expands until its pres-

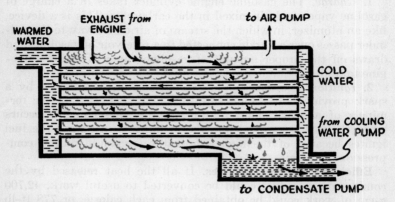

**The Steam Condenser. Cold water pumped through the tubes
cools and condenses the surrounding exhaust steam, producing a
high vacuum in the condenser. The condensate is returned to the
boiler for re-use.**

sure falls to that of the atmosphere. By attaching a condenser to
the exhaust outlet, the steam can expand to a much lower pressure. The condenser is simply an airtight chamber in which the
exhaust steam is condensed by cold water. The condensation results in great reduction of volume and hence produces a high
vacuum.

Internal Combustion Engines. The efficiency of an internal
combustion engine can be improved by raising its *compression
ratio*—the ratio of the volume of gas in the cylinder at the end of
the intake stroke to its volume at the end of the compression
stroke. It is clear that if this ratio is made larger, the gases
formed during combustion expand further and do more work.
However, the temperature of the gases in the cylinder rises as
the gases are compressed; therefore, if the compression ratio of
a gasoline engine is made too high, the high temperature produced will cause the mixture to explode prematurely. This fact

limits the compression ratio in modern gasoline engines to about 6-to-1. The Diesel engine is not limited in this way, since the charge is pure air; therefore compression ratios as high as 16-to-1 (corresponding to a temperature of about 1000°F) are common in Diesel engines. This explains the higher efficiency of these engines as compared with gasoline engines. However, the high pressures in the Diesel engine require heavy cylinder walls, making this engine much heavier per horsepower output than the gasoline engine. As a result, the Diesel engine is at present limited to applications where weight is not an important factor—ships, locomotives, stationary power plants. The gasoline engine is still supreme in automobiles and aircraft.

Valve Timing and Spark Advance in the Gasoline Engine. It has been found that the efficiency of the gasoline engine can be materially increased by careful regulation of the time during which each valve is open, and the point in the cycle at which the spark occurs. Valve *timing* is controlled by a *camshaft* geared to the crankshaft. The cams are set around the shaft at positions which will give maximum efficiency.

It has also been found that an engine will operate more efficiently if the spark occurs slightly before the piston completes its upward compression stroke, provided that the gasoline mixture burns slowly and smoothly. If the gasoline explodes too rapidly, the ascending piston will receive a sudden jolt or "knock" which greatly reduces efficiency. A *high-octane* gasoline is one which produces very little knock, and allows a considerable spark *advance*. (Octane is a constituent of petroleum which has an anti-knock rating of 100. The anti-knock rating of a gasoline is measured in terms of its performance compared with that of pure octane.) The use of high-octane gasoline in American military aircraft partly accounts for their superior performance.

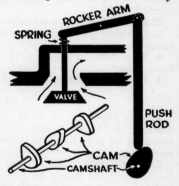

A Cam Opening an Engine Valve. The camshaft is geared to the engine crankshaft so that the valves always open at the proper time.

ASSOCIATION TEST

I
1. _____ Comparatively little vibration
2. _____ Utilizes fuel injector
3. _____ Contains no pistons
4. _____ Used to propel automobiles
5. _____ Highest compression ratio
6. _____ Valves operated by cam ring
7. _____ Lowest efficiency

II
1. Gasoline engine
2. Diesel engine
3. Reciprocating steam engine
4. Steam turbine
5. Radial aircraft engine

COMPLETION TEST

Increasing the number of cylinders in a gasoline engine _____(9)_____ the vibration. In a 4-stroke Diesel engine, the _____(10)_____ stroke follows the exhaust stroke. In the ordinary gasoline engine, there are _____(11)_____ crankshaft revolutions for every power stroke in one cylinder. The driving force in the reciprocating steam engine comes from the _____(12)_____ of the steam. 1 BTU is equivalent to _____(13)_____ foot-pound(s) of mechanical work. The efficiency of a steam engine can be increased by allowing the exhaust steam to escape into a _____(14)_____. The chief function of the carburetor is to _____(15)_____.

QUESTIONS

1. Why is a rotating turbine more efficient than a reciprocating steam engine?
2. Describe Joule's mechanical equivalent of heat experiment.
3. Compare the Diesel engine and 4-stroke gasoline engine in as many ways as you can.
4. Why does an engine need a flywheel? Why don't aircraft engines have them?
5. What is meant by "valve timing"? Why is it important?

PROBLEMS

1. In a repetition of Joule's experiment, a 15-lb weight fell a total distance of 75 feet. Using Joule's mechanical equivalent of heat, and assuming no heat loss, what would be the temperature rise of 15 lb of water? Ans. 0.096°F
2. If a certain grade of coal yields 12,000 BTU per lb, how much mechanical work should be obtained by the transformation of the energy in 1 ton, assuming an over-all efficiency of 30%? Ans. 5,600,000,000 ft-lb
3. An airplane engine develops 640 brake horsepower at 2200 rpm. It burns 54 gal of gasoline per hour. What is the thermal efficiency of the engine if the heat value of the fuel is 127,500 BTU per gal?
Ans. 23.6%

FOURTEEN—   LIGHT—ITS NATURE AND
                                        MEASUREMENT

Concept of a Wave. If a rope is fastened to a wall, and the free end held in the hand and given a rapid up-and-down motion, a series of bends or crests will be seen to pass along the rope from the hand to the wall. This passage of a series of fluctuations past a point is called a *wave*.

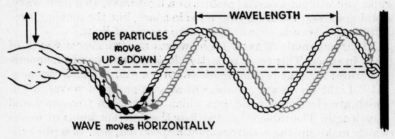

A Transverse Wave. The first position of the rope is shown in black. Its position a moment later is shown in red.

Frequency, Wavelength, and Velocity of a Wave. At any moment, the wave in the rope consists of a series of crests and troughs; a moment later, the crests and troughs have moved along to a new position, but the shape of the wave remains the same. One complete fluctuation is called a *cycle*. The number of crests which pass a given point each second is called the *frequency* of the wave, and is expressed in *cycles per second*. The distance between one crest and the next is the *wavelength*. In every wave:

$$\text{frequency} \times \text{wavelength} = \text{velocity}$$
$$fl = v$$

The velocity of a given type of wave depends only on the medium in which the wave is traveling. Increasing the frequency of the wave therefore simply shortens the wavelength. Thus frequency and wavelength are inversely proportional to each other.

Transverse Vibrations in a Wave. In the rope wave, the *form* of
the wave moves along the rope, but the rope itself does not move
in this direction since both ends are fixed. All that happens is that
each small piece of the rope moves up and down as the wave
goes by. This can be described by saying that the pieces of the
rope vibrate at right angles to the direction of propagation of the
wave. Such vibrations are called *transverse*.

A Wave as a Fluctuating Force. Since each piece of the rope
moves up and down, it must be acted upon by a force which produces this motion. This force is a fluctuating one which acts upwards half the time and downwards the other half. *If you think of
the wave as being just this varying force which travels along the
rope,* you will get a partial picture of a light wave. In a light wave,
nothing moves; but a varying force in space, like the moving force
in the rope, travels outward from the source of light.

Electromagnetic Waves. Light waves are transverse waves of
force in space. This force is partly electrical and partly magnetic
in nature; for that reason, light waves are said to be *electromagnetic.* Light waves are members of a large group of waves, all of
which are electromagnetic, but which differ as to frequency and
wavelength. The table on p. 181 lists the different kinds of waves
which make up the *electromagnetic spectrum,* and describes the
special effects of each.

Speed of Light. All electromagnetic waves travel through space
with the same speed—about 186,000 miles per second. Despite the
tremendous speed which this figure represents, the speed of light
has been measured very accurately by several ingenious methods.
For example, as early as 1676 the Danish astronomer Roemer
measured the speed of light by means of observations of Jupiter's
moons. Roemer was able to calculate just when one of the moons
should pass out of sight behind the planet each time the moon
made one revolution. But when Jupiter and the earth were on
opposite sides of the sun and farthest apart, the moon disappeared
1000 seconds later than the calculations predicted. Roemer con-
cluded, correctly, that this delay was only an apparent one, caused
by the time taken by light to cross the earth's orbit, a distance of
186,000,000 miles. Dividing by 1000 seconds gives the speed of
light—186,000 miles per second.

A long series of experiments by Albert A. Michelson, in this
century, using various methods, gave a result of 186.254 miles per

THE ELECTROMAGNETIC SPECTRUM

Wavelength in cm	Name	How Produced	Chief Effects	Uses
Up to .000 000 014	Gamma rays	Atomic disintegration	Penetrate all matter; affect photographic plates; produce phosphorescence; ionize gases; refracted by crystals	Atomic investigations
.000 000 006 to .000 001 360	X-rays	Sudden stoppage of high speed electrons	Same as gamma rays, but less vigorous and penetrating	X-ray photography and fluoroscope
.000 001 360 to .000 040	Ultra-violet rays	Very hot bodies and ionized gases	Affect photographic plates; produce phosphorescence, ionization, chemical effects	Photography, medicine, disinfecting
.000 04 to .000 08	Visible light	Hot bodies and ionized gases	Sensation of vision; photographic and chemical effects	Illumination, photography, signaling
.000 08 to .04	Infra-red rays	Heat radiations from all bodies	Produce heat in bodies; photographic effect on special emulsions	Heat lamps in medicine; special photographic effects
.01 to 1000	Ultra-high-frequency radio waves	Vacuum tube oscillators	Produce currents in conductors; travel in straight lines, can be reflected and focused	Television, FM, radio-location of aircraft
1000 to 3,000,000	Radio waves	Vacuum tube oscillators	Produce currents in conductors; reflected by Kennelly-Heaviside layer in atmosphere	Radio communication
Above 3,000,000	Alternating currents	Coil rotating in magnetic field	Electromagnetic induction	Generators, motors, transformers

second. This figure is probably correct within a few miles per second either way.

Astronomers use the distance covered by a ray of light *in one year* as their unit of distance—the *light year*. An idea of the distances involved in astronomy can be obtained from the fact that the nearest star is more than four light years (23,000,000,000,000 miles) away from the earth, and entire star systems have been discovered at distances of 900,000 light years and more. Light arriving at the earth today from such stars started out long before modern man appeared on the earth.

Energy in Electromagnetic Waves. The fluctuating forces propagated through space as waves carry energy with them, as do all waves. The wave in the rope is a package of energy; in a whip, for example, the energy transmitted to the end of the cord can be used to produce serious cuts in the skin or a loud snap in the air. Ocean waves may carry large amounts of energy, which some day may be tapped as sources of power. The energy of electromagnetic waves is usually released when the wave enters a body of matter. The energy of light waves for example produces chemical changes in the retina of the human eye which account for vision.

Quantum Theory of Light. According to the modern theory of electromagnetic radiations, the energy in a wave exists in separate packets called *quanta* (plural of *quantum*). The amount of energy in a single quantum depends on the wavelength of the radiation, but is the same for all waves of the same wavelength. In a given wave there are usually many quanta, but all the quanta are alike, and each is indivisible—there is no such thing as half a quantum of energy. In many ways the quanta of radiations are similar to the atoms of matter; it is thus correct to say that energy is composed of "particles" just as matter is composed of particles. A quantum of light is also called a *photon*.

Polarization of Light. The transverse vibrations in a light wave occur in all possible directions at right angles to the direction of motion of the wave. When light passes through certain crystals, all vibrations except those in one particular direction are absorbed. The light is then said to be *polarized*.

Tourmaline crystals possess this ability to polarize light; they absorb from a beam of light all of its vibrations except those that vibrate in a particular plane. The light that comes through one tourmaline crystal cannot get through a second tourmaline crystal unless this latter crystal is turned to the position where its axis is parallel to the axis of the first crystal. "Polaroid" is a commercial preparation in which many tiny polarizing crystals are embedded parallel to each other in transparent plastic (cellulose acetate). This material has come into common use in sun glasses because Polaroid can be set at an angle at which it absorbs reflected glare. (Reflected light is often polarized.)

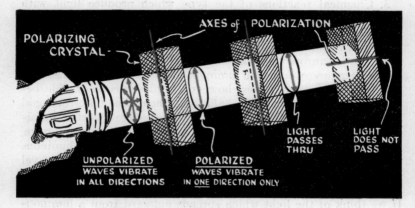

Action of Polarizing Crystals on Light

Disposal of Light Energy. Light cannot penetrate different substances equally well. Some substances are *transparent;* that is, they transmit light so well that objects are clearly visible through them. Some materials, such as the frosted glass bulbs of electric lamps, transmit light, but scatter the light so that objects cannot be readily seen through them; such objects are said to be *translucent.* Then, of course, there are the *opaque* substances through which light cannot pass. The degree to which a material transmits light is determined to some extent by its thickness. Although gold is normally considered to be opaque, very thin layers of gold are translucent. Even the materials which are classified as being transparent absorb light to some extent, so that no substance is perfectly transparent.

Sources of Light Energy. We see objects by the light that comes from them to our eyes. A body like the sun or an incandescent lamp which is a *source* of light is said to be a *luminous* body.

This light energy is given off when electrons within the incandescent body oscillate. This disturbance of the particles of a substance may be due to:

1. *Non-chemical heating of a substance to a high temperature,* as, for example, heating of the filament of an electric lamp.

2. *Chemical burning or combustion,* and chemical reactions which give off heat and light.

3. Chemical reactions of the type which produce light with relatively little heat, as in the firefly.

4. *Electrical disturbances,* such as those in vapor lamps or those which occur in the upper atmosphere during displays of the northern lights or aurora borealis.

5. *Phosphorescence,* as in luminous paints and in some minerals.

In the majority of cases, however, bodies become visible because they *reflect* light which falls upon them. They are then said to be *illuminated* bodies. The moon is thus a huge reflector illuminated by sunlight. You are now reading from an illuminated page.

Propagation of Light. The light that is given off by a luminous point travels outward in all directions and continues to travel *in straight lines* if the medium in which it is traveling remains the same throughout. If the medium is variable, the light may be bent. If we think of the light which spreads outward from a luminous point as being composed of many diverging lines of light, each line is called a *ray*. Parallel rays taken together comprise a *beam* of light.

Through experience with the sense of sight and the sense of touch we have come to assume that light rays from an object always travel to us in straight lines. Therefore, every time an image falls on the retina, the brain automatically assumes that the object producing the image is directly in front of the eyes, and we "see" the object "out there" in front of us. This is generally a true conclusion, and can be verified by going over and feeling the object. However, if the direction of the light rays has been changed before reaching the eyes, we are fooled—we see an object which is not really there. The most obvious example of this, of course, is the image in a mirror. This point will be studied more fully in Chapter 15.

Shadows and Eclipses. If an opaque object is placed before a point source of light, all rays which strike the object are prevented from proceeding further. Other rays continue in straight lines, but none of them enters the region behind the object. The unlighted space behind the object is called a *shadow*. The shadow formed by a point source is sharp, and is similar in shape to the object.

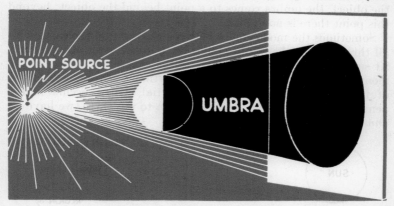

A point source casts a sharp shadow.

If the source of light is larger than a point, there will be regions in which the light from part of the source is cut off, but through which light from the remainder of the source passes. This partially illuminated region is the *penumbra* of the shadow, and it surrounds the region of total darkness which no rays reach, called the *umbra*. The penumbra is darkest near the umbra and gradu-

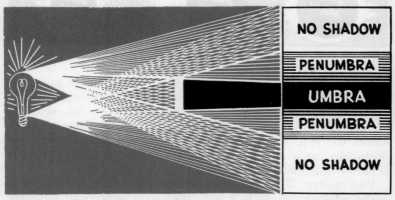

A large source produces a black shadow (umbra) surrounded by a partially illuminated penumbra.

ally lightens as the distance from the umbra increases, until it fades off into the region of no shadow. If the source is larger than the object, the umbra comes to a point behind the object; beyond this point there is no umbra.

Sometimes the moon comes between the sun and the earth with all three of these heavenly bodies lying in the same straight line. At such times we have an *eclipse* of the sun. If the umbra of the moon's shadow reaches as far as the earth, we have a *total* eclipse of the sun within the umbra. A partial eclipse occurs in the penumbra. If the umbra does not reach to the earth, we have an *annular*, rather than a total, eclipse.

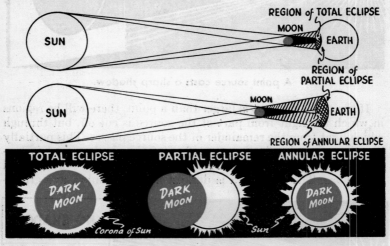

Three Types of Solar Eclipses

Eclipses of the sun occur only at the time of the new moon. At full moon, the moon occasionally enters the shadow of the earth, in which case the *moon* is eclipsed—its source of illumination, the sun, is cut off. An eclipse of the moon is total when the moon enters the earth's umbra. When the moon passes through the penumbra (as it always does before and after a total eclipse) it is partly illuminated, and is visible, though dim.

Photometry. The measurement of light and light sources is called *photometry*. It is known that some sources of light are "brighter" than others; that is, the rate at which light energy is radiated varies among different sources. This rate of radiation of light is measured in units called *candle power*. One candle power is the rate at which a certain standard lamp (called the standard candle) radiates light in a fixed direction. As an indication of the size of this unit, a 60-watt lamp has a candle power of about 50. A searchlight used in airplane detection may have several million candle power in the direction of its beam.

Most light sources have different candle powers in different directions. Special reflectors are often used to concentrate the light in one direction, thus increasing the candle power in that direction at the expense of candle power in other directions.

Illumination. *A surface one foot from a point source of light of one candle power is illuminated with an intensity of one foot-candle.* By examining the following diagram it is seen that the *intensity of illumination* decreases as the distance from the source increases. The same light which passed through the one-inch square at a distance of one foot, has spread out to cover an area three inches square at a distance of three feet—nine times the area. The intensity at three feet is therefore one-ninth of that at one foot; at four feet, it is one-sixteenth of that at one foot. Thus intensity of illumination is inversely proportional to the square of the distance from the source.

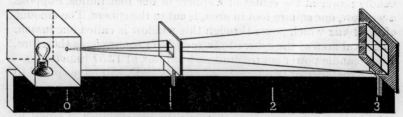

The Law of Inverse Squares. Illumination from a point source is inversely proportional to the square of the distance from the source.

Since intensity is also directly proportional to the candle power of the source, we obtain the following formula:

$$\text{intensity of illumination} = \frac{\text{candle power of source}}{\text{square of distance from source}}$$

where d is in feet. $\text{foot-candles} = \dfrac{cp}{d^2}$

TYPICAL PROBLEMS

What is the intensity of illumination 5 ft from a 100 cp lamp?

$$\text{ft candles} = \frac{cp}{d^2} = \frac{100}{25} = 4 \text{ ft candles}$$

At what distance from this lamp would the intensity be 10 ft candles?

$$10 \text{ ft candles} = \frac{100}{d^2}, \text{ or } d^2 = 10, \ d = \sqrt{10} = 3.16 \text{ ft}$$

What cp lamp is needed to furnish an illumination of 8 ft candles on a surface 6 ft away?

$$8 \text{ ft candles} = \frac{cp}{6^2}, \text{ or } cp = 8 \times 6^2 = 288 \text{ cp}$$

The number of foot-candles needed in order to avoid eye strain varies with the kind of task being done. It varies from the 10 to 20 foot-candles needed for reading ordinary print to 100 or more foot-candles for fine needlework on dark goods.

The Lumen and Light Flux. Imagine a point source of one candle power at the center of a sphere of one foot radius. Suppose a window, one square foot in area, is cut in the sphere. The amount of *light flux* which pours through this window is called *one lumen*. The total area of the sphere is 4π (or 12.57) square feet; therefore, a one-candle power source emits a total flux of 12.57 lumens.

At a distance of two feet, this lumen of light will have spread to cover four square feet. The intensity of illumination at the one-foot sphere is 1 foot-candle; at the two-foot sphere, ¼ foot-candle. It can be seen that intensity in foot-candles is equal to lumens per square foot falling on the surface:

lumens received = foot-candles × area in square feet

The lumen is the unit used by illumination engineers when measuring the total light output of a lamp, or the total light energy available in a room. The engineer's job is to direct these lumens so as to obtain proper intensity of illumination at all important points in the room.

The Bunsen Photometer. The Bunsen photometer makes it possible to determine the candle power of a light source of unknown brightness by comparing it with a light source whose intensity is known. As shown in the diagram, the instrument consists essentially of a white screen with a translucent "grease" spot. The screen can be moved back and forth between a standard light source (s) whose candle power is known and the light (x) whose candle power is to be determined. Light from no other source except those two should reach the screen. The grease spot disappears when the screen is in such a position that both of its sides are *equally illuminated*.

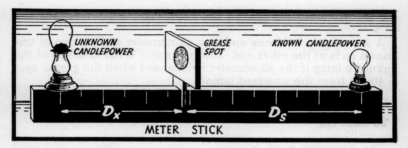

The Bunsen Photometer. When the grease spot disappears, the candle powers of the lamps are directly proportional to the squares of their distances from the spot.

In this position the following equation is true, because illumination from each lamp is the same:

$$\text{intensity of illumination} = \frac{cp}{d^2} = \frac{cp_s}{d_s^{\,2}} = \frac{cp_x}{d_x^{\,2}}$$

Therefore

$$cp_x = cp_s \times \frac{d_x^{\,2}}{d_s^{\,2}}$$

Electric Foot-Candle Meter. A convenient method of determining light intensity has been developed, largely for use in photography. The instrument is really a combination of a photoelectric cell and a sensitive galvanometer. Photoelectric cells contain metals such as potassium, rubidium, and cesium. When visible light strikes these metals, a feeble electric current is produced. The size of the current depends upon the intensity of the light, and is measured by the sensitive galvanometer.

Instead of having a scale to show the size of the current, the meter usually has a scale devised to indicate directly in foot-candles the intensity of the illumination which caused the current. The electric foot-candle meter is a useful instrument for checking the adequacy of the illumination in school rooms, factories, and elsewhere.

TYPICAL PROBLEM

A 32 cp lamp is at one end of a photometer and a lamp of unknown cp is at the other end (200 cm away). What is the cp of the unknown lamp if the photometer is balanced when the grease spot is 40 cm from the standard lamp?

Given: $cp_s = 32$; $d_s = 40$ cm; $d_x = 200 - 40 = 160$ cm

To find: cp_x

$$cp_x = cp_s \times \frac{d_x{}^2}{d_s{}^2}$$

$$cp_x = 32 \left(\frac{160^2}{40^2} \right) = \frac{32 \times 25600}{1600} = \textbf{512 cp}$$

QUESTIONS

1. Mention an example of (a) a luminous body, (b) an illuminated body, (c) a transparent substance, (d) a translucent substance, (e) an opaque body.

2. Galileo and his assistants attempted to measure the velocity of light by observing the time required by light to travel from a group of experimenters on one hill to a group on a second hill. Explain why this attempt was unsuccessful.

3. Describe how Roemer was able to measure the velocity of light by means of astronomical observations.

4. (a) Draw a diagram to show the type of shadow cast by an opaque object when the luminous body is larger than the object. (b) Draw a diagram to show the type of shadow cast by an opaque object when the light-source is a point.

5. Make a labeled diagram showing how an eclipse of the sun is formed

6. How is polarized light obtained and how is it used?

7. Distinguish between 1 foot-candle and 1 candle power.

CLASSIFICATION TEST

Give the number of the term which includes all the others.

1. (1) X-rays; (2) visible light; (3) electromagnetic waves; (4) ultra-violet rays; (5) cosmic rays.

2. (1) opaque; (2) translucent; (3) transparent; (4) diffusing; (5) optical property.

3. (1) light waves; (2) transverse; (3) polarized; (4) 186,000 mi/sec.

4. (1) shadow; (2) umbra; (3) penumbra; (4) eclipse.

5. (1) candle power; (2) foot-candle; (3) photometry; (4) lumen; (5) photometer.

ASSOCIATION TEST

I

6. _____ Shorter wave-length than visible light.

7. _____ Rate of emitting light energy.

8. _____ First determined velocity of light.

9. _____ Produces sun-burn and sun-tan.

10. _____ First proposed corpuscular theory of light.

11. _____ Longer wave-length than visible light.

12. _____ Light resulting from electrical disturbance.

13. _____ Light resulting from overcoming electrical resistance.

14. _____ A luminous body.

15. _____ An illuminated body.

II

1. Roemer
2. Venus
3. Incandescent electric lamp
4. Ultra-violet
5. Candle-power
6. Newton
7. Fluorescent lamp
8. Galileo
9. Radio waves
10. Polaris

PROBLEMS

1. Calculate the miles in a *light year*.   Ans. 5,880,000,000,000 miles

2. What intensity of illumination is obtained (*a*) 10 ft from a 1000 cp lamp? (*b*) 5 ft from a 100 cp lamp? Ans. (a) 10 ft-candles (b) 4 ft-candles

3. What candle power lamp will furnish an intensity of illumination of 9 ft candles (*a*) at a distance of 3 ft? (*b*) 5 ft?
                                        Ans. (a) 81 cp (b) 225 cp

4. At what distance from a 90 cp lamp is the intensity of illumination (*a*) 10 ft candles? (*b*) 20 ft candles?   Ans. (a) 3 ft (b) 2.12 ft

5. At what distance should a 50 cp lamp be placed to give the same illumination as a 100 cp lamp at a distance of 6 ft?   Ans. 4.25 ft

6. A 32 cp lamp is at one end of a photometer and a lamp of unknown candle power at the other end. What is the candle power of the unknown lamp if the grease spot disappears when placed (*a*) 40 cm from the known lamp? (*b*) 80 cm from the known lamp? Assume that the photometer is a meter in length.   Ans. (a) 72 cp (b) 2 cp

7. A piece of cardboard 6 in square is held vertically at a distance of 2 ft from a candle. What will be the dimensions of the shadow cast on a wall 4 ft beyond the cardboard square?   Ans. 18 inches square

FIFTEEN—   REFLECTION OF LIGHT

Definitions and Meanings of Terms. When light strikes a surface, much or little of it may be turned back or reflected. If there were no reflection, this would indicate that all of the light had been absorbed or transmitted. The very fact that illuminated objects are visible indicates that these objects are reflectors because we see them by means of the light which they do reflect. A ray which falls upon a surface is called an *incident ray;* a ray which rebounds from the surface is called the *reflected ray.* A line drawn perpendicular to the reflecting surface at the point where the incident ray strikes is called the *normal.* Between the incident ray and the normal lies the *angle of incidence,* and between the normal and the reflected ray lies the *angle of reflection.*

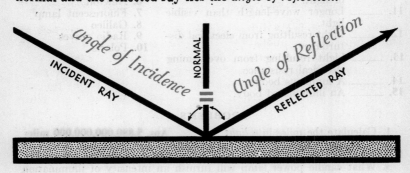

The Law of Reflection

The Law of Reflection. Measurement shows that *the angle of reflection is always equal to the angle of incidence.* This generalization is called *the law of reflection of light.* In the case of a ray which coincides with the normal, the reflected ray takes the same path and the angles of incidence and reflection are both equal to zero. The incident ray, the reflected ray, and the normal all lie in the same plane.

Regular and Diffuse Reflection. A smooth, plane surface, such as that of a mirror or still water, reflects light regularly. When the incident rays are parallel, the reflected rays are also parallel. If the surface upon which the incident rays fall is rough, diffuse reflection occurs. The rays reflected from rough surfaces are not parallel, even if the incident rays were. This explains why a

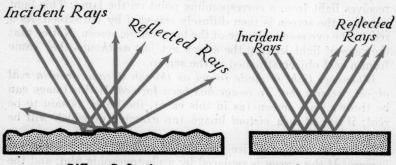

Diffuse Reflection   **Regular Reflection**

surface which reflects diffusely can be seen from any position at which there is an unobstructed straight line path between the surface and the observer's eye. If it were possible to make a perfect reflector which gave no diffuse reflection, it would be invisible. If a light were held in front of such a mirror but where the observer could not see the light directly, the image in the mirror would appear to be the real source of light. The illusion would be much more striking than it is with the imperfect mirrors to which we are accustomed.

Images. The following diagram shows an opaque card in which a pinhole has been made. On one side of the card is a carbon-

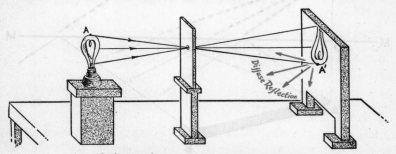

A pinhole produces a real image on a screen.

filament lamp; on the other is a white screen. The only light which reaches the screen must pass through the pinhole. Since light travels in straight lines, the rays which reach point A' can come only from point A on the lamp; similarly, each point on the screen receives light from a corresponding point on the lamp. This light reaching the screen is then diffusely reflected by the screen. As a result, the eye sees an image of the lamp on the screen. Notice that the rays of light leaving the screen act *just as though* they came from a real object attached to the screen.

Whenever light is made to act as though it came from a real object, we say that an image has been formed. If this image can be thrown on a screen (as in this case), the image is said to be *real*; if not, it is a *virtual* image (an example of which will be given presently).

The experimental device just described is known as a pinhole camera. If the screen is replaced by a photographic film, and the whole enclosed in a light-tight box, a picture of any object in front of the pinhole will be made on the film. Notice that the image formed is inverted with respect to the object. *Real images are always inverted.*

Images in the Plane Mirror. The following diagram shows what happens when light rays from an object strike a plane mirror

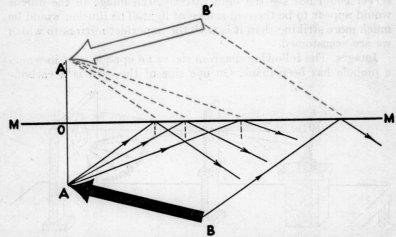

Formation of a Mirror Image. Virtual rays are shown in red.

(smooth reflecting surface). All the rays from a given point, A, are reflected in such a way that the reflected rays *seem* to be coming from the point A'. In other words, the eye sees the image of point A at A'. From the geometry of the diagram it can be shown that A' is as far behind the mirror as A is in front of it, and the line AA' is perpendicular to the mirror.

These facts are easily verified by standing a mirror on the table, sticking a pin at point A, and sighting along a ruler at the image of A from various positions. If each sight line is drawn, and then extended beyond the mirror, they will all meet at A'.

What applies to the point A is true of every point on the object AB. Therefore the image of AB is the arrow $A'B'$, which is exactly the same size as AB and as far behind the mirror as the object is in front of it.

But this image is a *virtual image*. The rays of light only *seem* to come from $A'B'$, but actually don't. $A'B'$ exists only in the mind, and cannot be thrown on a screen.

Notice that the image in a mirror is always erect—a point at the top of the object is at the top of the image also. The "mirror image," however, is reversed—a point on the right side of the object (as you look at it) is on the left side of the image. Hold this page up to a mirror to obtain proof of this statement.

This is a mirror image

Definitions Relating to Curved Mirrors. By applying the law of reflection, we can also construct diagrams for the images formed in curved mirrors. A part of the surface of a sphere is commonly used in the construction of a curved mirror. If we employ the inside of the sphere for our reflector, we have a *concave mirror;* if the reflecting surface is a portion of the outside surface of the sphere, we have a *convex mirror.*

In the diagram, MN, an arc of a circle, is used to represent a concave spherical mirror. C is the *center of curvature*, that is, the center of the sphere of which MN is a section. O is the middle of the mirror and the line drawn through the points C and O is the *principal axis.* Any other line, such as CP, drawn through the center of curvature to the mirror, is called a *secondary axis.* When rays of light parallel to the principal axis fall upon a concave mirror, they are reflected so that they meet at a point half way between the center of curvature and the mirror (*F*). This point is called the *principal focus* and the distance between it and the center of the mirror (*FO*) is called the *focal length* of the mirror.

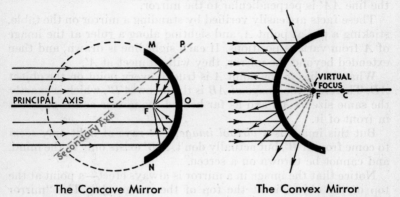

The Concave Mirror　　　　The Convex Mirror

When parallel rays strike a *convex* mirror, the reflected rays are divergent, but they seem to come from a focus in back of the mirror. Such an apparent focus is called a *virtual focus*.

Images Formed by the Concave Mirror. To locate the image of any point on an object placed before a concave mirror, all we need are the paths of two rays from the point. Where these rays eventually meet, or seem to meet, is the location of the image. From the

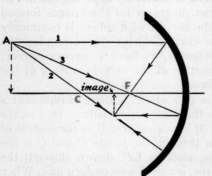

properties of the concave mirror we can trace the paths of three rays:

1. The ray which is parallel to the principal axis will be reflected through the principal focus.

2. The ray which passes through the center of curvature will be reflected back upon itself, because the radius of a sphere is normal to the surface.

3. The ray which passes through the principal focus on its way to the mirror, will be reflected parallel to the principal axis.

We usually use the first two of these rays, although in special cases we may have to use the third. All three reflected rays meet at the same point.

The diagrams on pages 198–199 show object and image in various positions, and describe what happens as the object moves in from infinity toward the mirror.

Shaving mirrors are concave mirrors placed so that the object (face) is between *F* and the mirror.

Images Formed by Convex Mirrors. Using the same methods, the images in a convex mirror can be constructed. The chief difference is that the ray parallel to the principal axis is reflected as though coming from the virtual focus behind the mirror, ●and the ray which would pass through the center of curvature is the one reflected back on itself. As a result, all the images formed are virtual, erect, and smaller than the object, as shown in the diagram.

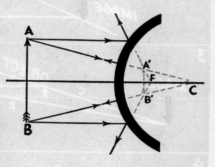

The Mirror Formulas. From the geometry of the diagrams, definite mathematical relations between image and object can be derived. These are expressed in the following formulas:

$$(1) \quad \frac{1}{\text{distance from object to mirror}} + \frac{1}{\text{distance from image to mirror}} = \frac{1}{\text{focal length}}$$

$$\frac{1}{D_o} \qquad + \qquad \frac{1}{D_i} \qquad = \qquad \frac{1}{F}$$

$$(2) \quad \frac{\text{size of image}}{\text{size of object}} = \frac{\text{distance from image to mirror}}{\text{distance from object to mirror}}$$

$$\frac{S_i}{S_o} \qquad = \qquad \frac{D_i}{D_o}$$

If the image is virtual (behind the mirror), then D_i is negative.

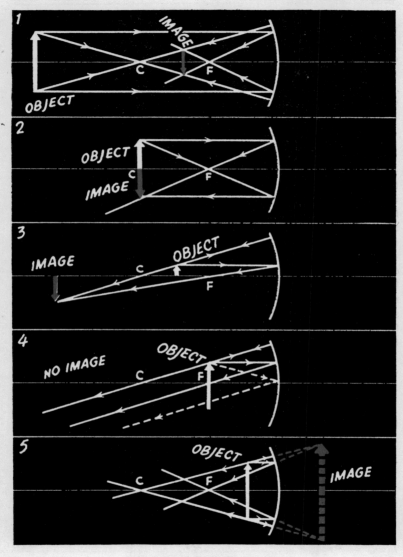

1

IMAGE

OBJECT

C   F

2

OBJECT

IMAGE   C   F

3

IMAGE

C   OBJECT

F

4

NO IMAGE   OBJECT

C   F

5

OBJECT

C   F   IMAGE

IMAGES FORMED BY

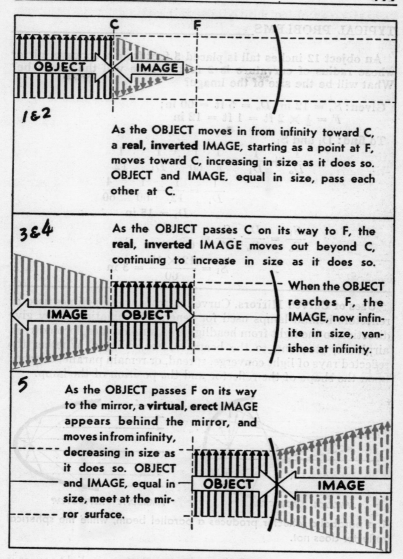

1 & 2

As the OBJECT moves in from infinity toward C, a **real, inverted** IMAGE, starting as a point at F, moves toward C, increasing in size as it does so. OBJECT and IMAGE, equal in size, pass each other at C.

3 & 4

As the OBJECT passes C on its way to F, the **real, inverted** IMAGE moves out beyond C, continuing to increase in size as it does so.

When the OBJECT reaches F, the IMAGE, now infinite in size, vanishes at infinity.

5

As the OBJECT passes F on its way to the mirror, a **virtual, erect** IMAGE appears behind the mirror, and moves in from infinity, decreasing in size as it does so. OBJECT and IMAGE, equal in size, meet at the mirror surface.

THE CONCAVE MIRROR

TYPICAL PROBLEMS

An object 12 inches tall is placed 5 feet from a concave mirror whose radius of curvature is 2 feet. Where will the image be? What will be the size of the image?

Given: $S_o = 12$ in; $D_o = 5$ ft $= 60$ in;
$\quad\quad\quad F = \frac{1}{2} \times 2$ ft $= 1$ ft $= 12$ in

To find: D_i and S_i

$$\frac{1}{D_o} + \frac{1}{D_i} = \frac{1}{F}; \frac{1}{60} + \frac{1}{D_i} = \frac{1}{12}$$

$$\frac{1}{D_i} = \frac{1}{12} - \frac{1}{60} = \frac{4}{60}$$

$$D_i = 15 \text{ in}$$

$$\frac{S_i}{S_o} = \frac{D_i}{D_o}; \frac{S_i}{12} = \frac{15}{60}$$

$$S_i = \frac{12 \times 15}{60} = 3 \text{ in}$$

Uses of Curved Mirrors. Curved mirrors are sometimes used as reflectors behind lamps used for general illumination. They give direction to the light from headlights on automobiles, locomotives, airplanes, etc., and to the beams of searchlights. Whether the reflected rays of light converge, spread, or remain parallel depends upon the shape of the reflector and the position of the lamp.

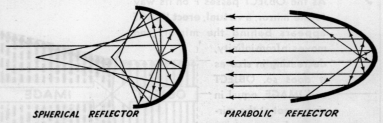

SPHERICAL REFLECTOR   PARABOLIC REFLECTOR

The parabolic reflector produces a parallel beam, while the spherical reflector does not.

When a spherical mirror is used as a reflector, the light source is commonly placed at the principal focus. A spherical mirror actually does not focus parallel rays sharply at a point, and this causes some distortion in the images formed by these mirrors. This failure to focus sharply at the principal focus is called *spherical aberration*. Conversely, when an electric lamp is placed at the principal focus of a spherical mirror, the rays which are reflected from the mirror are not parallel—they converge. For this reason the reflectors in automobile headlights are usually parabolic mirrors rather than spherical ones. A parabolic mirror focuses parallel rays sharply at a point; conversely, it furnishes parallel light rays when a light source is placed at the mirror's principal focus. One of the U.S. Army's anti-aircraft searchlights is sixty inches in diameter and has at the mirror's focal point a carbon arc of 800,-000 candle power. The light beam cuts the sky for a distance of five and one-half miles.

Signals by Reflected Light. Light beams are commonly used to communicate between army positions or between ships at sea. The use of radio communications during engagements may be unwise since they might be intercepted by the enemy. During the day, plane mirrors can be used to reflect the sun's rays and at night searchlights flash the messages. These devices have the advantage of being clearly visible only in the direction toward which they are directed.

It is possible for ships which lie over the horizon from each other to communicate by intermittently flashing a spotlight against the base of a cloud. This is also the technique used by the meteorologist who flashes his ceiling light against the clouds. He observes the spot on the clouds through his telescope, or *clinometer*, located a known distance from the test light. Noting the

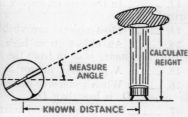

Signaling by Reflected Light   **Measuring the Height of a Cloud**

angle of elevation of the clinometer then makes it possible for the observer with the help of his trigonometric tables to calculate the *ceiling,* or elevation of the clouds.

In warfare, signaling by reflected light has the advantage that there is a limit to the distance at which it can be seen. When visibility is limited, nearby ships can signal to each other without fear that the distant enemy will be able to see the flashes.

ASSOCIATION TEST

I	II
1. _____ Angle of incidence = angle of reflection.	1. Spherical aberration
2. _____ Reflection from a rough surface.	2. Law of reflection of light
3. _____ Image always erect and reduced in size.	3. Concave mirror
4. _____ A defect of spherical mirrors.	4. Diffuse reflection
5. _____ Type of reflector used in searchlights.	5. Plane mirror
6. _____ Image always same size as object.	6. Convex mirror
7. _____ Enables object or surface to be seen from any angle.	7. Virtual focus
8. _____ Image distance always equal to object distance.	
9. _____ Rays of light only apparently travel to a focus.	
10. _____ Forms real images either larger or smaller than object.	

TRUE-FALSE TEST

Write a plus sign in the space provided if the statement is true, and a zero if the statement is false; if the statement is false, correct it by substituting for the underlined part of the statement.

11. _____ The incident ray and the reflected ray are in the same straight line only when the angle of incidence is 0°.

12. _____ In the case of convex mirrors, the principal focus is always virtual.

13. _____ Most objects are visible by regular reflection.

14. _____ An object 10 in high is placed 2 ft in front of a plane mirror. The image is 20 in from the object.

15. _____ A parabolic mirror is used to avoid spherical aberration.

16. _____ When a concave mirror forms an image that is larger than the object, D_i is less than D_o.

17. _____ The small curved mirror used by dentists to give an enlarged image of a tooth is a plane mirror.

18. _____ The shortest plane mirror in which a person 5 ft tall can see a complete image of himself is one that is 2.5 ft high.

19. _____ The incident ray makes an angle of 30° with respect to the normal; the angle between the incident ray and the reflected ray is 60°.

20. _____ A plane mirror set at an angle of 45° will enable one to see around the corner of a rectangular object.

QUESTIONS

1. Compare the reflection of light from white blotting paper with that from a plane mirror. Which of these objects is more easily seen from a distance? Why?

2. Mention three characteristic properties of an image formed by a plane mirror.

3. If the image is 1 ft high when the object is at a distance of 4 ft from a plane mirror, what is the height of the image when the object is 2 ft from the mirror?

4. What kinds of mirrors are used in automobiles and on trucks to give the driver a view of the traffic behind him? Describe the characteristics of the images formed by these mirrors.

5. Give the physical explanation of each of the following statements: (*a*) Book paper which is highly glazed is injurious to the eyes. (*b*) If you move toward a mirror, your image approaches you twice as fast as you approach the mirror. (*c*) If a beam of light is allowed to fall upon a plane mirror, and the mirror is then turned through 1°, the reflected beam is turned through 2°. (*d*) A perfect mirror is invisible.

PROBLEMS

1. An illuminated object is held 40 in in front of a concave mirror whose focal length is 15 in. Calculate where the image will fall and describe its characteristics. Ans. 24 in from mirror, real, inverted, smaller

2. If the object in problem 1 is 6 in tall, how tall will the image be?
Ans. 3.6 in

3. The focal length of a concave mirror is 20 in. An object 3 in tall is at a distance of 40 in from the mirror. What is the size of the image?
Ans. 3 in

4. If the object in problem 3 were placed 10 in in front of the mirror (*a*) Where would the image appear? (*b*) What would the size of the image be? (*c*) Describe the rest of its characteristics.
Ans. (a) 20 in behind mirror (b) 6 in (c) erect, virtual

5. The focal length of a convex mirror is 8 in. (*a*) Where will the image be formed of an object 4 in high held 2 ft in front of the mirror? (*b*) What will be the size of the image?
Ans. (a) 6 in behind mirror (b) 1 in

6. (*a*) How far in front of a concave mirror, whose radius of curvature is 2 ft, should an object 10 in long be placed to produce an image 15 inches in front of the mirror? (*b*) Describe the image produced.
Ans. (a) 60 in from mirror (b) real, inverted, 2.5 in high

7. (*a*) What is the radius of curvature of a concave mirror that produces an image of a lamp 10 ft away, on a screen 2 ft in front of the mirror? (*b*) Describe the image. Ans. (a) 3⅓ ft (b) real, inverted, smaller

SIXTEEN— REFRACTION OF LIGHT

SIXTEEN

Velocities in Different Media. The velocity of light depends on the medium in which it is traveling. In general, the velocity is less in denser substances. For example, in air it is **186,000 miles per second**, in water, **140,000 m.p.s.**, in flint glass, **111,000 m.p.s.**, etc. If the speed in one substance is less than in another, the first is said to be *optically denser* than the second, regardless of the actual densities of the materials.

What Refraction Is. As long as a light beam is traveling in a medium of constant optical density, it travels in a straight line. If, however, it enters a medium of different optical density, at an oblique angle, the direction of the beam changes. This change of direction, or bending of a beam of light in passing from one medium to another of different optical density, is called *refraction*. Refraction does not occur if the rays pass from one medium to the other at right angles to the surface between the media.

Explanation of Refraction. Refraction is the result of the different speeds of light in the two media. The middle diagram shows what happens when a beam of light passes from air to glass at an oblique angle. The line *AB* is the *wave front* of the beam in air. (The wave front is a line perpendicular to the direction of

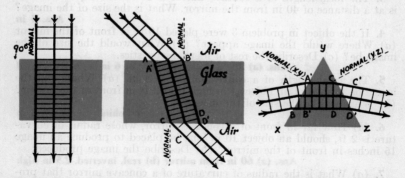

Refraction of Light. The refracted ray always bends toward the normal on entering the denser medium, and bends away from the normal on leaving.

the beam at all points.) As soon as part of the wave front enters the glass, it is slowed up, since the speed of light in glass is less than that in air. When the entire front has entered the glass, the light from point A has moved to point A' in the same time that light from point B moved to point B'. Since the direction of the beam is always perpendicular to the wave front, the change in direction of the wave front inside the glass results in a change in direction of the beam.

At the other edge of the glass, the first part of the beam to emerge into air speeds up, resulting in another change in direction, as shown. If both surfaces of the glass are parallel, the amount of bending at each surface is the same, and the ray emerges parallel to its original direction, but not along the same line. If the glass is a prism, the beam takes the direction shown in the diagram.

If the beam enters perpendicular to the surface, no refraction occurs, because all parts of the wave front enter at the same time and are slowed up simultaneously.

Laws of Refraction. When light passes obliquely into a *denser* medium, it bends *toward* the normal to the surface of the medium. When it passes from a dense to a less dense medium, it bends *away* from the normal. The incident ray, refracted ray, and normal all lie in the same plane.

Index of Refraction. The index of refraction is a number which determines the amount of bending which light undergoes in passing from air into a given substance. As would be expected, the index of refraction of a substance depends on the speed of light in that substance. It is given by the following formula:

$$\text{Index of Refraction} = \frac{\text{Speed of Light in Air}}{\text{Speed of Light in Substance}}$$

Index of refraction is constant for a given substance, that is, it does not depend on the angle of incidence. However, light of long wavelength (such as red light) travels faster in matter than light of short wavelength (such as violet light); as a result, the index of refraction for red light is always less than that for violet light, for a given medium.

An instrument called a *refractometer* enables the scientist to determine these indexes very quickly. With it he can easily distinguish between a genuine diamond for which the index of refraction is 2.417 and a glass or "paste" imitation whose index of refraction would be just slightly under two. Likewise, the refractometer is useful in identifying crystals, precious stones, etc.

Examples of Refraction. Light that comes to us from the sun, moon, and stars is refracted when it enters our atmosphere. The amount of refraction increases as the light penetrates because the density of the atmosphere becomes greater as the earth's surface is approached. The initial refraction is due to the fact that light travels faster in interstellar space (an almost perfect vacuum) than it does in air. As a result of refraction, we never see the heavenly bodies in their true positions except when they are directly overhead. Since the bending is toward the normal we really see the sun and other heavenly bodies before they rise above the horizon and after they set below the horizon. Keep in mind the fact that it is the final path of a light ray as it strikes the eye that determines where we see the object from which the light comes.

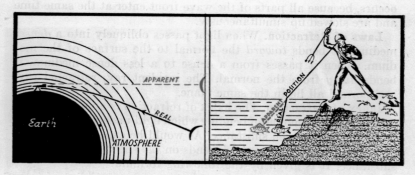

Two common optical illusions resulting from refraction.

The shimmering scene over a hot roadway or over a hot radiator is due to varying refraction. Convection currents set up by these hot surfaces give rise to layers of air of different densities, which are constantly moving because the warmer, less dense air rises. The light which comes through these shifting layers undergoes varying amounts of refraction from instant to instant. This type of refraction causes the "wavy" result. Obviously, the common saying that we "see heat waves rising" is false since heat waves are invisible.

When viewed obliquely, a stick partly immersed in water appears broken and a fish swimming in water appears to be closer to the surface than it really is. Refraction accounts for these optical illusions.

Critical Angle and Total Reflection. Whenever a ray of light strikes the surface between two mediums of different optical densities, part of the ray is *reflected* from the surface back into the first medium; the remainder of the ray is usually *refracted* and enters the second medium. *If the ray is passing from a more dense to a less dense medium,* the refracted ray is bent *away* from the normal. As the angle of incidence is increased, the angle of refraction also increases, until an angle of incidence is reached for which the angle of refraction is 90°—the refracted ray emerges along the surface. This angle of incidence is called the *critical angle.* If the angle of incidence is greater than the critical angle, no light can leave the denser medium, and the entire ray is totally reflected within the medium. As the diagram shows, the amount of light reflected inside the medium increases as the angle of in-

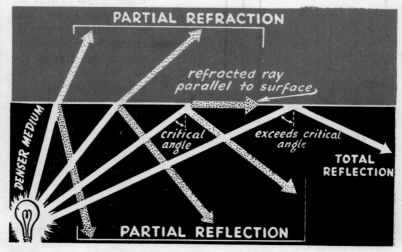

Refraction and Reflection at the Inner Surface of an Optically Dense Medium. As the angle of incidence within the denser medium increases, the amount of light reflected at the surface increases; the entire ray is reflected internally when the angle of incidence exceeds the critical angle. The less dense medium is shown in red.

cidence increases, until eventually all the light is reflected for angles exceeding the critical angle. *The critical angle applies only to rays striking the surface from within the denser medium.* Some refraction always occurs when rays strike the surface obliquely from the less dense medium.

The critical angle depends on the index of refraction of the material. Water has a critical angle of about 49°, crown glass about 42°, but the diamond only 24°. The small critical angle of the diamond accounts for its brilliance. Light that enters it does not escape unless it strikes a surface at an angle of incidence less than 24°. The prolonged internal reflection of a large portion of the light which enters a diamond makes it so brilliant.

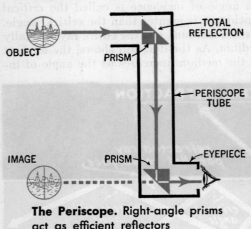

The Periscope. Right-angle prisms act as efficient reflectors

The following diagram illustrates how two right angle prisms are used in the periscope of a submarine. Right angle prisms set as shown to give total reflection are more efficient reflectors than are mirrors because no absorption occurs at the reflecting surface in a prism. Such prisms are also used as reflectors in binoculars, reflecting telescopes, and range finders.

Lenses. A lens is simply a piece of glass, quartz, or other transparent material which is shaped to have curved surfaces, or one curved and one flat surface. When these surfaces are properly shaped, the refraction of light passing through the lens can be put to a number of practical uses, since such a lens will produce real or virtual images.

Definitions. Lenses which are thicker at the center than at the edges are called *convex*. A convex lens will cause rays parallel to the principal axis to bend in such a way that they intersect at a single point or focus on the other side of the lens (as shown on the next page). This lens is therefore *convergent*. A lens thinner at the center than the edges is *concave*, and will cause parallel rays to diverge as though coming from a single point, a virtual focus. This lens is *divergent*.

The *optical center* of a lens is that point through which all rays pass without undergoing appreciable refraction. In a symmetrical lens, this point is the actual center of the lens. You can see that rays approaching the optical center will be slightly refracted on entering the lens, and refracted in the opposite direction on leaving the lens; if the lens is thin, however, the ray emerges practically along the same straight line.

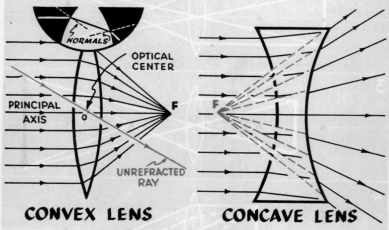

The distance OF is the focal length.

The line normal to the lens surface and passing through the optical center is the *principal axis*. The *principal focus* is defined as for curved mirrors.

Formation of Images by Lenses. The foregoing definitions enable us to construct the images formed by a lens much as we did in the case of curved mirrors. We use (1) the ray parallel to the principal axis, which is refracted through the principal focus, and (2) the ray through the optical center, which is unrefracted. The intersection of these rays upon emerging from the lens locates the image of the point selected. Image formation by convex lenses is illustrated on pages 210–211. Compare the results with those for the concave mirror.

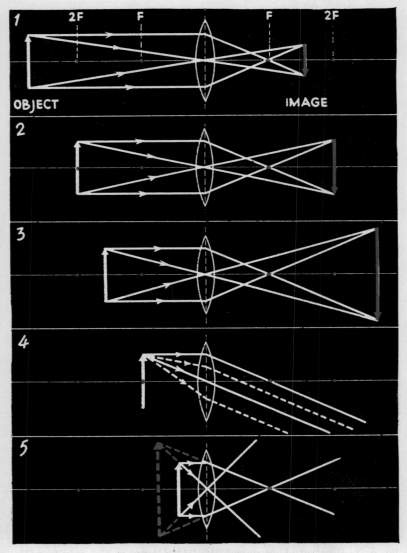

IMAGES FORMED BY

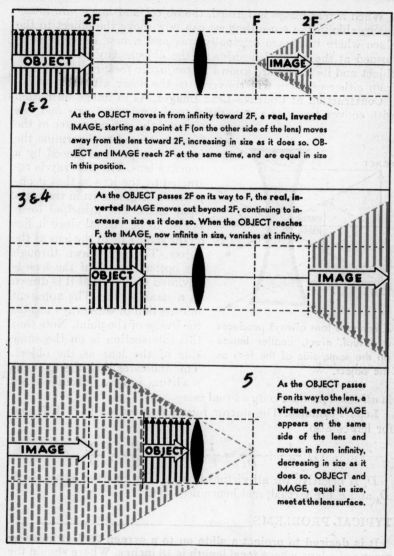

1 & 2 As the OBJECT moves in from infinity toward 2F, a **real, inverted** IMAGE, starting as a point at F (on the other side of the lens) moves away from the lens toward 2F, increasing in size as it does so. OBJECT and IMAGE reach 2F at the same time, and are equal in size in this position.

3 & 4 As the OBJECT passes 2F on its way to F, the **real, inverted** IMAGE moves out beyond 2F, continuing to increase in size as it does so. When the OBJECT reaches F, the IMAGE, now infinite in size, vanishes at infinity.

5 As the OBJECT passes F on its way to the lens, a **virtual, erect** IMAGE appears on the same side of the lens and moves in from infinity, decreasing in size as it does so. OBJECT and IMAGE, equal in size, meet at the lens surface.

THE CONVEX LENS

When a real image is formed, the object and image are interchangeable in the sense that we can now move the object to the place where its image originally was and a new image will be formed at the original position of the object. Any point on the object and its image are known as *conjugate foci;* rays diverging from either of them will converge to the other after refraction.

Construction of Concave-Lens Images. As in image formation with convex lenses, a ray parallel to the principal axis and one

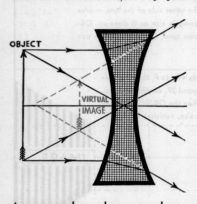

OBJECT

VIRTUAL IMAGE

A concave lens always produces a virtual, erect, smaller image on the same side of the lens as the object.

through the optical center of the lens are traced to determine the image of a point produced by a concave lens. The first ray is refracted by the lens so that it appears to originate from the principal focus. The principal focus is said to be virtual since it lies on the same side of the lens as the object. The ray drawn through the optical center of the lens is deviated so little that it is drawn as a straight line. The apparent intersection of these rays locates the image of the point. Note that this intersection is on the same side of the lens as the object. This indicates that the image is a virtual image. *Concave lenses in all cases produce only virtual images.*

Lens Formulas. The mirror formulas given on page 197 hold for lenses also.

$$(1) \ \frac{1}{D_o} + \frac{1}{D_i} = \frac{1}{F} \qquad (2) \ \frac{S_i}{S_o} = \frac{D_i}{D_o}$$

D_i is negative for all virtual images. For concave lenses, both D_i and F are virtual, and hence negative.

TYPICAL PROBLEMS

It is desired to project a slide on to a screen 75 feet away by means of a lens whose focal length is 18 inches. Where should the slide be placed?

Given: $F = 18$ in $= 1.5$ ft; $D_i = 75$ ft
To find: D_o

$$\frac{1}{D_o} + \frac{1}{D_i} = \frac{1}{F}: \qquad \frac{1}{D_o} + \frac{1}{75} = \frac{1}{1.5} = \frac{2}{3}$$

$$\frac{1}{D_o} = \frac{49}{75}; \; D_o = \frac{75}{49} \text{ ft} = 1.53 \text{ ft} = \mathbf{18.36 \text{ in}}$$

A boy wishes to construct a photographic enlarger which will make a print 8″ × 10″ from a 2″ × 2½″ negative. The enlarging lens is to be mounted 18″ above the photographic paper. In purchasing his lens, what focal length should he specify? How far above the lens must the negative holder be placed?

Given: $\dfrac{S_i}{S_o} = \dfrac{8''}{2''} = 4; \; D_i = 18''$

To find: F and D_o

$$\frac{S_i}{S_o} = \frac{D_i}{D_o}; \; 4 = \frac{18}{D_o}; \; D_o = \frac{18}{4} = 4\tfrac{1}{2}'' = \frac{9}{2}$$

$$\frac{1}{D_o} + \frac{1}{D_i} = \frac{1}{F}; \; \frac{2}{9} + \frac{1}{18} = \frac{1}{F}; \; \frac{1}{F} = \frac{5}{18}; \; F = \frac{18}{5} = 3\tfrac{3}{5}''$$

The Camera. The camera is essentially a light-tight box in the dark interior of which a real, inverted image is produced on a sensitive film. While it is possible to take pictures with a pin hole camera (page 193), a camera is usually equipped with a convex lens because this makes it possible to concentrate more light from the object. The use of more light decreases the time required for the exposure. This result cannot be obtained by enlarging the pinhole because the image then becomes blurred.

In the simple box-type camera, the lens is fixed, and the image distance cannot be varied. As a result, there is only one distance at which an object will produce a sharp image on the film. At other distances, a more or less blurred image is produced. This effect is minimized in manufacturing the camera by using only a small opening near the center of the lens. Such a lens is less sensitive to the distance of the object, and is usually set so that a satisfactory picture can be taken at any distance from about 8 feet to infinity. If you try to get too close to the object in an attempt to get a larger image, a badly blurred image results. Another disadvantage of this lens is that it admits relatively little light, requiring bright sunlight for a good picture, and an exposure of at least $\frac{1}{25}$ second.

More expensive cameras are designed so that the lens may be moved toward or away from the film in order to obtain a sharp image of the object being photographed, regardless of distance. This permits use of a lens with a larger effective diameter, letting more light enter and making possible high speed snapshots, or snapshots under poor lighting conditions.

As the useful diameter of the lens is increased, more and more care must be taken in the shape of the lens, since the outer portions of a purely spherical lens would distort or blur the image.* A lens of large diameter which produces undistorted images is called an "anastigmat." A lens is said to be "fast" if it permits short exposures, even in poor light. The speed of a lens is measured by its "f" rating, obtained by dividing the focal length by the useful diameter of the lens. A faster lens has a smaller "f" rating —the speed varying inversely as the square of the "f" rating. Thus an $f8$ lens is about twice as fast as an $f11$ lens.

The lens is covered by an adjustable *diaphragm* which may be opened to the proper amount, depending on the amount of light available and the speed at which the picture is to be taken. Thus on a bright day, even an $f3.5$ lens would be "stopped down" to $f11$ or $f16$ for an ordinary snapshot at $\frac{1}{25}$ second. However, the diaphragm would be opened wider to take a picture at $\frac{1}{100}$ second. The exposure meter is used to determine just what "f" opening is correct for existing light conditions. Lenses also tend to disperse light into colors. This undesirable feature, called *chromatic aberration*, can be eliminated by constructing the lens of a combination of two kinds of glass (one usually crown glass and the other flint glass) fitted together. Such a lens is called an *achromatic lens*.

The Human Eye. The human eye is analogous to a camera in its parts. Light from the object or scene being viewed is focused by the *crystalline lens* and *cornea* to form an image on the *retina*. The retina is essentially the spread out end of the optic nerve. The *iris* (colored portion of the eye) is a diaphragm which automatically controls the amount of light that enters through the pupil. In strong light, the iris contracts and the pupil becomes small; in the dark, the iris relaxes and the pupil becomes larger.

* This type of distortion in lenses is called *spherical aberration*.

The principal difference between the operation of the eye and that of a camera is the fact that focusing of the eye is accomplished by *changing the focal length* of the lens. *Ciliary* muscles attached to the lens contract and thicken the lens when we look at nearby objects. A shorter focal length is needed then because rays from nearby objects are diverging more when they strike the eye and hence must be refracted more sharply to be bought to a focus. This ability of the eye to change the focal length of its lens is called the *power of accommodation.*

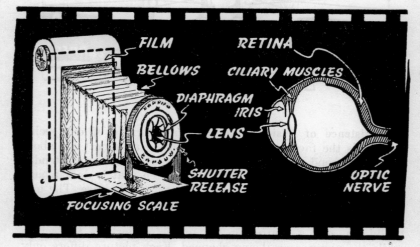

The Camera Compared With the Human Eye

Correction of Defects. If the lens of the eye fails to flatten sufficiently as the ciliary muscles relax for far vision, the images for distant objects fall in front of the retina and the vision is blurred. An eye which focuses well for nearby objects but fails to do so for distant objects is said to be near-sighted. *Near-sightedness* is corrected by wearing glasses with diverging lenses of the correct concavity.

If the lens of the eye accommodates correctly for distant objects, but the ciliary muscles fail to increase the curvature of the lens sufficiently for satisfactory observation of nearby objects, the defect is called *far-sightedness.* This defect can be corrected by glasses with converging lenses.

Unequal curvature of the cornea or lens produces blurring because lines in some directions are not focused as sharply ·as others. For example, vertical lines may be clear, and horizontal lines blurred. This defect, known as *astigmatism*, can be corrected by wearing properly ground cylindrical (instead of spherical) lenses.

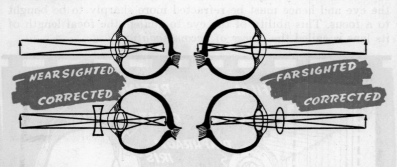

Persistence of Vision. Another characteristic of our seeing process is the fact that we continue to see an object for about ¹⁄₁₀ of a second after the object is removed. When we attend a motion picture theatre, we look at a screen that is dark nearly half of the time without realizing that this is the case. The motion picture projector flashes a series of pictures upon the screen (usually 16 per second for silent films and 24 per second for "talkies"), and a shutter on the projector darkens the screen while the pictures are being changed. Each picture differs only slightly from the previous one. The lag and blending in our vision creates the illusion that we are seeing continuous motion.

Projection Lanterns. A projection lantern consists of a light tight box with an opening in back of which, in order, are the slide holder, one or more convex, condenser lenses, and a powerful light source (either an electric arc or incandescent lamp). The lens is placed a little farther from the slide than its focal length and the slide is inverted and reversed left to right. The image is then erect upon the screen.

The Simple Microscope. A convex lens used to examine an object within the focal length of the lens is called a simple microscope. As shown previously, the lens used in this manner produces an enlarged, erect, virtual image. If the lens is placed close to the object and slowly drawn away, the image is seen to increase in size until it reaches a maximum when the object is just within the focal length. The image vanishes if greater magnification is attempted. The image may be placed at any distance from the eye by slight movements of the lens. Since the eye sees best at a distance of about 10 inches, we automatically adjust the position of the lens until the image is at 10 inches. For a short focal length lens, the object is then practically at F. Therefore the ratio of image size to object size is $10/F$—that is, the maximum magnification of the simple microscope is:

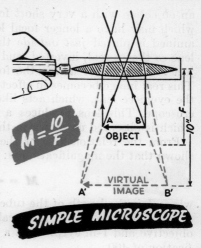

$$M = \frac{10}{F}$$

SIMPLE MICROSCOPE

where F is in inches. (If F is in cm, the formula is $M = 25/F$.)

The reading glass and the biological dissecting microscope are examples of the simple microscope.

The Compound Microscope. A compound microscope permits much greater magnification than is possible with any practical single lens. (For example, a magnification of 100 with a simple microscope requires a lens with a focal length of only $\frac{1}{10}$ in.)

The compound microscope employs two convex lenses: (1)

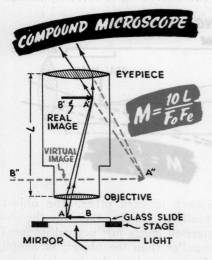

COMPOUND MICROSCOPE

$$M = \frac{10L}{F_o F_e}$$

an *objective* with a very short focal length, and (2) an *eyepiece* which may have a longer focal length. The object *AB* to be examined is placed *just outside* the focal length of the objective lens so that a real, inverted, and enlarged image *A'B'* of the object is formed *just within* the focal length of the eyepiece lens. This real image becomes in effect the object to be viewed through the eyepiece lens, which acts like the magnifier of a simple microscope. This lens produces a virtual, enlarged image *A"B"*, which is observed as shown in the diagram.

From the relationships of the images and objects, it can be shown that the magnification is:

$$M = \frac{10L}{F_o F_e}$$

where *L* is the length of the tube in inches, F_o is the focal length of the objective, and F_e the focal length of the eyepiece. A ¼-in objective and 1-in eyepiece in a 10-in tube would give a magnification of 400.

A concave mirror and a condensing lens (convex) are usually provided below the stage to concentrate a great deal of light on the object to be examined (which must be transparent).

Telescopes. The refracting telescope, like the compound microscope, consists, essentially, of two convex lenses correctly chosen

REFRACTING TELESCOPE

$$M = \frac{F_o}{F_e}$$

and properly placed with respect to each other. The object viewed by the telescope is virtually at infinity; therefore the objective lens produces a real, inverted image just beyond its focal length. This image is much smaller than the object, in actual size, but is now much nearer the eye and can be examined conveniently. The eyepiece of the telescope, as in the microscope, is used to magnify this real image. While even this virtual image is still smaller than the object, it is so much nearer the eye that a great effective magnification is produced. In this case, the magnification is:

$$M = \frac{F_o}{F_e}$$

To obtain large magnifications, F_o must be made large; that is why astronomical telescopes are so long.

In both the compound microscope and the refracting telescope, the image seen is inverted in relation to the object, since the inversion by the objective lens is the only inversion. In a surveyor's transit and other telescopes for viewing objects upon the earth, inverted images would be undesirable. For this reason telescopes of this type have another convex lens placed between the objective and eyepiece to re-invert the image so that objects will not seem to be upside down. Telescopic sights used for aiming guns very accurately are of this kind.

Binoculars are really telescopes whose tubes have been shortened by using total reflecting prisms.

The Range Finder. The military range finder is a device used to sight an object simultaneously from two different positions several feet apart. As the diagram shows, it consists essentially of

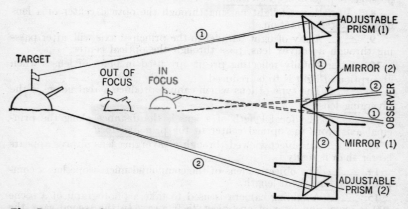

The Range Finder. The prisms are rotated until the images produced by both coincide.

a long support with a movable reflecting prism at each end. Rays from both prisms are reflected to a single eyepiece.

A double image of the object appears in the eyepiece except when the prisms are turned so that they both point directly at the object. In this position, the angle at which each prism is set can be measured and the distance of the object computed by trigonometry. Actually, of course, the dial which is used to rotate the prisms is marked off to read distance directly.

TRUE-FALSE TEST

Write a plus sign in the space provided if the statement is true, and a zero if the statement is false; if the statement is false, correct it by substituting for the underlined part of the statement.

1. _____ Converging lenses are thicker at the center than at the edges.

2. _____ The image thrown on the screen by a motion picture projector is a virtual image.

3. _____ In order to have total internal reflection, the incident ray must be in the medium of greater optical density.

4. _____ In order to have total internal reflection, the angle of incidence must exceed the angle of refraction.

5. _____ The image formed by a farsighted eye of a relatively nearby object occurs in front of the retina.

6. _____ To correct farsightedness, diverging lenses are used in spectacles.

7. _____ The characteristic of the eye which makes motion pictures possible is persistence of vision.

8. _____ Rays of light passing through the optical center of a lens undergo total refraction.

9. _____ A ray of light parallel to the principal axis will, after passing through a convex lens, pass through the optical center.

10. _____ Totally reflecting prisms are used in place of lenses when absorption of light is to be reduced.

11. _____ The type of lens which cannot produce a real image is the diverging lens.

12. _____ The focal length of a lens is the distance along the principal axis from the optical center to the principal focus.

13. _____ An object viewed through a diverging lens always appears larger than it really is.

14. _____ The objective lens of the compound microscope has a comparatively long focal length.

15. _____ A folding camera is used to take a photograph of a scene 100 ft away and later of an object 25 ft away. In the second case, the distance from lens to film is longer than in the first case.

ASSOCIATION TEST

I

16. _____ Ratio of speed of light in another medium to speed in air
17. _____ Military range finders
18. _____ Forms either real or virtual images
19. _____ Regulates amount of light entering eye
20. _____ Light obliquely entering rarer optical medium
21. _____ Defect of human eye
22. _____ Sun's rays entering earth's atmosphere obliquely
23. _____ Submarine periscope
24. _____ Simple magnifying lens
25. _____ Defect of a lens

II

1. Spherical aberration
2. Astigmatism
3. Index of refraction
4. Totally reflecting prisms
5. Bent towards the normal
6. Concave lens
7. Convex lens
8. Bent away from the normal
9. Pupil
10. Iris

QUESTIONS

1. Explain or define: (a) Optical density; (b) Refraction; (c) Critical angle; (d) Law of refraction of light.

2. By means of diagrams show what happens to a ray of light falling obliquely upon (a) a triangular glass prism; (b) a rectangular glass plate.

3. Construct a diagram to show how it is possible to see the sun (a) before it rises above the horizon; (b) after it sets below the horizon. How does this affect the hours of daylight upon the earth?

4. Explain or define: (a) Optical center; (b) principal axis; (c) principal focus; (d) conjugate foci.

5. Distinguish between (a) virtual focus and conjugate foci; (b) principal focus and focal length.

6. Where, with respect to the principal focus of a convex lens, should the film be placed in a motion picture projector? Why?

7. Make a diagram showing how an image is formed by a convex lens when it is used as in a projector.

8. Make a diagram showing how a double convex lens may be used to magnify a pin. Indicate the position of the principal focus and the position of the image.

9. Describe an experiment to show how the principal focus of a convex lens is found.

10. Make labeled diagrams of two converging lenses, one of them forming an enlarged virtual image, and the other forming a real diminished image.

11. If a pupil can read easily only when the printed page is held closer to the eye than it is customary for the average person to hold it, will glasses of the converging type (convex) correct the difficulty? Give a reason for your answer.

12. Compare the compound microscope and the telescope in as many ways as you can.

PROBLEMS

1. The index of refraction of one type of glass is 1.5. Calculate the velocity of light in the glass.   Ans. 124,000 mi/sec

2. An object 12 in high is placed 24 in in front of a convex lens having a focal length of 6 in. Calculate (*a*) the distance from lens to image; (*b*) the height of the image.   Ans. (a) 8 in (b) 4 in

3. The object in problem 2 is moved up to a distance of 4 in from the lens. Calculate (*a*) image distance; (*b*) size of the image.
     Ans. (a) −12 in (b) 36 in

4. A concave lens has a focal length of 3 in. What is the size of the image seen when a drawing 8 × 10 in in size is held 1 ft from the lens and is viewed through it?   Ans. 1.6 × 2 in

5. How far from a camera must a 6-foot person stand, if a full length picture is to be obtained on a film 3 inches by 3 inches, the focal length of the camera lens being 6 inches?   Ans. 150 in, or 12.5 ft

6. The photograph of a child 4 feet high is to be taken by a camera the lens of which has a focal length of 9 inches. The child stands 10 feet from the camera lens. How large is the image?   Ans. 3.9 in

7. An airplane camera lens with a focal length of 18 in is focused on a building 800 ft long from an altitude of 24,000 ft. (*a*) How far is the film from the lens when making this picture? (*b*) How long will the building appear on the negative? (*c*) If the building is ¾ in from a highway on the negative, actually how far apart are they?
     Ans. (a) 18 in (b) 0.6 in (c) 1000 ft

SEVENTEEN—   COLOR

Dispersion of White Light. If a narrow beam of white light (such as sunlight or the light from an arc lamp) is passed through a glass prism, the beam will be spread out during the refraction which occurs. If the emerging light is thrown on a screen, it will be found that the light has been separated into a continuous *spectrum* of colors, ranging from red at one end to violet at the other. This effect is called *dispersion*.

The dispersed light can be passed through another prism placed in the reverse position, and the colored rays will be recombined into the original beam of white light.

Dispersion of White Light

Dispersion always accompanies refraction of white light. The rainbow is a spectrum produced by refraction of sunlight in passing through water droplets in the air.

Cause of Dispersion. As explained on page 205, the amount of refraction of a light ray depends, in part, on its wavelength. Visible light varies in wavelength from .00004 cm to .00008 cm. It happens that the longest of these waves (those about .00008 cm in length) produce the color sensation *red* when they strike the retina; the shortest produce the sensation *violet;* waves of intermediate length produce the various other colors that we experience in daily life. However, when waves of all wavelengths strike the eye simultaneously, we experience the color sensation *white.* In other words, color is a special sensation which depends on the wavelength or combination of wavelengths present in the light reaching the retina.

When white light, consisting of waves of all lengths, enters a refracting medium obliquely, the long red waves are refracted least, the short violet rays the most, and the other colors are arranged in between in the order of their wavelengths. A beam of light of just one wavelength is called *monochromatic* (single-colored).

Color by Reflection. The color of an opaque object depends upon the color of the light that the object is able to reflect. In white light a body appears white if it reflects all the colors of white light about equally. A body appears black if it cannot reflect any color, i.e., if it absorbs all colors of the light which falls upon it. In white light a green body appears green because it reflects only green light and absorbs the others. If it reflects principally green light but also some other color or colors to a lesser extent, the color of the object then is some *shade* of green, rather than a pure green.

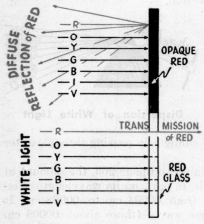

Color by Reflection and by Transmission

An opaque object which has a pure color appears *black* in light that contains no wavelengths for that particular color. A red object appears black when placed in blue, green, or yellow light which furnish no red light for it to reflect. Similarly, a blue object appears black in any light except blue light or a mixture of light which contains wavelengths for blue.

Color by Transmission. The color of a transparent body depends upon the color of the light which it transmits. A piece of blue glass appears blue because it absorbs all the colors of the spectrum except blue, which it transmits. Similarly red glass transmits red and absorbs all other colors composing white light. If more than one color is transmitted by a transparent object its color is the result of the combination of the transmitted colors. An ordinary window pane is colorless because it transmits all the visible colors of white light equally well.

More About Color Vision. It might be thought that the retina of the eye responds to each color individually. This is not true. We can obtain the sensation yellow *either* by a monochromatic beam of yellow light *or* by mixing two beams, one red and the other green, in certain proportions. The red and green beams contain no yellow wavelengths, yet we "see" yellow as a result of the combination. Red and blue light will similarly produce violet.

The theory of this is that the retina contains separate nerves or *color receptors* for each of just three colors—red, green, and blue. If red and green light strike the retina, the "red" and "green" nerves are stimulated, and the mind sees "yellow." If yellow light falls on the retina, it also stimulates both the red and green nerve endings, because each color receptor is more or less sensitive to the spectral colors on either side of its chief color. Thus the mind responds again "yellow." All colors are the result of greater or lesser stimulation of each of the three color receptors; when all three are stimulated to the proper extent, we see white.

As might be expected, blue light combined with yellow light can produce white light—the yellow serving to stimulate both red and green color receptors.

Color by Addition. Red, green, and blue are called the *primary colors*, because all others may be produced by combinations of these three in various proportions. Such combinations can be produced by shining spotlight beams of different colors on the same spot, or by rapidly rotating a wheel made up of colored segments. This is known as color by *addition*.

Color by Subtraction from White Light. The mixing of paint pigments is a subtraction rather than an addition process and the results are quite different. When yellow and blue *pigments* are mixed, the resulting color is green, not white, which you recall results upon mixing yellow and blue *light*. Yellow pigment reflects the red and green portions of white light in addition to the yellow; it absorbs the other colors. Blue pigment reflects only blue and green rays and absorbs the others. Consequently, when these pigments are mixed, green is the only color not absorbed by either of them and it becomes dominant. Thus, producing colors by mixing pigments is a subtractive process since the resulting color is determined by what the pigments together *fail to remove* from white light.

Color-Blindness. About five per cent of humans (more men than women) suffer from some degree of color-blindness which they have inherited and for which there is no known cure. The commonest color-blindness is for the color red. A red-color-blind person sees some shades of red as black and others as a different color. Rarely is anyone completely color-blind. To those who *are* blind to all colors, objects simply appear in varying degrees of light and dark. Good color vision is a strict requirement for pilots, since colored signal lights are widely used for identification and communication.

Camouflage. The purpose of camouflaging an object is to make it seem a part of the environment about it and thus escape notice. When we wish to have something stand out from its environment we create *contrast*. Thus on this printed page you find black print on white paper. In camouflage, the opposite effect is desired. Strong contrasts are removed. A sniper with green clothing and green equipment is difficult to see among the branches of a tree. In wartime, ships are painted a color which blends well with that of the ocean and the horizon in order to make it difficult for enemy submarines and surface ships to see them.

Types of Spectra. The spectrum that is obtained upon using a prism to analyze the light from an incandescent solid, liquid, or certain gases under great pressure is found to merge from red on one end to violet on the other. Since there are no breaks, this type of spectrum is called a *continuous spectrum*.

Most incandescent gases or vapors under atmospheric pressure give a *bright line spectrum*. If the light given off by very hot bodies in which such gases are present is separated by a prism into a spectrum, the spectrum is found to be interrupted by bright lines. For example, sodium vapor always produces a bright line in the yellow part of the ordinary spectrum. Each such vapor or gas gives one or more bright lines which are characteristic of it and by which it can be identified.

When light which ordinarily would give a continuous spectrum passes through a cool gas or vapor, these gases or vapors absorb the waves of the same length that they themselves would give off when incandescent. The spectrum obtained from such light is continuous, except for breaks where some color or colors have been removed in this manner. Such a spectrum is called an *absorption spectrum*. The positions of the absorption lines indicate what element or elements have done the absorbing. Since the atmosphere of the sun contains relatively cool gases, the solar spectrum is an absorption spectrum. Its many dark lines are called Fraunhofer lines.

The Spectroscope; Its Uses. The spectroscope is an instrument used in studying spectra. It consists of:

1. A slit which allows only a narrow beam to enter the instrument through a tube called the *collimator* tube.

2. A convex lens so located that the slit is at the principal focus. Hence, the rays emerge parallel from this lens.

3. A triangular prism which causes the dispersion.

4. Usually a telescope to examine the spectrum. Since the collimator tube and the telescope are mounted on a circular protractor, the amount of refraction of any line can be readily measured and its wavelength determined.

BEST ANSWER TEST

1. _____ Red light differs from blue light in (1) velocity; (2) wave length; (3) intensity; (4) Fraunhofer lines.

2. _____ An American flag dyed with pure colors and viewed in pure green light will appear to be (1) red, white, and green; (2) black and white; (3) green and black; (4) solid green.

3. _____ The color of light which is bent the least by a spectroscope prism is (1) red; (2) green; (3) violet; (4) white.

4. _____ The color of a transparent body is due to the wave lengths which it (1) transmits; (2) absorbs; (3) transforms; (4) reflects.

5. _____ Dark lines seen in the spectrum of the sun are called (1) primary colors; (2) interference patterns; (3) Fraunhofer lines; (4) shadows.

QUESTIONS

1. Describe briefly an experiment that tends to show how the observed color of an object depends in part on the kind of light in which it is viewed.

2. Draw a diagram to show how a glass prism may separate white light into its component colors.

3. What determines the color of (*a*) an opaque body; (*b*) a transparent body? Explain why a piece of red cloth appears black when seen by blue light.

4. A ray of white light passes perpendicularly through a piece of green glass and then obliquely through an ordinary triangular glass prism. Make a labeled diagram showing the complete path of the light ray.

5. Why is it advisable to match colors either in sunlight or under "daylight" lamps?

6. Explain how the spectroscope may be used to determine the composition of a star.

7. In preparing a window display, as for a department store, why must attention be given to the colors of light used?

8. What are some ways in which colored lights are used to produce theatrical effects?

EIGHTEEN

Magnets and Magnetic Materials. Some 2000 years ago, it was found that the mineral *magnetite,* or *lodestone* (now known to be an oxide of iron, Fe_3O_4), has the ability to attract small pieces of iron. This force of attraction is called *magnetism,* and any object or device which exerts magnetic force is called a *magnet.* Magnetite is a *natural* magnet. Man-made magnets are called *artificial* magnets. These are generally composed of an alloy steel (mostly iron), and may assume various shapes. Magnetism is also produced whenever an electric current flows through a wire. Usually the wire is wound in the form of a coil around a soft iron *core.* Such a device is termed an *electromagnet.*

Iron and its alloys are not the only materials attracted by a magnet, although, for practical purposes, they are virtually the only ones used. Other magnetic materials include nickel, cobalt, liquid oxygen, certain alloys such as Alnico (composed of aluminum, nickel, and cobalt), and a few others. *Non-magnetic* materials are exemplified by copper, brass, tin, glass, water, etc.

Magnetic Polarity. An ordinary bar magnet dipped into iron filings will collect them at its ends, but not at its center. Such spots where magnetic attraction is most pronounced are called

IRON FILINGS   LIKE POLES REPEL   UNLIKE POLES ATTRACT

The iron filings indicate that the magnetic field is strongest at the ends (poles) of a magnet. Like poles repel and unlike poles attract.

poles. So far as is known, a magnet must have at least two poles.

If a long bar magnet is suspended or supported so that it rests horizontally and can swing freely, it will be found to come to rest pointing approximately north and south. The end pointing to the north is called the *north-seeking pole,* or simply, the *north pole.* The other end is the *south-seeking* or *south pole.*

If another magnet is brought near the suspended magnet, it will be found that the two north poles, or the two south poles, repel each other, whereas the north pole of one and the south pole of the other attract each other. Thus we have the *law of magnetic force: like magnetic poles repel each other; unlike magnetic poles attract each other.*

Magnetic Fields. Every magnet is surrounded by a space where its magnetic effects are present. This is called the *magnetic field.* Every magnetic field is said to contain magnetic *lines of force,* or lines of *magnetic flux.* These are lines drawn in the magnetic field so as to show at every point the direction in which a small compass would point. Magnetic lines of force have very definite and important properties.

1. *Lines of force never cross one another.* At a given point in the field, a compass can point in only one direction.

2. *Lines of force form closed curves.* By agreement, magnetic lines of force are considered to run from the north pole around

Soft iron is much more permeable than air; hence the magnetic lines of force are concentrated in the iron.

to the south pole of the magnet, and to complete their path through the magnet itself. However, nothing *flows* along the lines of a magnetic field.

3. *The concentration of the lines of force indicates the strength of the magnetic field.* That is, the number of lines perpendicular to a unit area of the field is a measure of field strength.

4. *Lines of force follow the path of least resistance.* Magnetic lines of force pass more readily through a piece of iron placed between the poles of a magnet than they do through air. The ability of a substance to concentrate magnetic lines of force is called its *permeability.* Iron is much more permeable than air. All materials are permeable to some extent. *Permalloy,* an alloy of iron and nickel, has extremely high permeability.

Typical Magnetic Fields. 1. *Around a bar magnet.* The lines of force about a bar magnet leave the north pole and enter the south pole. They are crowded together at the poles but there are relatively few lines outside the center of the bar.

2. *Between unlike poles.* The lines of force between two unlike poles connect the poles and are most concentrated in the space between them. The lines of force tend to draw the poles together.

3. *Between like poles.* The lines of force between two like poles change their direction abruptly. A line originating at one pole does not terminate at the other. The repelling lines of force tend to keep the two unlike poles apart.

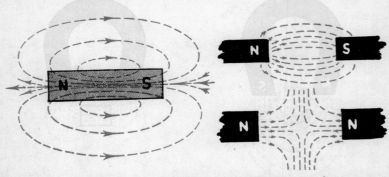

The diagram at the left shows the magnetic field about a bar magnet. At the right is shown the magnetic field between two unlike poles (top) and two like poles (bottom).

Theory of Magnetism. The modern theory of magnetism attempts to account for the magnetization of an object and for some of the observed facts of magnetism.

The basic assumption is that each individual atom of a magnetic substance is, in effect, a tiny magnet with a north pole and a south pole. This magnetism is believed to be due to the motion of the electrons in their orbits. (The flow of electricity always produces magnetism.) In an unmagnetized bar, the arrangement of the atoms is such that all of their magnetic fields are neutralized and exert no magnetic influence at all outside the bar.

In a magnetized bar, it is believed that many, if not most, of the atoms are arranged so that their magnetic fields are aligned in the same direction. Thus the magnetic field is strengthened and extends outside the bar itself.

The bar at the left is unmagnetized; its atoms are disarranged. The bar at the right is magnetized because the atomic poles are aligned.

This theory of magnetism seems highly plausible in view of the many facts of magnetism which it explains.

1. *Magnetic saturation.* There is a limit to which a piece of magnetic material can be magnetized, beyond which its field cannot be made any stronger. Such a magnet is said to be *saturated.* When this condition is reached, it is believed that *all* of the atoms have been aligned with their north poles in the same direction.

2. *Decrease in strength.* Most magnets gradually lose their strength, especially if care is not taken in storing and handling them. Anything which promotes increased atomic motion disturbs the orderly arrangement of the aligned atoms and thereby destroys the magnetism of the object. Heating magnets, dropping or jarring them, storing them with like poles adjacent, and passing electric currents through them weaken the strength of magnets.

3. *Breaking a magnet.* When a bar magnet is broken in two, each half becomes a magnet with a north pole and a south pole.

This breaking in two can be continued until the pieces are quite small,—theoretically, until the pieces are the atoms themselves, when they would still be magnets.

4. *Production of magnets.* An unmagnetized iron bar can be made into a magnet simply by holding another magnet close to it. This is called *magnetic induction.* The magnetic lines of force from the magnet pass through the iron bar and align many of its

Induced Magnetism. The U-magnet induces magnetism in each of the iron tacks brought within the magnetic field of the U-magnet. Note that the tacks become magnetized whether or not they actually touch the magnet. In the diagram at the right, the atoms in the magnetized bar are aligned by the N-pole as it passes over them.

atoms. By magnetic induction a *north* pole is set up in the end of the bar nearest the south pole of the magnet and a *south* pole in the end nearest the north pole of the magnet. Magnetic induction is clear if we remember that the material to be magnetized is composed of atoms which are in themselves minute magnets, but not aligned. When a magnetic field is introduced the atoms are aligned and induced magnetism results. Induced magnetism is usually only temporary and disappears when the magnet is removed. An unmagnetized iron bar can also be made into a magnet by stroking it with a magnet or by using the magnetic field around an electric current. If the material being magnetized is hard steel (cobalt steel, for example), rather than soft iron, the magnetism tends to be permanent.

Highly permeable materials are very easily magnetized but

just as easily lose their magnetism when removed from the influence of the magnet. *Retentivity* is the ability of a material to retain its magnetism. In general, materials having high permeability have low retentivity.

Magnetism of the Earth. The earth acts like a huge magnet with one pole located at the extreme north of the middle of Canada just inside the Arctic Circle, and the other pole nearly diametrically opposite, in the Antarctic region. The lines of force that form the earth's magnetic field have been mapped for use by navigators, surveyors, explorers, etc., for finding direction.

In making use of the earth's magnetic field, an instrument called a *compass* is used. It consists of a magnetized needle carefully balanced and supported at its mid-point so that it is free to turn in a horizontal plane. On the inside bottom of the case con-

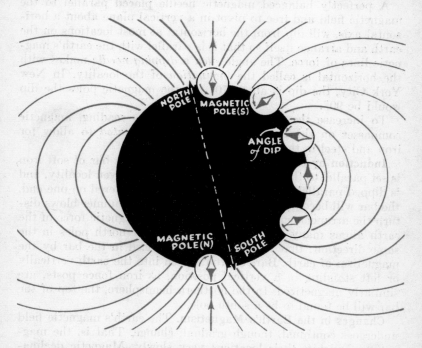

Magnetic Field of the Earth. Note how the angle of dip is determined by the direction of the earth's magnetic lines of force at that point.

taining the compass, there is usually a circular card marked in degrees from 0° to 360°. This enables the navigator (of a ship or a plane) to determine the angle between the direction in which the craft is going and the direction of the compass needle. (The card may be attached to the needle and rotate with it. A fixed pointer at the edge of the card gives the reading in this case.)

Magnetic Declination. The earth's magnetic poles and its geographic poles do not coincide. The angle by which a compass needle deviates from geographic north at any location is called the *declination* of that locality. Thus in New York City, the average declination is about 10° west, which means that a compass needle points in a direction 10° west of true north. The declination at Cincinnati, Ohio, is 0°. Places to the west of Cincinnati have east declination.

A perfectly balanced magnetic needle placed parallel to the magnetic field and free to pivot in a vertical plane about a horizontal axis, will dip from the horizontal at most locations on the earth and arrange itself so that it is parallel with the earth's magnetic lines of force. The angle such a *dipping needle* makes with the horizontal is called the *inclination* of the locality. In New York City, the dip is about 70°. At the magnetic poles the dip would be 90°.

To increase the accuracy of the compass reading, magnetic compasses on ships and aircraft are *compensated* to allow for iron and steel in the ship.

Induction by the Earth's Magnetic Field. If a bar of soft iron is set parallel to the earth's lines of force for a given locality, and is dipped parallel to a dipping needle and hammered on one end, the bar will become a temporary magnet. The hammer blows disturb the arrangement of the atoms, and the magnetic force of the earth aligns many of these atoms with their north poles in the same direction; that is, magnetism is induced in the bar by the magnetism of earth. Bars of iron driven into the earth vertically or left standing in a vertical position, as iron fence posts, are similarly magnetized. In the northern hemisphere, the top of the bar will be found to be a south pole.

Changes in the Earth's Magnetism. The earth's magnetic field undergoes continual, though gradual, change. That is, the magnetic poles shift their locations very slowly. Magnetic declination of any place on the earth is not exactly the same every year.

Magnetic storms, seemingly associated with sunspot activity, occur irregularly over the earth. These magnetic disturbances produce sudden and violent fluctuations in the compass reading. They may completely disrupt long-distance telephony, telegraphy, and radio communication, and they produce greatly increased static on radios.

MULTIPLE ANSWER TEST

I. *Two magnetic poles*

1. _____ attract each other if they are both north poles;
2. _____ repel each other if they are both south poles;
3. _____ attract each other if one is a north, and the other a south pole;
4. _____ attract or repel each other with one-fourth as much force if the distance between them is doubled.

II. *Magnetic lines of force*

5. _____ frequently cross one another;
6. _____ repel one another;
7. _____ tend to contract like stretched elastic bands;
8. _____ run from the north pole to the south pole of a magnet.

III. *An unmagnetized steel bar may be magnetized by*

9. _____ holding another magnet near to it;
10. _____ wrapping insulated wire around it, and passing an electric current through the wire;
11. _____ stroking it from end to end repeatedly with either end of another magnet;
12. _____ bending it U-shaped.

QUESTIONS

1. What is the difference in behavior between soft iron and hard steel after they have been left for some time in a magnetic field and later removed from the field?

2. Can a magnet be made with only one pole? Explain.

3. State three ways in which a magnet may be de-magnetized.

4. How can you determine whether a piece of steel is magnetized or not?

5. Iron posts placed in the ground are found, after some time, to be magnetized. Which end would be found to be a north pole? Explain.

6. How might a magnetic compass be used to detect the presence of large bodies of iron ore?

7. Explain how a magnet attracts several nails, each hanging from the other.

8. How does the atomic theory of magnetism explain the results obtained by (*a*) breaking a permanent magnet into two pieces; (*b*) heating a magnet; (*c*) sending an electric current through a magnet?

NINETEEN—   STATIC ELECTRICITY

Electric Charges. An ebonite (hard rubber) rod is rubbed with fur and the rod suspended from a silk thread. If a second ebonite rod is similarly rubbed and brought near the suspended rod, it will be found that the suspended rod is repelled. If the same procedure is repeated using glass rods rubbed with silk, it will be found that the two glass rods will repel each other. But if the rubbed glass rod

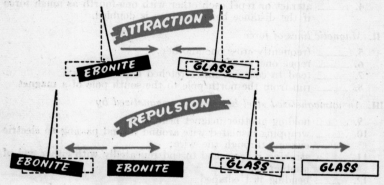

Unlike charges attract; like charges repel.

is brought near the rubbed ebonite rod, the two will be found to *attract* each other. Apparently, rubbing the ebonite rod with fur and the glass rod with silk imparted a special property to the rods. Objects which behave in this manner are said to be *charged* or *electrified*. Many such experiments have resulted in two important conclusions.

1. *There are two kinds of electric charges*—the kind produced on ebonite by rubbing it with fur, and the kind produced on glass by rubbing it with silk. The terms suggested by Benjamin Franklin to distinguish between these two kinds of charges are still used, namely, *positive* for the charge or electrification on the ebonite, and *negative* for the charge on the glass. It has further been determined that both kinds of charges occur in definite units, and that one unit of positive charge exactly equals one unit of negative charge.

2. *Like charges repel each other and unlike charges attract each other.* The force of attraction or repulsion depends upon the magnitudes of the charges and varies inversely as the square of the distance between them.

Differences Between a Magnetized Body and an Electrified Body. 1. A charged body attracts any material. A magnetized body attracts only magnetic materials, such as iron, steel, nickel, and cobalt.

2. All materials may be charged, but only magnetic materials can be magnetized.

3. A body may be charged either negatively or positively. A magnet must have two poles.

4. A charged body loses some or all of its charge if touched with any uncharged body. A magnet does not lose any of its magnetism by touching other bodies.

Electric Field of Force. An electric field of force surrounds all charged bodies. As in the case of magnetism, this field can be represented by imaginary lines of force indicating the direction and intensity of the field. The diagrams show the conventional

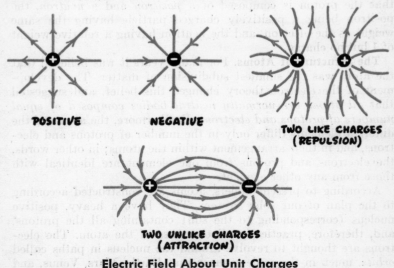

POSITIVE

NEGATIVE

TWO LIKE CHARGES (REPULSION)

TWO UNLIKE CHARGES (ATTRACTION)

Electric Field About Unit Charges

representations of the fields of force surrounding bodies possessing unit positive and negative charges.

Work is required to overcome the force of repulsion and bring two similar charges closer together. Work is also required to overcome the force of attraction if two unlike charges are to be separated.

Electrical Nature of Matter. The production of electric charges and the interpretation of their effects can best be explained by the theory that *all ordinary matter is composed of positive and negative electricity in equal amounts.* In other words, there is reason to believe that both positive and negative electricity are everywhere and in all things, such as glass, ebonite, paper, metals, water, air, etc. This belief is commonly explained by the *electron theory* of matter.

Positive electricity occurs in units called *protons,* while the units of negative electricity are called *electrons.* The electron and the proton each have the same charge, although the weight of the proton is about 1850 times the weight of the electron. The proton has a relative weight (compared with a hydrogen atom) of practically 1; thus the electron weighs approximately $\frac{1}{1850}$ as much as the hydrogen atom. There is some evidence to suggest that the proton is composed of a *positron* and a *neutron,* the positron being a positively charged particle having the same weight as the electron, and the neutron having a relative weight of 1 but no charge.

The Structure of Atoms. For many years it was believed that the atom was the smallest subdivision of matter. The development of the electron theory changed this belief, and suggested that *all atoms are normally neutral bodies composed of equal numbers of protons and electrons.* Furthermore, the atoms of the different elements differ only in the number of protons and electrons, and in their arrangement within the atoms; in other words, the electrons and protons from one element are identical with those from any other element.

According to present beliefs, atoms are constructed according to the plan of our solar system. They have a heavy, positive nucleus (corresponding to the sun) containing all the protons, and, therefore, practically all the mass of the atom. The electrons are thought to revolve around the nucleus in paths called *orbits,* much in the same manner that Earth, Mars, Venus, and the other planets revolve around the sun. These electrons are held within their orbits by the force of attraction existing between the nuclear protons and the planetary electrons.

The hydrogen atom has the simplest structure. It has one proton for a nucleus and one electron revolving around it. Other atoms are more complex, having many protons in their nuclei and an equal number of electrons revolving in the outside orbits. (The nucleus is believed also to contain neutrons (n), neutral particles weighing about as much as a proton.) The diagrams show the probable structure of the atoms of several elements.

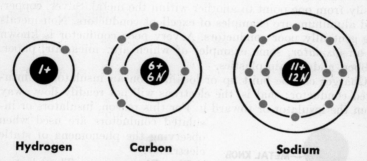

Hydrogen   **Carbon**   **Sodium**

Note that in each case the number of protons ($+$) equals the number of electrons ($-$). The electrons are shown in red.

How Bodies Become Charged. The electrons within the atoms of all substances are in constant motion. There is a tendency, moreover, for some of these moving electrons to leave the atoms to which they belong and move to neighboring atoms. These moving or circulating electrons are called "free" electrons.

Some substances have more free electrons than others. Consequently, when two dissimilar substances are placed in contact, the substance with more free electrons will lose some of these electrons to the other substance with which it is in contact. The substance which loses electrons becomes positively charged; the substance which gains electrons becomes negatively charged.

Bodies become charged only by acquiring or losing electrons and not by any transfer of protons, which are in the nuclei of atoms and are not free to move.

When the ebonite rod was charged by contact with fur (the rubbing merely brought more atoms into contact; friction has nothing to do with it), some of the electrons left the fur and attached themselves to the rod. Likewise, when the glass rod was rubbed with silk, electrons moved from the glass to the silk. Whenever electrification is caused by contact, two opposite kinds of charges are produced in equal amounts.

Insulators and Conductors. Different substances vary greatly as to the freedom of motion of their electrons. Substances in which the free electrons move readily are called *conductors*. Metals are good conductors because their free electrons move easily from one point to another within the metal. Silver, copper, and aluminum are examples of excellent conductors. Non-metals are generally poor conductors. A very poor conductor is known as an *insulator*, some examples of which are: mica, air, paper, rubber, and certain plastics.

Charges can be built up or localized on an insulator or insulated conductor; that is, the electrons will not readily flow away from the insulator or toward it. For this reason, insulators or insulated conductors are used when observing the phenomena of static electricity.

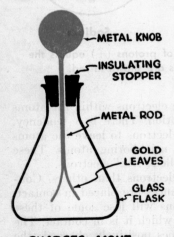

The Gold Leaf Electroscope

The Electroscope. The electroscope is a device for detecting the presence of an electric charge, and also for determining whether this charge is positive or negative. The gold leaf electroscope consists of a glass flask with an insulating stopper, through which a metal rod passes. A metal knob is fastened to the outer end of the rod and two very thin leaves of gold are fastened to the end of the rod inside the flask. Other kinds of metal foil may be substituted for the gold. The flask, or other housing, of the electroscope prevents the delicate leaves from being affected by drafts of air, while the insulating stopper (sulfur, rubber, etc.) prevents the leaves of the electroscope from losing their charge.

Charging the Electroscope by Contact. If a charged body is touched against the knob of an electroscope, it will be found that the gold leaves of the electroscope will diverge, indicating that like charges have been produced upon the leaves, causing them to repel each other. The extent to which the leaves diverge is an indication of the amount of charge. The reason for this phenomenon becomes apparent upon examination of the diagram. Nor-

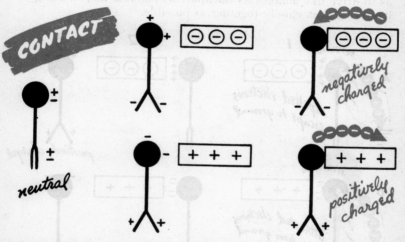

Charging by Contact. Since all matter is composed of protons and electrons, only a deficiency or excess of electrons imparts a charge to a body.

mally, the positive and negative charges within the electroscope balance each other, leaving it neutral. When a charged body (assume it is negative) is brought near the knob of the electroscope, some of the electrons in the knob are repelled to the gold leaves, thus causing them to diverge. The knob now is deficient in electrons. As the charged body touches the knob, the electrons flow from the charged body into the knob. When the charged body is removed, the electroscope is left with an excess of electrons; the gold leaves remain diverged, and the electroscope is said to be negatively charged. If a positively charged body is touched to the knob, the electrons will leave the electroscope, leaving it positively charged.

Whenever any body is charged by *contact,* the sign of the charge produced is the *same* as the sign of the charge producing it.

Charging the Electroscope by Induction. As we have just seen, even the approach of a charged body is sufficient to move the electrons in an electroscope, and cause the leaves to diverge. We have also seen that the force of attraction and repulsion is such as to drive like charges as far apart as possible and to bring unlike charges as closely together as possible.

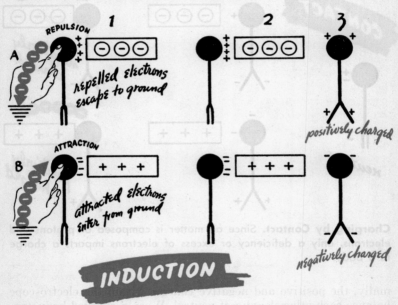

Charging by Induction. The charged and charging bodies do not touch; electrons enter or leave the body being charged through the action of an electric field of force.

1. *Inducing a Positive Charge.* If a negatively charged body is brought *near* (but not in contact with) a neutral electroscope (diagram A), some of the electrons in the knob will be driven

away from the charged body. If we now provide a path of escape for the negative charges by touching the knob of the electroscope with the finger (1) or with any other conductor connected with the earth (ground), the negative charges will leave the electroscope. If the finger is first removed (2), thus breaking the link with the ground, and then the charged body is removed, the electroscope will be found to be charged positively (3).

2. *Inducing a Negative Charge.* To induce a negative charge (diagram B), a positively charged body is brought near the electroscope. When the knob is touched with the finger (1), electrons are attracted from the earth into the electroscope. When first the finger (2) and then the charged body are removed, the electroscope will have an excess of negative charges and thus will be negatively charged (3).

Whenever any body is charged by *induction,* the sign of the charge produced is *opposite* to the sign of the charge producing it.

Determination of the Sign of the Charge. To determine whether the charge on a body is positive or negative, a *charged* electroscope is used. Suppose a charged body is brought near a negatively charged electroscope and the leaves are observed to diverge still more. We know that like charges repel. Since the leaves were already negative, additional electrons must have been repelled from the knob into the leaves to make them diverge still more. Hence the unknown charge on the body must have been negative.

The following table shows the effect of bringing (1) a positive body, (2) a negative body, near (a) a neutral electroscope, (b) a positively charged electroscope, and (c) a negatively charged electroscope.

	(a) Neutral Electroscope	(b) Positively Charged Electroscope	(c) Negatively Charged Electroscope
1. Positive body	Leaves diverge	Leaves diverge farther	Leaves come together
2. Negative body	Leaves diverge	Leaves come together	Leaves diverge farther

Thus the presence of a charged body can be detected by the use of either a neutral or a charged electroscope, but the sign of the charge can be determined only by the use of a charged electroscope of known sign.

Electric Potential. You will recall from the discussion in Chapter 7 that potential energy is the energy possessed by an object by virtue of its position. Thus, the water at the top of Niagara Falls possesses potential energy because of its position in the gravitational field of the earth. As the water pours over the brink of the falls, this potential energy is converted into kinetic energy.

In a similar manner a charge in an electrical field possesses potential energy. This energy is measured by the amount of work required to move the charge from infinity up to that point and is similar to the work required to raise water from the center of the earth to the top of Niagara Falls. (1) If the work must be done to move a positive charge up to the point, the point is said to be at positive potential. (2) If the work must be done to move a negative charge up to the point, the point is said to be at negative potential.

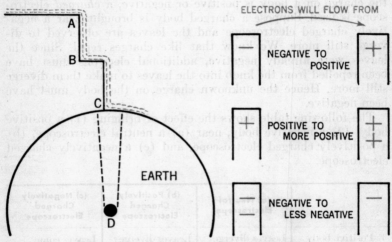

Electrons flow from low to high potential.

Potential Difference. We said above that when the water at the top of Niagara Falls fell to the bottom of the falls the potential energy stored at the top was used up. Actually, this is not strictly true. If there were a shaft at the bottom of the Falls extending to the center of the earth, we know that the water would fall to the center of the earth. Therefore, the water at the bottom of the Falls still possesses some potential energy. The work done by the falling water was really a measure of the *difference* in potential energy between the top and the bottom of the Falls. An examination of the diagram will make this clearer. The water at point *A* will flow to point *B*. The water at point *B* will also flow to point *C*. The water at point *C* would (if there were a shaft) flow to point *D*. A power station at point *B*, in harnessing the work performed by the water falling from *A* is really utilizing only the *difference in potential* energy between points *A* and *B*. The water at *B* still has potential energy, which can be utilized by a power station at the lower level, *C*.

A parallel situation exists with regard to electric potential. The free electrons in a conductor will flow from a point of low (or relatively negative) potential to a point of high (or relatively positive) potential. The difference in potential energy between two given points is what causes electrons to flow from one point to the other until the potential of the two points is the same. An electric difference in potential exists between two points if (1) one is positive and the other negative, or (2) both are positive but one is more positive than the other, or (3) both are negative but one is more negative than the other. The diagram illustrates the flow of electrons in these three situations.

The flow of electrons produced by a difference in potential constitutes an electric current. We get only intermittent currents from a static electricity machine because the potential difference that is built up by the separation and localization of positive and negative charges drops to zero every time a spark discharge permits the electrons to reunite with the positive charges. Chemical cells, batteries, and mechanical generators maintain a steady difference of potential and so produce continuous currents of electric charges. Difference of potential (p.d.) is measured in *volts*. *Electromotive force* (emf or "electron-moving force") and *electrical pressure* are other terms used to express a difference in potential.

The Condenser. Any charged conductor can be looked upon as a storehouse or source of electric charge. If an uncharged conductor is connected to it, some of the charge in this "storehouse" will flow into the second conductor. In certain applications of electricity it is desirable to store large quantities of charge upon a conductor or group of conductors, so that these conductors can act as sources of electric charge. A device which is designed so that it will readily hold large amounts of charge is called a *condenser*.

In general, practical condensers consist of two conductors quite close to each other, but separated by an insulator or *dielectric*. The conductors are usually thin sheets or plates of metal. The action of this condenser depends upon electrostatic attraction between charges of opposite sign upon the two conductors, as will now be explained.

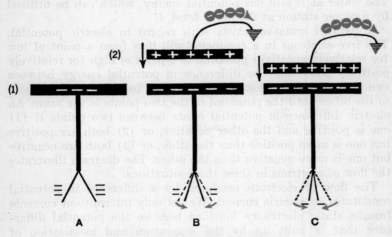

The Principle of the Condenser

In the diagram, *A* is a negatively charged electroscope, with a metal plate (1) instead of a knob at the top. Plate (1) has a certain amount of negative charge upon it. There is also a negative charge on the leaves of the electroscope, causing them to diverge. We shall now see how the charges can be redistributed so that more negative charge appears on plate (1).

In *B*, a grounded metal plate (2) has been brought close to plate (1). As a result, the leaves of the electroscope have moved closer together, indicating that some of their negative charge has left them and moved onto plate (1). The explanation is as follows. Electrons on plate (2) have been repelled to the ground by the electrons on plate (1). The resulting positive charge on plate (2) has attracted additional electrons from the leaves into plate (1). In other words the ability of plate (1) to hold a negative charge has been increased by the approach of the grounded plate (2).

If plate (2) is brought closer to plate (1), as shown at *C,* the electroscope leaves will come still closer together, showing that more negative charge has been drawn onto plate (1) and bound there by the increased positive charge on plate (2). We thus see that *the ease with which each plate holds a charge is increased when the distance between them is decreased.*

The charge on each plate will also increase if a pane of glass or other non-conductor is inserted between the plates. The glass increases the strength of the electric field between the plates, thus strengthening the attractive forces upon which the condenser action depends. This phenomenon is similar to that produced by inserting a soft iron core in a magnetic field to increase the field strength. Any non-conductor or dielectric will have a similar effect on the condenser—the amount depending on a property called the *dielectric constant* of the substance. Dielectric constant in electricity is similar to permeability in magnetism.

As might be expected, *increasing the area of the plates will also increase the amount of charge on the plates.*

The Capacitance of a Condenser. The relative ease with which a condenser holds or stores a charge is called its *capacitance.* We have just seen that the capacitance of any condenser depends upon the distance between its plates, the kind of dielectric between them, and the area of the plates.

The capacitance of a condenser is like the volume of a gas container. By increasing the pressure, more and more gas molecules can be forced into the container even though the volume does not change. Similarly, by increasing the electrical pressure more and more charge can be forced onto the plates of the condenser.

Experiments have shown that the amount of charge on a given condenser is directly proportional to the potential difference or electrical pressure acting upon the plates. On the other hand, applying the same potential difference to different condensers will result in different accumulations of charge in proportion to the capacitance of each particular condenser. That is,

Charge = Capacitance × Potential Difference

$$Q = CE$$

If Q is measured in *coulombs* (p. 262), and E is measured in *volts*, then C is measured in *farads*.

Back EMF of a Condenser. The right-hand diagram on the opposite page shows a condenser connected to a source of voltage. The electrons from the negative terminal flow to plate (A), where they produce a negative potential. The negative plate (A) repels electrons from plate (B), thus producing a positive potential on plate (B). The electromotive force of the battery or generator continues to drive electrons to plate (A) and draw electrons from plate (B) until the difference in potential across the two plates is the same as that across the two terminals of the battery or generator.

A "back pressure" builds up at the plates of the condenser as the charge on it accumulates. The electrons already on plate (A) tend to repel additional electrons coming from the negative terminal of the battery. Equilibrium results when this "back pressure" of the electrons on plate (A) exactly equals the forward pressure from the battery.

This back pressure may itself be used as a source of voltage. If after charging the condenser, the battery is removed, the charged condenser is left with a potential difference between its plates. If a conductor is then connected from one plate to the other, electrons will flow from the negative plate to the positive plate through the conductor.

The concept of back emf will be better understood if an analogy is drawn between electric pressure and air pressure. In the left diagram, the molecules of air would be equivalent to electrons. Assume that two pipes are connected to a pump as shown in the diagram and that the pump is capable of creating a pressure difference of 3 lb/in^2. The pump draws molecules of air from pipe (B) and pushes them into pipe (A). This continues until a difference in pressure of 3 lb/in^2 is produced between the two pipes, at which time the air pressure in pipe (A) will counterbalance the force exerted by the pump and no additional air molecules can be pumped into it. If the pump is now disconnected from the two pipes and the latter are connected as shown, it is apparent that the air will flow from one pipe to the other in the direction of the greater force. This is exactly what happens with the electrons in a condenser.

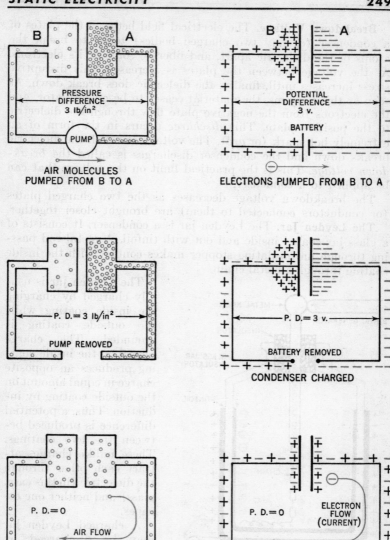

PRESSURE
DIFFERENCE
3 lb/in²

PUMP

AIR MOLECULES
PUMPED FROM B TO A

POTENTIAL
DIFFERENCE
3 v.

BATTERY

ELECTRONS PUMPED FROM B TO A

P. D. = 3 lb/in²

PUMP REMOVED

P. D. = 3 v.

BATTERY REMOVED

CONDENSER CHARGED

P. D. = 0

AIR FLOW

PIPES CONNECTED

P. D. = 0

ELECTRON
FLOW
(CURRENT)

CONDUCTOR

CONDENSER DISCHARGED

Action in a Condenser during Charging and Discharging

Breakdown Voltage. The electrical field between the plates of a condenser (or any two charged bodies) tends to break the atoms of the dielectric apart, and liberate some of its electrons. As the voltage between the plates is increased, this disruptive stress increases until, finally, the dielectric does break down. As soon as this happens, the material ceases to be an insulator, and the electrons from the negative plate flow through the dielectric to the positive plate. This *discharge* occurs in the form of an extremely hot spark (or *arc*). The voltage at which the dielectric breaks down and the condenser discharges is called the *breakdown voltage.* This is the practical limit on the voltage that can be applied to a condenser.

The breakdown voltage decreases as the two charged plates (or conductors connected to them) are brought closer together.

The Leyden Jar. The Leyden jar is a condenser. It consists of a glass jar coated inside and out with tinfoil. A metal rod passing through an insulating stopper makes contact with the inside coating through a metal chain.

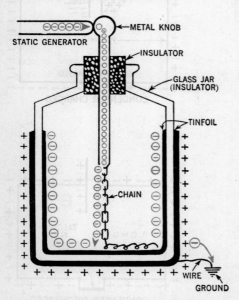

The Leyden jar is usually charged by charging the inside coating while the outside coating is grounded. The charge placed on the inside coating produces an opposite charge in equal amount on the outside coating by induction. Thus, a potential difference is produced between the two coatings. These unlike charges attract each other through the dielectric (in this case, glass) and neither one escapes.

A charged Leyden jar may be discharged by connecting the two coatings to each other by a wire or by a curved metal

The Leyden jar is a condenser.

rod provided with an insulated handle. If one end of this rod is touched to one coating and the other end is brought near the other coating of a charged Leyden jar, a large spark will be obtained. A ¼-inch spark indicates a potential difference between the coatings of about 10,000 volts.

The Leyden jar was one of the early condensers. Modern commercial condensers vary in materials and in construction. They may be made of silver and mica, tinfoil strips and waxed paper, aluminum foil and aluminum oxide film, etc. They may have a

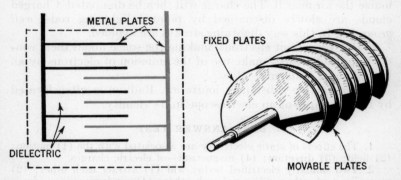

Fixed and Variable Condensers. The capacitance of the variable condenser is changed by rotating the movable plates, which thus changes the effective area of the plates.

fixed capacitance, or may be *variable*. Condensers have many applications in connection with induction coils, alternating current circuits, and radio, all of which are discussed later.

Lightning. Lightning takes place as the result of the breakdown of the air, which acts as a dielectric. The uprush of warm, moist air causes condensation of the water vapor as the cold of higher altitudes is reached. When larger droplets of water are formed, these rain particles are positively charged. The finer spray is negatively charged. In this manner, a difference of potential is established between the larger drops and the fine droplets. Under the influence of this voltage (usually tremendous), the air breaks down and becomes conducting. Then a discharge of electricity, *i. e.*, lightning, may follow. The conditions are similar to those in a charged condenser; therefore, lightning is a type of condenser discharge. Of course, the discharge may also occur between a highly charged cloud and the earth, or objects (trees, houses, etc.) on the ground.

Ionization of the Air. Air is ordinarily an insulator, and all of its atoms are neutral. If, however, some electrons are separated from their atoms, the latter become charged particles, or *ions,* which move when a charged body is near them. In other words, the ionized air becomes a conductor. Air may be ionized as follows:

1. A charged body, provided with a point, concentrates most of its charge at the point. This charge may become large enough to ionize the air near it. The charge will then be dissipated. Charged clouds are slowly discharged by pointed lightning rods, *well grounded.* In this way, lightning strokes are avoided.

2. Hot wires emit electrons, making the space about them conducting. Radio tubes make use of the emission of electrons by an incandescent filament.

3. Radioactive substances ionize air. Radium is often located by the discharge of an electroscope in its vicinity.

BEST ANSWER TEST

1. The effects of static electricity are associated with the (1) motion; (2) field; (3) direction; (4) magnetism—of electric charges.

2. Two similarly electrified bodies will (1) attract each other; (2) neutralize each other; (3) repel each other; (4) condense.

3. To give an uncharged body a positive charge, (1) add protons; (2) add electrons; (3) remove protons; (4) remove electrons; (5) touch it with a proof plane.

4. If the force of attraction between two charged bodies is 9F, and the distance between them is reduced to ⅓ as much, the force will become (1) 27F; (2) 3F; (3) 12F; (4) 81F.

5. Modern beliefs hold that atoms (1) are indivisible; (2) have a neutral core with electrons around it; (3) have a positive core with protons around it; (4) have a positive core with electrons around it; (5) have a negative core with protons around it.

6. The electroscope is a device for (1) analyzing electric charges; (2) producing electric charges; (3) neutralizing electric charges; (4) isolating electric charges.

7. An electroscope has a positive charge, and when a charged body is brought nearby, the leaves diverge still more. The sign of the charged body is (1) neutral; (2) negative; (3) positive; (4) unknown.

8. An electroscope has a negative charge. A negatively-charged body is brought near it, the electroscope is grounded momentarily, and the charged body is then withdrawn. The electroscope will be (1) charged positively; (2) charged negatively; (3) neutral; (4) broken.

9. An electrical condenser (1) creates electric charges; (2) stores electric charges; (3) destroys electric charges; (4) consists of two insulating plates separated by a conductor.

10. Lightning occurring during an electrical storm (1) is really quite harmless; (2) is really a condenser discharge; (3) never strikes twice in the same place; (4) has no relation to static electricity.

ASSOCIATION TEST

I		II
11. _____ Silver, copper, iron		1. Leyden jar
12. _____ Sulfur, glass, rubber		2. Voltage
13. _____ Measure of potential difference		3. Insulators
14. _____ Increased capacity of condenser		4. Coulomb
15. _____ Used to detect electric charge		5. Plates brought closer together
16. _____ Electromotive force		6. Plates moved farther apart
17. _____ A simple condenser		7. Conductors
18. _____ Practical unit is microfarad		8. Electroscope
19. _____ 6.28×10^{18} electrons		9. Proof plane
20. _____ 2 factors determining Q of a charged condenser		10. Capacitance

QUESTIONS

1. Mention two ways in which free electrons may be obtained.

2. Describe a simple experiment to show the difference between an electrified body and a non-electrified body.

3. Explain in physical terms each of the following statements of fact: (a) A positively charged body will be discharged if a glowing body is brought near it. (b) Lightning is a condenser discharge. (c) A condenser may be used to store electricity. (d) An electroscope is used to determine the kind of electric charge.

4. State one method of charging an electroscope so that it is in proper condition to test the charge of another electrified body.

5. (a) What kind of an electric charge has the electron? (b) Making use of the electron theory, account for the charge on hard rubber when rubbed with wool or cat's fur.

6. (a) Mention the essential parts of a condenser. (b) Mention one practical use of the condenser.

7. Mention (a) three respects in which the behavior of magnets is similar to that of electric charges; (b) two respects in which it is different.

8. A charged body when brought near a suspended pith ball will first attract it, and then repel it. Explain.

9. Large sparks can frequently be seen jumping from leather belts which are driving machinery. Explain.

10. An ebonite rod rubbed with fur will attract the fur with which it is rubbed. Explain.

TWENTY—

ELECTRIC CURRENTS AND CIRCUITS

THE PRIMARY CELL

Importance of Difference in Potential. As we have seen, electrons flow from one point to another only when there is a difference in potential between the two points. In order to maintain a continuous flow of electrons (current of electricity), there must be a continuous difference of potential. The marvels of our present electrical age were made possible as a result of the discovery and development of two ways to maintain a constant difference in potential: (1) by chemical action in cells and batteries; (2) by mechanical generators (discussed in chapter 21). The first chemical cell that successfully delivered a continuous current of electricity was devised by the Italian physicist, Volta, and announced in the year 1800. Simple chemical cells are called *voltaic* cells in his honor. Voltaic cells depend upon *ionization* for their operation.

Ionization. The hydrogen atom is neutral because the negative electron balances the positive charge of the proton in the nucleus. If the electron were removed, a positively charged hydrogen *ion* would remain. *Ions are electrically charged atoms or groups of atoms.* Acids, bases, and salts, when they are dissolved in water, break up into ions, which wander about (migrate) freely in the solution. This process is called *dissociation* and the solution containing ions is called an *electrolyte*.

Chemical Action Within a Voltaic Cell. The essential parts of the voltaic cell are: (1) two dissimilar *electrodes* composed, usually, of two unlike metals or a metal and carbon; (2) an *electrolyte*. A simple cell for experimental study can be made by immersing strips of zinc and copper in a water solution of sulfuric acid. A potential difference of 1.10 volts is generated.

When sulfuric acid, $H_2(SO_4)$, is put into solution, it separates into two kinds of ions: H^+ and $(SO_4)^{--}$. When the strips of copper and zinc are connected by a wire, action occurs at both electrodes.

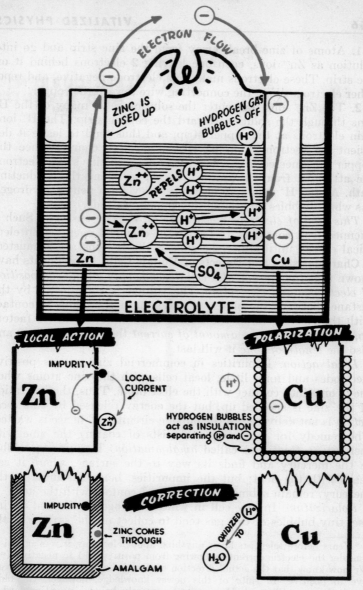

Action in a Voltaic Cell, and Correction of Its Defects

1. Atoms of zinc break away from the zinc strip and go into solution as Zn^{++} ions, each one leaving 2 electrons behind it on the strip. These electrons make this electrode negative, and repel other electrons along the connecting wire toward the copper.

2. The Zn^{++} ions that enter the solution repel many of the H^+ ions through the solution toward the copper strip. The H^+ ions gain electrons at the copper strip, and thus tend to leave it deficient of electrons, that is, with a positive charge. Since the copper is connected to the negatively charged zinc strip, electrons are attracted from the zinc to the copper along the conducting path. As the H^+ ions gain electrons, they form neutral hydrogen gas which bubbles up around the copper electrode.

*This flow of electrons constitutes an electric current.** Such a chemical cell continues to transform chemical energy into electrical energy until either the zinc or the H^+ ions are exhausted.

Characteristics and Defects of Voltaic Cells. Experiments have shown that *the voltage of a cell depends only on the composition of electrodes and electrolyte.* The voltage is not affected by the distance between the plates, or the area of the plates in contact with the electrolyte, or the size of the cell. These latter factors do, however, affect the *amount of current* the cell can deliver and also the *length of time* it will last.

Local action. Impurities in commercial zinc act as positive electrodes and form little, local cells with the zinc atoms when they come into contact with the electrolyte. Thus, the ionization of the zinc is speeded up, but the energy released by this *local action* is not delivered to the outside circuit, and hence is wasted. The remedy for local action consists of coating the zinc with mercury, a treatment called *amalgamation.* The zinc is soluble in the mercury and finds its way to the surface, where it can react with the acid; but the impurities, being insoluble in the mercury, remain submerged and out of contact with the acid.

Polarization. In any cell in which hydrogen is formed during use, tiny bubbles of this gas tend to collect on the surface of the

---

* Years before scientists knew anything about electrons, it was agreed to consider the electric current as flowing from positive (+) to negative (−). We now know that the actual direction of flow (of electrons) is from negative to positive. In spite of this newer knowledge, however, the older terminology is still used. Hence, we are merely being conventional when we say that the electric current flows from plus to minus.

positive plate. This layer of gas acts as an insulator and offers increased resistance to the transfer of electrons, thus causing the current to decrease. The effect is termed *polarization*. If manganese dioxide is added to the electrolyte solution in the copper-zinc-sulfuric acid cell, polarization is overcome by the oxidizing action of this chemical; it converts the hydrogen into water about as fast as the gas is formed.

The Dry Cell. The term "dry cell" is somewhat misleading since the cell is not really dry. Instead of a liquid electrolyte solution, the active chemical is in paste form. Actually, the cell is sealed so that externally it is dry. The negative plate of the cell is a zinc cup. A carbon rod placed at the center of the cell serves as the positive electrode. The zinc cup is lined with blotting paper soaked in ammonium chloride solution, and the space between it and the carbon rod is filled with ammonium chloride, manganese dioxide, and granulated carbon, all mixed to form a paste. The manganese dioxide serves as the depolarizer. The cell generates about 1.5 volts

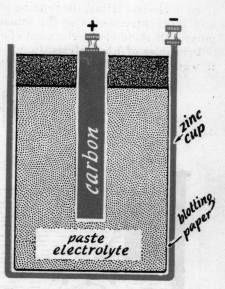

The Dry Cell. The electrodes are shown in red.

on open circuit. It is termed a *primary cell*, because once the chemicals are used up, it cannot be recharged but must be replaced by a new cell. (See page 273 for cell circuits.)

CHEMICAL EFFECTS OF AN ELECTRIC CURRENT

Up to now, we have considered how chemical action produces an electric current. We shall now see how a current produces chemical action.

Electrochemistry. Several important chemical industries are founded on chemical changes that take place when an electric current is passed into certain conducting solutions. These *electrochemical* industries supply some of the most vital materials our country needs today, such as chlorine, sodium hydroxide, metallic sodium, aluminum, calcium, magnesium, etc. In addition, *electrolysis* (chemical change brought about by electricity) is applied in electroplating, the refining of copper, the storage battery, and other processes. Certain fundamental *laws of electrolysis* govern all these electrochemical effects.

Principles of Electrolysis. In our discussion of the voltaic cell, it was seen how the ions in an electrolyte generate an electric

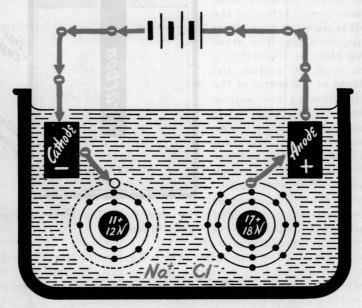

Electrolysis of Sodium Chloride. The positive sodium ion is attracted to the cathode, where it gains an electron and thus becomes neutral. The negative chlorine ion is attracted to the anode, where it gives up an electron and thus becomes neutral. For each electron given up by the cathode, one is gained by the anode. The electron flow is shown in red.

current. Electrolysis is substantially the action of a voltaic cell in reverse. In electrolysis, two electrodes connected to a source of direct current (DC) are inserted in an electrolyte. The ions in the electrolyte respond to the law of electrical attraction and repulsion; that is, the positive ions migrate toward the negative pole, or *cathode,* and the negative ions migrate toward the positive pole, or *anode.* A typical electrolytic action is shown in the diagram on page 258.

Electrolysis of Water. The electrolysis of water is carried out in a similar manner. A little sulfuric acid is generally added to the water to make it a conductor. When current is passed into the solution, oxygen collects at the positive pole and hydrogen collects at the negative pole. The volume of hydrogen is twice the volume of the oxygen.

Electroplating. Electroplating is essentially the act of putting a thin coating of one metal on the surface of another by means of electrolysis. The purpose is usually to make the plated object more resistant to corrosion, or to simulate the appearance of a more costly article (silverplated ware, for example). The object to be plated is thoroughly cleansed and is attached to the cathode. A bar of the pure plating metal (nickel, cadmium, silver, chromium, etc.) is attached to the anode. The solution contains a dissolved salt of the plating metal.

The refining of copper is also accomplished by electroplating. The action is explained in the diagram on page 260.

Laws of Electrolysis. Michael Faraday conducted experimental studies which led him to formulate *three laws of electrolysis,* as follows. The amount of metal deposited by electrolysis is directly proportional to **(1)** *the length of time the current flows;* **(2)** *the strength of the current in amperes;* and **(3)** *the electrochemical equivalent of the metal.* By definition, the electrochemical equivalent of an element is the *weight in grams* of that element which deposits from solution when a current of *1 ampere* flows for *1 second.* For example, if 3.354 g of silver are deposited by a current of 10 amperes in 5 min, then 1 ampere would deposit 0.3354 g in 5 min (300 sec), and 1 ampere would deposit 0.001118 g in 1 sec; thus the electrochemical equivalent of silver is 0.001118 g. This value can be determined so accurately that it is used in calibrating ammeters and is the basis of the *standard international ampere.*

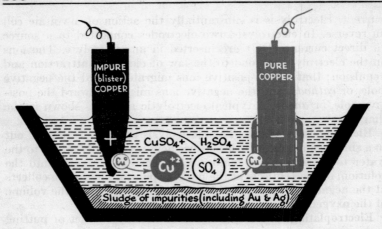

Refining of Copper. The positive copper ions in the solution are attracted to the cathode, become neutral, and deposited as pure, metallic copper. Simultaneously, copper atoms leave the anode and enter the solution as copper ions. All electroplating operates on this principle. Pure metal is deposited on the cathode (object to be plated); the anode is made of the plating metal.

THE SECONDARY CELL

The Lead-Acid Storage Battery. Storage batteries consist of two or more secondary cells, that is, cells which can be discharged and recharged repeatedly. The active material on the positive electrode of the lead-acid cell is lead peroxide (PbO_2); the negative electrode consists of spongy lead. The electrolyte is a dilute sulfuric acid solution.

When the battery is charged, it contains stored *chemical energy*. This energy is transformed into *electrical energy* by the reactions that ensue when the terminals of the cell are connected; that is, when the cell is discharging.

On discharge, hydrogen ions of the sulfuric acid remove oxygen from the lead peroxide electrode and unite with them to form water. The electrode is reduced to lead, which then combines with sulfate ions to form a deposit of lead sulfate. These reactions give this electrode a positive charge. At the other electrode, lead atoms unite with sulfate ions to form a deposit of lead sulfate. By this action, the electrode acquires a negative charge.

When discharging, (1) the cell delivers current to the outside; (2) sulfuric acid is removed from the solution, thus decreasing the specific gravity of the electrolyte; (3) the electrodes gradually become similar in composition, both being coated with lead sulfate; (4) the voltage of the cell drops to less than 2 volts.

When the positive terminal of a charging outfit is connected to the positive terminal of the cell (and negative is connected to negative), current is forced through the cell. To accomplish this, the voltage of the charging current must be higher than the voltage of the cell or battery being charged. Under these conditions, (1) acid is restored to the solution and the specific gravity (specific weight) increases; (2) the electrodes again become dissimilar, the positive becoming lead peroxide and the negative spongy lead; (3) the voltage rises to about 2.2 volts when the cell is fully charged.

The condition of charge of a lead-acid storage battery is best determined by using a hydrometer to test the specific gravity of

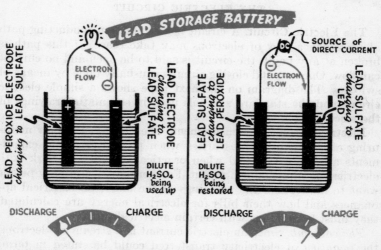

When the storage battery is discharging, its action is that of the voltaic cell. When it is being charged, the action is that of electrolysis.

the electrolyte solution. A voltmeter is of little value for testing this kind of battery since it may show a high terminal voltage and yet the battery may not be fully charged. The hydrometer indicates the quantity of sulfuric acid present. The specific gravity of a fully charged lead-acid cell is about 1.3 (1300 on the hydrometer). When completely discharged, the specific gravity falls to about 1.1 (1100 on the hydrometer).

Lead-acid storage batteries are commonly used for ignition and lighting on automobiles and airplanes; they drive the electric motors of submerged submarines; large ones serve as reservoirs of electrical power for emergency use in hospitals, telephone exchanges, etc; and they have dozens of other miscellaneous uses. The usual battery is made up of 2, 3, or 6 cells in series, thus giving approximately 4, 6, or 12 volts. (See page 273 for explanation of cells in series.) The common automobile battery has 3 cells, while the Army airplane battery contains 6 cells and thus gives 12 volts. It is designed so that the electrolyte will not spill, even if the plane should turn upside down.

THE ELECTRIC CIRCUIT

The Electric Circuit. A circuit is an unbroken conducting path along which a flow of electrons may take place. If this path is broken at any point, the circuit is said to be open and no current can flow. Opening and closing circuits is usually done by means of switches. The diagram on the next page shows a simple electric circuit and the standard symbols used in schematic drawings of the electric circuit.

Electrical Units of Measurement. The need of units for measuring electrical quantities arises when precise electrical experiments are carried on and when practical electricians work with electrical circuits and equipment. Furthermore, if ordinary people want to understand the meanings of the labels on electrical appliances and how their bills for electrical energy are calculated, they must be familiar with certain electrical units.

The coulomb. Since an electric current is a stream of electrons, the *quantity* of electricity transferred could be stated in terms of electrons. One coulomb of electricity contains 6.3 billion billion (6.3×10^{18}) electrons. This is a measure of quantity for electricity just as the quart is for milk, the pound for butter, etc.

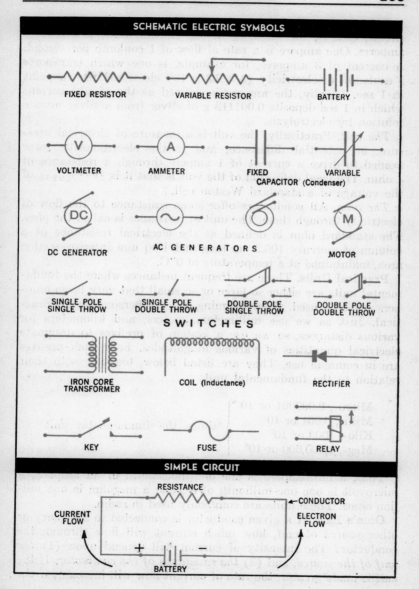

SCHEMATIC ELECTRIC SYMBOLS

FIXED RESISTOR   VARIABLE RESISTOR   BATTERY

VOLTMETER   AMMETER   FIXED CAPACITOR (Condenser)   VARIABLE

DC GENERATOR   AC GENERATORS   MOTOR

SINGLE POLE SINGLE THROW   SINGLE POLE DOUBLE THROW   DOUBLE POLE SINGLE THROW   DOUBLE POLE DOUBLE THROW

S W I T C H E S

IRON CORE TRANSFORMER   COIL (Inductance)   RECTIFIER

KEY   FUSE   RELAY

SIMPLE CIRCUIT

RESISTANCE
CURRENT FLOW   CONDUCTOR   ELECTRON FLOW
BATTERY

The ampere. The *time rate* at which electricity flows in a circuit, that is, the *intensity* of the electron flow, is stated in amperes. One ampere is a rate of flow of 1 coulomb per second. A current of 3 amperes, for example, is one which transports 3 coulombs of electricity ($3 \times 6.3 \times 10^{18}$ electrons) past a point in 1 sec. Legally, the ampere is defined as the steady current which in 1 sec deposits 0.001118 g of silver from a silver nitrate solution by electrolysis.

The volt. Practically, the volt is a measure of electrical pressure, or potential difference, and is the electromotive force needed to drive a current of 1 ampere through a resistance of 1 ohm. The legal definition of the volt is that it is $^{1000}\!/_{10183}$ of the voltage of a standard Weston cell.

The ohm. All conductors offer some resistance to the flow of electricity through them. The unit of resistance is called the *ohm.* The standard ohm is defined as the electrical resistance of a column of mercury 106.3 cm long and 1 sq mm in cross-section area, maintained at a temperature of 0°C.

Practical Units. There are frequent instances where the fundamental units are either so large or so small that very large numbers must be used, thus becoming too cumbersome to be practical. Just as we use millimeters, meters, and kilometers for various distances, so we use a system of prefixes to designate electrical quantities of various magnitudes. Four such prefixes are in common use. They are listed below, together with their relation to the fundamental unit:

$$\left.\begin{array}{l} \text{Micro-, } 0.000001 \text{ or } 10^{-6} \\ \text{Milli-, } 0.001 \text{ or } 10^{-3} \\ \text{Kilo-, } 1000 \text{ or } 10^{3} \\ \text{Meg-, } 1{,}000{,}000 \text{ or } 10^{6} \end{array}\right\} \text{ times the fundamental unit}$$

Thus, a milliampere is one one-thousandth of an ampere; a microvolt is one one-millionth of a volt; a megohm is one million ohms. These units are commonly used in radio.

Ohm's Law. If a given conductor is connected to a battery or other source of emf, how much current will flow through the conductor? The intensity of current will depend upon (1) *the emf of the source,* and (2) *the resistance of the conductor.* If the emf is made greater, the rate of current flow will increase; if the resistance is reduced, the current will also increase. The German physicist, Ohm, discovered that the current through any conductor is directly proportional to the emf applied to the conductor, and inversely proportional to the resistance of the conductor. This is called Ohm's law, and may be expressed in the following formula:

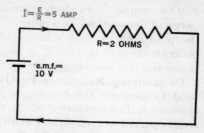

An Illustration of Ohm's Law

$$current = \frac{electromotive\ force}{resistance}$$

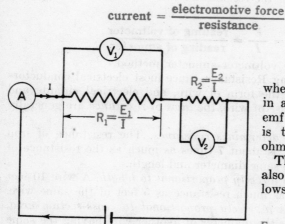

$$I = \frac{E}{R}$$

where I is the current in amperes, E is the emf in volts, and R is the resistance in ohms.

The formula may also be written as follows:

$$E = IR, \text{ or, } R = \frac{E}{I}$$

The Voltmeter-Ammeter Method of Determining Resistance. The resistance of any part of a circuit is equal to the voltage drop across that part divided by the current flowing through it. Voltage and current are measured by meters properly connected. In the diagram, R_1 is found by dividing its voltage drop (reading of voltmeter V_1) by the current (reading of ammeter A). The value of R_2 is similarly found by using the reading of V_2.

Voltage Drop. To make current flow from any point in a circuit to any other point, there must be a difference in potential between the two points. This difference in potential which exists between any two points in an electric circuit is called the *voltage drop* between or across those two points. The current which flows between the points obeys Ohm's law, where E is now the voltage drop between the points, and R is the resistance of the conductor between the two points.

Determining Resistance by Ohm's Law. Ohm's law may be used to measure the resistance of any conductor or part of a conductor. The conductor whose resistance is to be determined is connected in an electric circuit, so that a current will flow through it. The amount of current flowing is measured by an ammeter inserted in the circuit; at the same time, a voltmeter is connected to the ends of the unknown resistance and the voltage drop across the resistance is thereby measured. Applying Ohm's law:

$$R = \frac{E}{I} = \frac{\text{reading of voltmeter}}{\text{reading of ammeter}}$$

This is called the voltmeter-ammeter method.

Factors Affecting Resistance. Since most electrical conductors are fabricated in the form of wire, and electrical circuits and appliances make use of wire, the *laws of resistance* are generally stated as follows.

1. *Composition determines resistance.* The resistance of iron wire, for example, is about **7** times as much as the resistance of copper wire of the same diameter and length.

2. *Resistance is directly proportional to length.* A wire 10 feet long offers twice as much resistance as 5 feet of the same wire.

3. *Resistance is inversely proportional to cross-section area.* A wire three times the diameter of another wire having the same length and composition, offers only one-ninth the resistance; it has nine times the cross-section area (since area varies with the square of the diameter), and it is nine times as easy for a given current to flow through it.

These laws of resistance are expressed by the formula,

$$R = \frac{kl}{d^2}$$

in which $R =$ the resistance in ohms, $l =$ the length in feet, $d =$ the diameter in mils (1 mil = .001 in), and $k =$ a constant depending for its value on the material used.

4. *Temperature affects resistance.* All conductors undergo changes of resistance with changes in temperature. In general, the resistance of a metal increases with a rise of temperature, while the resistance of most liquid and non-metallic conductors (carbon) decreases as the temperature rises.

TYPICAL PROBLEMS

An incandescent lamp has a resistance of 220 ohms when hot. Find the current through the lamp when it is operated on a 110-volt line.

$$R = 220 \text{ ohms}; E = 110 \text{ volts}; I = ?$$

$$I = \frac{E}{R}, \text{ or } I = \frac{110}{220} = \textbf{0.5 ampere}$$

An electric toaster operating on 120 volts emf draws a current of 6 amperes. What is the resistance of the coil of the toaster?

$$E = 120 \text{ volts}; I = 6 \text{ amperes}; R = ?$$

$$R = \frac{E}{I}, \text{ or } R = \frac{120}{6} = \textbf{20 ohms}$$

What emf is necessary to produce a current of 0.02 ampere through a resistance of 5000 ohms?

$$E = ?; I = 0.02 \text{ ampere}; R = 5000 \text{ ohms}$$
$$E = IR, \text{ or } E = 0.02 \times 5000 = \textbf{100 volts}$$

The voltage drop across a 1.5 megohm radio resistor is 30 volts. What current (in milliamperes) flows through it?

$$E = 30 \text{ volts}; R = 1.5 \times 10^6 \text{ ohms}; I = ? \text{ milliamps}$$

$$I = \frac{E}{R}, \text{ or } I = \frac{30}{1.5 \times 10^6} = 20 \times 10^{-6} \text{ amp} = 20 \times 10^{-3} \text{ milliamp}$$
$$= \textbf{0.02 milliamp}$$

Other Methods of Measuring Resistance. The value of a resistance may be determined by comparing it with a standard resistance whose precise value is known. The *Wheatstone bridge* method, which is highly accurate, is commonly employed for this purpose.

Resistance may also be measured directly by an instrument called an *ohmmeter*. The ohmmeter operates on the ammeter-

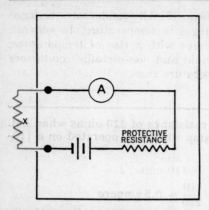

The Ohmmeter Method of Determining Resistance. The ohmmeter is shown in black; the resistance being measured, in red.

voltmeter method of measuring resistance. It contains a dry cell of fixed voltage, and an ammeter, connected as shown in the diagram. When the terminals of the ohmmeter are connected to the terminals of an unknown resistance (x), the circuit is completed and the ammeter reads the current which flows. Since the current depends on the resistance, the scale can be calibrated to read ohms directly—the voltage being fixed by the self-contained battery. Before using the ohmmeter, it should be adjusted to read zero when the terminals or test prods are touched together. Note that low resistance readings occur at the high current end of the meter scale. Zero current means infinite resistance (open circuit).

SERIES AND PARALLEL CIRCUITS

Series and Parallel Connections. For the purpose of circuit analysis, any electrical appliance or device is called a resistor, since all of them offer resistance to the passage of a current. Ordinarily, the connecting wires offer such small resistance as to be negligible.

When resistors are inserted between two points in an electric

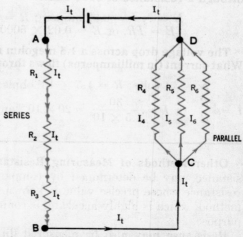

Resistances in Series and in Parallel

circuit in such a manner that *all* the current flows through *all* the resistors, one after the other, they are said to be connected *in series*. When resistors are inserted between two points in an electric circuit in such a manner that the current flowing between the two points is *divided* among the resistors, the resistors are said to be connected *in parallel*. In the diagram the total current (I_t) leaving point A flows through each of the three resistors (R_1, R_2, R_3) in turn. The total current (I_t) leaving point C in the circuit divides among the three resistors in parallel, part of the current (I_4) flowing through R_4, part (I_5) through R_5 and part (I_6) through R_6. Total current (I_t) flows from point D to the battery.

Characteristics of a Series Circuit.

1. *The current is the same throughout a series circuit.* There can be no loss or gain of current (electrons); hence, all of the electrons that flow out of the generator or battery must flow through the circuit and return. A break anywhere in a series circuit completely stops the flow of current.

$$I_1 = I_2 = I_3, \text{ etc.}$$

2. *The total or equivalent resistance (R_{eq}) of a number of resistors in series is the sum of their separate resistances.*

$$R_{eq} = R_1 + R_2 + R_3, \text{ etc.}$$

3. *The total voltage drop across a number of resistors in series is the sum of the voltage drops across the individual resistors.*

$$E_t = E_1 + E_2 + E_3, \text{ etc.}$$

TYPICAL PROBLEM

Three resistors of 20 ohms, 30 ohms, and 50 ohms respectively are connected in series. The current through R_1 (20 ohms) is 0.8 ampere. (*a*) What is the current through R_3 (50 ohms)? (*b*) What is the voltage across R_2? (*c*) What is the total voltage drop across the three resistors?

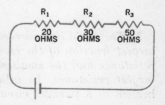

(*a*) In a series circuit, $I_1 = I_2 = I_3$, etc. $I_1 = 0.8$ ampere; hence
$$I_3 = \textbf{0.8 ampere}$$

(b) $I_2 = 0.8$ ampere; $R_2 = 30$ ohms; $E = ?$

$$E = IR, \text{ or } E = 0.8 \times 30 = \textbf{24 volts}$$

(c) In a series circuit, $E_t = E_1 + E_2 + E_3$, etc.

$$E_1 = IR_1, \text{ or } E_1 = 0.8 \times 20 = \textit{16 volts}$$
$$E_3 = IR_3, \text{ or } E_3 = 0.8 \times 50 = \textit{40 volts}$$
$$E_t = 16 \text{ volts} + 24 \text{ volts} + 40 \text{ volts} = \textbf{80 volts}$$

or

$$E_t = IR_{eq}, \text{ or } E_t = I(R_1 + R_2 + R_3);$$
$$\text{Hence, } E_t = 0.8 \times (20 + 30 + 50) = \textbf{80 volts}$$

Characteristics of Parallel Circuits. In a parallel circuit, the main-line current divides and flows simultaneously through the various branches. The type of circuit used in wiring our homes illustrates a parallel circuit. Each appliance is really connected separately across the main line. Series wiring cannot be used in homes because the total resistance of two or three ordinary lamps would be sufficient to prevent the flow of enough current from a 120-volt line to light them fully. Furthermore, we would have to use all of the appliances connected in series whenever we wished to use any one of them. Parallel circuits permit independent use of the various branches; a break in one branch of a parallel circuit does not interrupt the flow of current in other complete branches. The characteristics of parallel circuits are as follows.

1. *The total current* (I_t) *flowing in the main line is the sum of the currents in the separate branches.*

$$I_t = I_1 + I_2 + I_3, \text{ etc.}$$

2. *The voltage across each branch of a parallel circuit is the same.*

$$E_1 = E_2 = E_3, \text{ etc.}$$

3. *The main line current divides in a parallel circuit, with the largest fraction of the current going through the branch of least resistance and the smallest fraction going through the branch of largest resistance.* In other words, Ohm's law applies to each branch of a parallel circuit.

$$I_1 = \frac{E}{R_1}; \quad I_2 = \frac{E}{R_2}; \quad I_3 = \frac{E}{R_3}; \text{ etc.}$$

4. *The total or equivalent resistance* (R_{eq}) *of a number of resistors in parallel is less than the resistance of any one of them —even less than that of the separate branch offering the least resistance.* This fact is not difficult to understand if it is remembered that a resistance is a conductor, and each branch may be thought of as another pathway through which additional current flows; hence, as more conductors are added, the equivalent resistance becomes less.

The *conductance* of a device indicates how well it allows current to flow, in contrast to *resistance* which indicates just the opposite. Hence, *conductance* (symbol $= G$) *is the reciprocal of resistance* (R):

$$G = \frac{1}{R}$$

5. *The total conductance* (G_{eq}) *of a parallel circuit is the sum of the conductances of the separate branches.*

$$G_{eq} = G_1 + G_2 + G_3, \text{ etc.}$$

Substituting in this formula for the value of G, we derive the formula for the equivalent resistance of a parallel circuit:

$$\frac{1}{R_{eq}} = \frac{1}{R_1} + \frac{1}{R_2} + \frac{1}{R_3}, \text{ etc.}$$

The equivalent resistance of n equal resistors connected in parallel is $\frac{1}{n}$ times the resistance of one of them.

TYPICAL PROBLEMS

What is the equivalent resistance of 20 ohms, 40 ohms, and 80 ohms connected in parallel?

(*Note*: Answer must be less than 20 ohms.)

$$\frac{1}{R_{eq}} = \frac{1}{R_1} + \frac{1}{R_2} + \frac{1}{R_3}, \text{ or } \frac{1}{R_{eq}} = \frac{1}{20} + \frac{1}{40} + \frac{1}{80}$$
$$80 = 4R_{eq} + 2R_{eq} + R_{eq}$$
$$80 = 7R_{eq}$$
$$R_{eq} = \textbf{11.4 ohms}$$

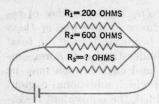

R₁= 200 OHMS
R₂= 600 OHMS
R₃=? OHMS

A resistor of 200 ohms, one of 600 ohms, and one of unknown value are connected in parallel to a source of emf. The voltage across R_1 (200 ohms) is 40 volts, and the main line current is 0.52 ampere. Calculate (a) I_1; (b) E_2; (c) R_3; and (d) R_{eq}.

(a) $R_1 = 200$ ohms; $E_1 = 40$ volts; $I_1 = ?$

$$I_1 = \frac{E_1}{R_1}, \text{ or } I_1 = \frac{40}{200} = \textbf{0.2 ampere}$$

(b) In a parallel circuit, $E_1 = E_2 = E_3$, etc. Hence, $E_2 = \textbf{40 volts}$

(c) $R_3 = ?$; $E_3 = 40$ volts; $I_3 = I_t - (I_1 + I_2)$. I_2 must be calculated.

$$I_2 = \frac{E_2}{R_2}, \text{ or } I_2 = \frac{40}{600} = 0.067 \text{ ampere}$$
$$I_3 = 0.52 - (0.2 + 0.067) = 0.253 \text{ ampere}$$
$$R_3 = \frac{E_3}{I_3}, \text{ or } R_3 = \frac{40}{0.253} = \textbf{158 ohms}$$

(d) $R_{eq} = ?$; $E = 40$ volts; $I_t = 0.52$ ampere

$$R_{eq} = \frac{E}{I_t}, \text{ or } R_{eq} = \frac{40}{0.52} = \textbf{77 ohms}$$

or

$$\frac{1}{R_{eq}} = \frac{1}{R_1} + \frac{1}{R_2} + \frac{1}{R_3}, \text{ or } \frac{1}{R_{eq}} = \frac{1}{200} + \frac{1}{600} + \frac{1}{158}$$
$$1{,}896{,}000 = 94{,}800 R_{eq} + 31{,}600 R_{eq} + 120{,}000 R_{eq}$$
$$1{,}896{,}000 = 246{,}400 R_{eq}$$
$$R_{eq} = \textbf{77 ohms}$$

Internal Resistance of a Cell. If the emf of a cell is measured with a high resistance voltmeter (so that very little current flows), the reading obtained is called the open-circuit voltage of the cell. It is the emf actually being developed by the chemical action within the cell. If this cell is now connected to a fairly low resistance, the current which flows will be less than what would be expected; and if the voltage across the cell terminals is now measured it will be found to be less than the open-circuit value. The reason for this is that the cell itself has an internal resistance, and the current flowing through this internal resistance produces a voltage drop inside the cell. Consequently the terminal voltage of the cell is reduced.

Cells in Series. When cells are connected so that the positive terminal of one is connected to the negative terminal of the next, etc., the cells are in series. The total emf of a number of cells in series is the sum of the emfs of all the cells; the internal resistance is likewise the sum of the separate resistances of each cell. Series connections of cells are used to obtain increased voltage—as in flashlights (where two or three 1.5-volt cells are connected in series with the bulb), in radio batteries of $4\frac{1}{2}$ volts (3 cells), $22\frac{1}{2}$ volts (15 cells), and 45 volts (30 cells), etc. The series connection does not make a greater current available. The maximum current which the combination can supply is still the maximum of any individual cell in the series.

Cells in Parallel. When more current is needed than a single cell can safely provide, several cells are connected in parallel—positive terminals connected together and negative terminals

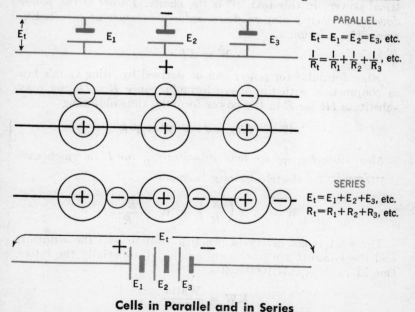

PARALLEL

$E_t = E_1 = E_2 = E_3$, etc.

$\frac{1}{R_t} = \frac{1}{R_1} + \frac{1}{R_2} + \frac{1}{R_3}$, etc.

SERIES

$E_t = E_1 + E_2 + E_3$, etc.

$R_t = R_1 + R_2 + R_3$, etc.

Cells in Parallel and in Series

connected together. The total emf of the combination is the emf of a single cell, but the internal resistance is reduced in accordance with the formula for connecting resistances in parallel. Since the currents from each cell now add together, a greater total current is available. *Note that cells connected in parallel should have the same emf;* otherwise the cells of lower emf will act as low-resistance short circuits on the cells of higher emf—thus producing a large current which would damage all cells.

The ordinary No. 6 dry cell should not be permitted to supply a current in excess of $\frac{1}{4}$ ampere. When more current is needed, enough cells should be connected in parallel so that no single cell supplies more than this safe current value. When more than 2 or 3 amperes are required, storage batteries are usually employed.

POWER AND ENERGY

Electrical Power. Power is defined as the rate of doing work, or of transferring or transforming energy. The unit of electrical power is the *watt*. W and P are both used as symbols for electrical power; in this text, W is the choice. *1 watt is the power developed when 1 ampere flows under a pressure of 1 volt.* Expressed as a formula,

$$W = EI$$

Other formulas for power can be derived by using Ohm's law in conjunction with the above formula. Since $E = IR$, we may substitute IR for E in the power formula, thus obtaining

$$W = (IR) \times I; \text{ or } W = I^2 R$$

Also, since $I = \dfrac{E}{R}$ we may substitute $\dfrac{E}{R}$ for I, in which case the formula for electrical power becomes

$$W = E \times \left(\frac{E}{R}\right), \text{ or } W = \frac{E^2}{R}$$

The watt is not always a practical unit to use; the *milliwatt* and the *kilowatt* are commonly employed, especially the latter. One kilowatt equals 1000 watts.

$$\text{KW} = \frac{\text{Watts}}{1000}$$

The relationship of mechanical and electrical power is shown by the following expressions:

1 Kilowatt = 1⅓ Horsepower
1 Horsepower = 746 watts, or 0.746 kilowatt

Neglecting frictional and heat losses, an electric motor, for example, develops 1 horsepower output for every 746 watts input. Efficiency of the motor would be calculated in the usual manner; that is, output/input.

Electrical Energy. *Energy = Power × Time.* To calculate how much electrical energy is consumed, therefore, we must know the rate at which it is consumed (power), and for how long (time). We know from experience, for example, that it costs more to operate a 100-watt lamp than a 50-watt lamp for the same length of time; but, of course, we get more light from the 100-watt lamp because it transforms energy at a faster rate. Likewise, we know that it costs more to operate a given lamp for 10 hours than for 5 hours.

The common units for expressing electrical energy are the *watt-hour* and the *kilowatt-hour*. A very small unit is the *watt-second*, also known as the *joule*.

Bills for "electricity" are calculated in terms of kilowatt-hours. If we use five 100-watt lamps for a period of 4 hours, the electrical energy transformed into heat and light is 5 × 100 watts × 4 hours = 2000 watt-hours, or 2 kilowatt-hours. If the rate is 8 cents per KWH, the cost of operating these lamps is 8 × 2 = 16 cents. Expressed as formulas,

$$\text{kilowatt-hours} = \frac{\overbrace{\text{volts} \times \text{amperes}}^{\text{watts}} \times \text{hours}}{1000}$$

$$\text{cost} = \text{kilowatt-hours} \times \text{rate}$$

HEATING EFFECTS OF AN ELECTRIC CURRENT

Converting Electrical Energy to Heat. Whenever an electric current flows through a resistance, the electrical energy consumed (power × time) is converted into heat. This conversion of electrical energy into heat is used in such devices as electric stoves, toasters, irons, etc. In the incandescent lamp (not fluorescent or neon lights, however) the heating effect of a current is used to produce useful light.

As among all forms of energy, there is a definite quantitative relationship between electrical energy and heat, given by the formula:

$$1 \text{ calorie} = 4.18 \text{ joules (watt-seconds)}$$

In the case of a conductor of resistance R carrying a current I, the heat developed in the conductor is given by the following formula:

$$H \text{ (calories)} = 0.24 \, I^2Rt$$

where I^2R is the power in watts, as shown on page 274, and t is the time in seconds.

Heat in Series and Parallel Circuits. In a series circuit, you will recall, the current is the same in every appliance or device. Since $H \propto I^2R$, and I^2 is the same for every appliance, the greatest amount of heat is developed where the resistance is largest. This is shown by the fact that the wire in an electric lamp becomes white hot, whereas the wire which carries the current into the lamp remains comparatively cold, since it offers low resistance.

In a parallel circuit, the voltage is the same across all branches. Since $H \propto I^2R$, and I^2R may be expressed as IE, it is apparent that the greatest amount of heat is developed in the branch carrying the largest current; that is, the branch offering the smallest resistance.

TYPICAL PROBLEM_____

(a) How much current will a 22-ohm electric iron draw when connected across a 110-volt line? (b) At what rate is energy used? (c) How many calories of heat are developed in 10 minutes?

(a) From Ohm's law, $I = \dfrac{E}{R}$; $I = \dfrac{110}{22} = $ **5 amperes**

(b) $W = EI$; $W = 110 \times 5 = $ **550 watts**

(c) $H = 0.24 \, I^2Rt$
$ H = 0.24 \times 25 \times 25 \times 22 \times 600$

Applications of the Heating Effect of the Current. *The incandescent lamp.* The incandescent electric lamp is essentially a fine wire with a high melting point, sealed in a glass envelope (bulb) in which provision is made to prevent oxidation when the passage of current heats the filament (wire) to incandescence. Early lamps contained a high vacuum, but modern lamps are usually filled with a mixture of argon and nitrogen. This gas mixture not only prevents oxidation of the tungsten filament, but also retards its evaporation. Evaporation of the tungsten filament during incandescence tends to destroy the filament and blacken the bulb. Modern gas-filled tungsten lamps of the type ordinarily used for home lighting develop about $1\frac{1}{3}$ candlepower per watt, as contrasted with the early carbon filament lamps which gave about $\frac{1}{3}$ candlepower per watt.

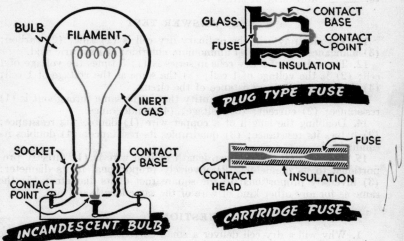

BULB   FILAMENT

GLASS   CONTACT BASE

FUSE   CONTACT POINT

INSULATION

INERT GAS

PLUG TYPE FUSE

SOCKET   CONTACT BASE

CONTACT POINT

FUSE

CONTACT HEAD   INSULATION

INCANDESCENT BULB

CARTRIDGE FUSE

Applications of the Heating Effect of an Electric Current

The fuse. A fuse is usually a strip of metal having a low melting point and fairly high resistance per unit length. Fuses are constructed to melt when more than the desired current passes through them; for example, a 10-ampere fuse melts when the current through it exceeds 10 amperes. Electrical meters and other devices are frequently protected from the effects of excessive currents by means of properly selected fuses. House circuits are commonly protected by 15-ampere fuses. Fuses are always connected in series. Consequently, when a fuse "blows," it opens the circuit and no current will flow until the fuse is replaced.

ASSOCIATION TEST

I

1. _____ Unit of electrical power
2. _____ Unit of electrical energy
3. _____ Incandescent electric lamp
4. _____ Requires DC electricity
5. _____ Electrical fuse
6. _____ Operates on either AC or DC
7. _____ Equals 1⅓ horsepower
8. _____ Electroplating
9. _____ More heat in smaller resistor
10. _____ More heat in larger resistor

II

1. Kilowatt-hour
2. 2 resistors in series
3. 2 resistors in parallel
4. Chemical effect
5. Heating effect
6. Kilowatt
7. Charging storage battery
8. Electric toaster

BEST ANSWER TEST

11. The electrolyte in the ordinary dry cell is (1) zinc; (2) carbon; (3) manganese dioxide; (4) ammonium chloride; (5) sulfuric acid.

12. The voltage of 5 dry cells in series is (1) 5 times the voltage of 1 cell; (2) ⅕ the voltage of 1 cell; (3) the same as the voltage of 1 cell; (4) dependent on the resistance of the circuit.

13. In a series circuit, the quantity that is the same throughout is (1) resistance; (2) current; (3) voltage; (4) conductance.

14. Doubling the length of a copper wire (1) doubles its resistance; (2) halves its resistance; (3) quadruples its resistance; (4) doubles its conductance.

15. The resistance of a given length of iron wire is (1) directly proportional to its diameter; (2) inversely proportional to its diameter; (3) inversely proportional to the square root of its diameter; (5) the same as for any other kind of wire of the same length and size.

QUESTIONS

1. Why will a dry cell deliver a small current for a fairly long time without polarization, but not a large one?

2. What is the effect of each of the following on (1) the voltage, (2) the internal resistance of a chemical cell? (*a*) Materials of which the cell is constructed; (*b*) size of the plates; (*c*) distance between the plates; (*d*) area of plates in contact with electrolyte.

3. What is the source of the electrical energy delivered by a dry cell?

4. Describe a procedure for determining the electric resistance of a toaster, making use of a voltmeter and an ammeter.

5. Explain the reasons for using parallel circuits instead of series circuits in house wiring.

6. What is meant by a *short circuit?* How do fuses act as safeguards against the effects of short circuits?

7. Is it advisable to use a 30-ampere fuse in a 20-ampere circuit? Why?

8. What is it that a storage battery really stores? Explain.

9. State Faraday's laws of electrolysis.

10. How would you go about plating a brass object with chromium? What kind of current would you need? Why?

PROBLEMS

1. Calculate the resistance of 200 ft of copper wire, the diameter of which is 32 mils. ($k = 10.4$) Ans. 2.03 ohms

2. How many feet of the wire in problem 1 must be used in winding a coil of 5 ohms? Ans. 492 ft

3. How much current will be sent through (a) 20 ohms, (b) 100 ohms, (c) 2000 ohms by a potential difference of 10 volts? Ans. (a) 0.5 amp (b) 0.1 amp (c) 0.005 amp

4. What difference of potential is required to send (a) 10 amperes through a 5-ohm resistance; (b) 0.5 ampere through a 500-ohm resistance; (c) 2 "mils" (milliamperes) through a 1-megohm resistance? Ans. (a) 50 v (b) 250 v (c) 2000 v

5. What resistance, when connected to a 550-volt line, will permit a current flow of (a) 50 amperes; (b) 2 amperes; (c) 11 mils? Ans. (a) 11 ohms (b) 275 ohms (c) 50,000 ohms

6. What is the resistance of 40 ohms, 60 ohms and 80 ohms connected (a) in series, (b) in parallel? Ans. (a) 180 ohms (b) 18.5 ohms

7. (a) How much line current will flow when five 100-ohm lamps are connected in parallel across a 110-volt line? (b) How much current does each lamp draw? (c) What voltage would be needed to send 1 ampere through these five lamps connected in series? Ans. (a) 5.5 amp (b) 1.1 amp (c) 500 v

8. What is the resistance of an electric heater drawing 4 amperes on a 110-volt circuit? Ans. 27.5 ohms

9. (a) What resistance should be put in series with a 110-volt lamp that draws 2 amperes, in order to light it from a 200-volt circuit? (b) What would be the voltage drop across this resistance? Ans. (a) 45 ohms (b) 90 v

10. The voltage at a power house supplying 50 amperes to a trolley car one mile away is 550 volts. (a) What is the voltage drop through the connecting wires whose resistance is 0.5 ohm? (b) What is the voltage at the trolley? Ans. (a) 25 v (b) 525 v

11. A 55-watt incandescent electric lamp is made so that it will operate properly on a 110-volt circuit. Answer the following, showing all necessary work: (a) If, when the lamp is in use, the voltage should rise to 125 volts, state whether there would be an increase, a decrease or no change in (1) the current flowing through the lamp, (2) the brightness of the filament. (b) Calculate the current for which the lamp was designed to operate. (c) Calculate the resistance that must be put in

series with the lamp in order that it may receive the current found in
answer to (b) while under a pressure of 125 volts.

Ans. (a) (1)—increase (2)—increase (b) 0.5 amp (c) 30 ohms

12. (a) What is the terminal voltage of a 6-volt storage battery,
whose internal resistance is 0.05 ohm when it is being charged at the
rate of 8 amperes? (b) When it is discharging at the rate of 10 amperes?

Ans. (a) 6.4 v (b) 5.5 v

13. Resistors of 800 ohms and 200 ohms are connected in parallel,
and the combination is then connected in series with a resistor of unknown value. When the voltage across the entire circuit is 160 volts, the
current through the 200-ohm resistor is 0.16 amp. Calculate: (a) the
voltage across the parallel branch; (b) the current through the 800-ohm
resistor; (c) the voltage across the unknown resistor; (d) the resistance
of the unknown resistor. Ans. (a) 32 v (b) 0.04 amp (c) 128 v (d) 640 ohms

14. How much current would 20 cells in series, each having an emf
of 2 volts and an internal resistance of 0.1 ohm send through three
resistances of 20, 30, and 60 ohms, respectively, connected in parallel?

Ans. 3.33 amp

15. An incandescent lamp draws 0.8 amp when connected to a 120-
volt line. Calculate (a) the wattage, (b) the resistance of the lamp.

Ans. (a) 96 watts (b) 150 ohms

16. What are the watts per candle-power in a lamp drawing 0.4 amp
from a 110-volt line and giving 25 candle-power?   Ans. 1.76 watts/cp

17. The label on an electric toaster reads, "550 watts; 110 volts." (a)
What current does the appliance draw? (b) What is its resistance?

Ans. (a) 5 amp (b) 22 ohms

18. Radio resistors made of carbon are available in ½-, 1-, and 2-
watt sizes. What (a) resistance, (b) wattage rating should a resistor
have if it is to carry 5 mils at 100 volts? (c) What size resistor would
you select if they are to be operated at only about 50% of capacity?

Ans. (a) 20,000 ohms (b) ½-watt (c) 1-watt

19. Calculate the calories of heat developed in 15 min by the electric
toaster in problem 17.   Ans. 119,000 cal

20. A 120-volt house circuit has a 15-ampere fuse. How many 60-watt
lamps in parallel can be operated at once without blowing the fuse?

Ans. 30

21. What is the cost of operating each of the following appliances for
120 hours at 8 cents per KWH: (a) 100-watt lamp; (b) the toaster in
problem 17; (c) an electric soldering iron of 20 ohms resistance connected to a 110-volt line.   Ans. (a) $0.96 (b) $5.28 (c) $5.81

22. The motor of an electric refrigerator operated on a 110-volt line
draws a current of 2.5 amp. To maintain the desired temperature inside
the refrigerator, the motor operates ⅓ of the time. What is the power
of the motor (a) in watts, (b) in horsepower? (c) Calculate the apparent resistance of the motor. (d) What will be the cost of operating
the refrigerator for 30 days if the rate is 5¢ per KWH?

Ans. (a) 275 watts (b) 0.369 HP (c) 44 ohms (d) $3.30

TWENTY-ONE— ELECTROMAGNETISM AND ELECTROMAGNETIC INDUCTION

ELECTRICITY IN MOTION PRODUCES MAGNETISM

Oersted's Discovery. A Danish physicist, Oersted, in the year 1819, discovered the presence of a magnetic field around a current-carrying wire. This field around a straight wire carrying a current consists of concentric circles in planes perpendicular to the wire. The presence and pattern of the field can be seen by passing current through a vertical wire which runs through a piece of cardboard supported horizontally. When iron filings are sprinkled on the cardboard and it is tapped lightly, the filings align themselves in circles around the wire, thus revealing the magnetic lines of force.

The direction of these circular lines of force can be determined by placing a small compass on the cardboard. The north pole of the compass points in the direction of the magnetic field (magnetic lines of force run from N through the air to S). If a straight, current-carrying wire is held *above* a compass in such a manner that the current flows from north to south, the north pole of the compass needle is deflected to the east. The needle points in the direction of the field. If the direction of the current is reversed, the needle is deflected to the west.

The *right-hand thumb rule* is useful in determining the di-

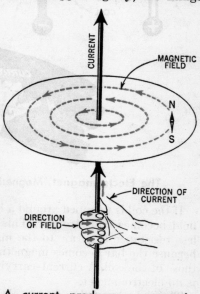

A current produces a magnetic field; the right-hand thumb rule shows the direction of the current and the field.

rection of the magnetic field about a current-carrying wire. *Grasp the wire with the right hand so that the thumb points in the direction of current flow (+ to −); then the fingers will curl around the wire in the direction of the magnetic field.*

Magnetic Field About a Current-Carrying Coil. A more intense magnetic field can be obtained from a small current flowing in a wire by looping the wire to form a coil. It is found that the coil closely resembles a bar magnet, both in its magnetic action on a compass needle and in the pattern of its magnetic field.

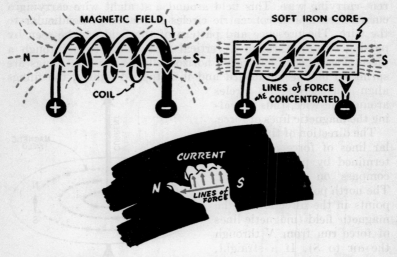

The Electromagnet. Magnetic lines of force are in red.

If the coil is wrapped around a bar of iron or steel, the magnetic field becomes still stronger. This is because iron and steel offer less resistance than air to the magnetic lines of force, and also because the bar becomes magnetized and its lines of force add to those of the coil. A current-carrying coil of wire with an iron core is an electromagnet.

The right-hand thumb rule also enables us to determine which end of an electromagnet is a north pole and which is a south pole: *Grasp the coil of the electromagnet with the right hand so that the fingers curl in the direction of current flow; then the thumb will point to the north pole of the electromagnet.* The polarity of an electromagnet thus depends upon the direction of the flow of current.

Characteristics of Electromagnets. The strength of an electromagnet depends upon (1) the number of amperes flowing in the coil; (2) the number of turns in the coil; (3) the permeability of the core. With a given material used as the core (usually soft iron), the strength of an electromagnet depends upon the number of *ampere-turns;* that is, the product of the current in amperes and the number of turns in the coil. An electromagnet having 1000 turns of wire carrying 4 amperes is equal to one having 2000 turns of wire carrying 2 amperes; both have 4000 ampereturns.

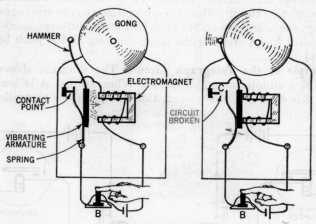

The Electric Bell

The principal advantages of electromagnets are: (1) they can be made much stronger than permanent magnets; (2) their field strength is easily controlled by regulating the current; (3) they lose practically all their magnetism almost immediately when the current is turned off, provided that the core is soft iron (low retentivity). If the core were hard steel (high retentivity), it would retain much of its magnetism and become a permanent magnet.

Applications of the electromagnet are found in the electric bell, the magnetic hoist, the relay, the telephone and telegraph;

in electric motors, generators, and transformers; and in electrical measuring instruments, such as galvanometers, ammeters, voltmeters, and others. In fact, an electromagnet is a part of nearly every electrical machine. The magnetic field is the most widely applied of the effects which current flow produces.

The Electric Bell. The essential parts of the electric bell are shown in the diagram on page 283. When the circuit is completed, by closing the push button *B*, the current flows through the electromagnet. The soft iron vibrating armature is attracted by the electromagnet and as it moves over, the circuit is broken at *C*. (See right side of diagram.) When the current stops, the electromagnet loses its magnetism and hence its attraction for the armature. A spring moves the armature back and it again makes contact at *C*, thus completing the circuit and re-energizing the electromagnet. In this way, the armature moves back and forth and the hammer attached to it keeps striking the gong—as long as the push button is closed.

Principle of the Telegraph Circuit. The diagram shows the set-up of a simple telegraph circuit. When station *A* is sending, switch *S* is open but *S'* is closed; thus the circuit is controlled by

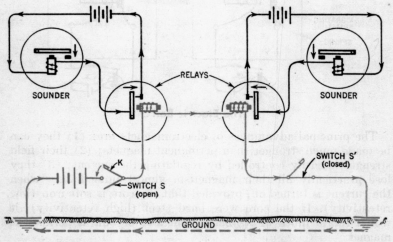

SOUNDER   ←RELAYS→   SOUNDER

K
←SWITCH S (open)   SWITCH S' (closed)

GROUND

Station A   **Station B**

The relay circuit is shown in red.

means of the sender key K. When this key is closed, the circuit is complete (the earth serves as one conductor between the two stations), and current flows through the coils of the relay at station B. The relay is really a sensitive electromagnetic switch having a coil of many turns of fine wire and a light-weight armature. When the feeble main line current flows through the coils of the relay, electromagnetism is produced which pulls the armature against a contact point. This closes the local circuit and allows a heavier current to flow through the coils of the sounder. Electromagnetism pulls the armature of the sounder downward against a setscrew.

When the key is released at A, the circuit is broken; the relay electromagnet is de-energized, the local circuit is opened, and the armature of the sounder is released. The sounder thus makes two clicks, one when it is pulled down and another when it is released. The time interval between these two clicks is interpreted as a dot or a dash by the operator, a short time interval representing a dot and a longer one a dash. Dots and dashes are translated into messages according to the Morse code.

ELECTRIC METERS

Many electric meters are of the indicating type; that is, the desired reading is obtained from the movement of a pointer across a calibrated scale. The device in this type of meter that causes the pointer to move is called the *meter movement*. Many meter movements depend for their operation upon magnetic attraction and repulsion.

The Weston Meter Movement. The meter movement used most extensively for measuring DC, and also with certain modifications for AC, is called the *Weston* movement, after its inventor. This type of movement is also known as the permanent-magnet moving-coil type.

The Weston movement consists essentially of a small rectangular coil of fine wire, suspended on jewel bearings between the poles of a permanent magnet, and free to rotate against the retarding force of two spiral springs. The springs also serve to carry current into and away from the coil. A non-movable soft iron core within the coil strengthens the magnetic field through it.

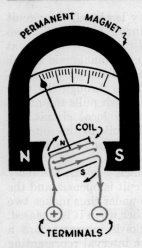

The Weston Meter. As current flows through the coil (shown in red) a magnetic field is set up with the polarity as indicated. The N-pole of the coil is repelled by the like pole of the permanent magnet, causing the coil to rotate.

When current flows through this coil, the magnetic field produced about the coil reacts with the magnetic field of the permanent magnet causing the coil to rotate and move the attached pointer across a scale. The amount of rotation of the coil depends upon the strength of the magnetic field produced by the coil, and hence depends upon the size of the current flowing in the coil. Modern Weston movements are carefully constructed so that the deflection of the pointer is directly proportional to the current in the coil.

The Galvanometer. A galvanometer is a device for detecting very small electric currents, and their direction, but not for measuring their value in practical units. Portable galvanometers commonly operate on the Weston principle. Their coils will be burned out by currents of more than a few microamperes.

The Ammeter. To extend the range of a galvanometer, that is, to enable it to read larger currents, it is only necessary to add a *shunt*. The galvanometer then becomes an *ammeter*. A shunt is a strip of metal of low resistance connected across the terminals of the coil of the meter, that is, in parallel with the coil. The shunt carries the major portion of the current entering the meter, while a small, fixed percentage of the total current flows through the coil. Thus if 10 amperes flow through an ammeter, 9.95 amperes may go through the shunt and only 0.05 amperes through the coil itself. Ammeters usually have two or three shunts from which one is selected to adapt the meter to the desired range; the larger the current to be measured, the smaller the resistance of the shunt must be. An ammeter is connected in series with the circuit in which the current is to be measured; that is, the circuit is opened at some convenient point and the ammeter is inserted.

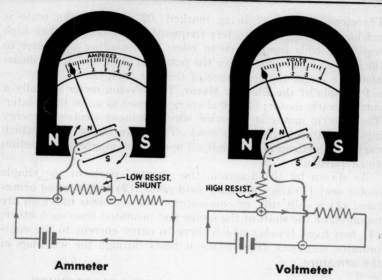

Ammeter

Voltmeter

The Voltmeter. A voltmeter is essentially a galvanometer with a high resistance (several thousand ohms) in series with the coil, so that it can safely be connected across a line, or other relatively large voltage. Such a high resistance connected in series protects the delicate coil, since only a very small current can flow through the meter. For example, if the voltmeter resistance is 10,000 ohms and the voltmeter is put across a 100-volt line, the current through the voltmeter will be only 0.01 ampere, as can be seen from Ohm's law:

$$I = \frac{E}{R}; \ I = \frac{100}{10,000} = 0.01 \text{ ampere}$$

Although the voltmeter movement actually measures the current flowing through it, the scale is calibrated to read voltage directly. For example, a voltmeter ($R = 10,000$ ohms) is connected across two points between which the difference in potential is to be measured, and a current of 0.02 ampere flows. The voltage, therefore, must be 200 volts:

$$E = IR; \ E = .02 \times 10000 = 200 \text{ volts}$$

Therefore, instead of being marked .02 amperes, the scale is marked 200 volts. Voltmeters frequently have two or more high resistance coils from which to select for adapting the meter to the desired range; the larger the potential difference to be measured, the larger the resistance of the coil must be.

Principle of the Electric Motor. The Weston meter is really a small electric motor; electrical energy is used to move the pointer. The electric motor is a device which changes electrical energy into mechanical energy, or work. There are many types which vary in structural details, but all operate on magnetic attraction and repulsion.

As shown by the diagram, the essential parts of the simple motor are: (1) the stationary *field poles;* (2) the *rotating armature;* (3) a split ring, or *commutator,* the segments of which are mounted on the shaft of the motor and insulated from each other; (4) two fixed *brushes* which serve to carry current to the commutator segments, from which it flows through the windings of the armature.

MAGNETISM IN MOTION PRODUCES ELECTRICITY

Faraday's Discovery. The development of the voltaic cell made it possible for scientists to experiment with and study electric currents, but voltaic cells could not furnish sufficient power to make possible the widespread use of electricity as of today. The production of large amounts of electric power had to await the development of the mechanical generator, that is, a device which can transform mechanical energy (or work) into electrical energy. The underlying principle of the generator was discovered by Michael Faraday, the renowned English scientist.

Faraday wondered, "If electricity can produce magnetism, can magnetism produce electricity?" By 1831, he had discovered that there is a flow of current whenever a bar magnet is *moved* in or out of a coil of wire, the ends of which are connected to form a closed circuit. The weak current can be detected by connecting the ends of the wire to a galvanometer.

The emf which makes this current flow is termed an *induced emf,* and its production, being dependent upon magnetism, is called *electromagnetic induction.*

Joseph Henry, in America, independently made many of the same discoveries as Faraday. These two scientists receive full

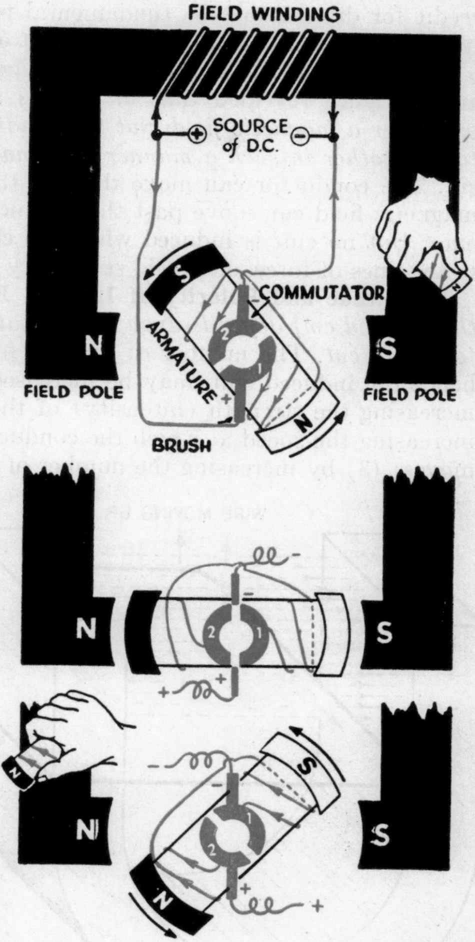

1. Starting with the source of DC, trace the flow of current through the armature from + to —, noting that the current enters segment (1) of the commutator and leaves through segment (2). Applying the right-hand thumb rule to the armature, we find that the white end of the armature is a north pole and the black end is a south pole. The forces of magnetic attraction and repulsion between the poles of the armature and the poles of the field cause the armature to rotate in a counterclockwise direction.

2. The middle diagram shows that when the armature poles are in line with the field poles, the brushes are at the gap in the commutator and no current flows in the armature.

3. Inertia, however, carries the armature past the field poles as shown in the bottom diagram. In this position, current enters the armature winding through segment (2) and leaves through segment (1), thus reversing the direction of current and hence the polarity of the armature. The black end is now north and the white end is now south. (Compare with top diagram.) The forces of attraction and repulsion again operate to keep the armature rotating in the same counter-clockwise direction.

credit for discovering the fundamental principles of electromagnetic induction, upon which our present electrical age is founded.

Production of an Induced EMF. The experiments of Henry and Faraday revealed that *an emf is induced in a conductor whenever a magnetic field and the conductor move with respect to each other in such a manner that magnetic lines of force are cut.* The conductor can move through the magnetic field, or the magnetic field can move past the conductor—it makes no difference. But no emf is induced when the conductor moves parallel to the lines of force, or is held stationary with respect to the field.

Magnitude and Polarity of Induced EMF. *The magnitude of the induced emf depends upon the rate at which magnetic lines of force are cut.* The number of lines of force cut per second, and hence the induced emf, may be increased in three ways: (1) by increasing the strength (intensity) of the magnetic field; (2) by increasing the speed at which the conductor or the magnetic field moves; (3) by increasing the number of loops or turns of wire in

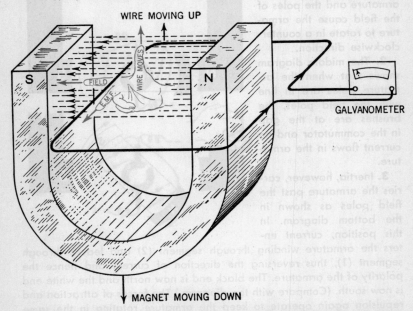

Fleming's Rule for Determining the Direction of an Induced EMF

the conductor. The magnitude of the current (termed the *induced current*) that flows in the circuit as a result of the emf produced depends, of course, on the resistance of the circuit; that is,

$$I = \frac{E}{R}.$$

The direction of the induced current may be determined by the *right-hand three-finger rule* (Fleming's Rule): *extend the thumb, forefinger, and center finger of the right hand at right angles to each other. If the thumb points in the direction in which the conductor moves through the field, and the forefinger points in the direction of the magnetic lines of force (toward the south pole), then the center finger points in the direction of the flow of current in the conductor.*

Principle of the AC Generator. It is apparent from Fleming's rule that if we change the direction in which the conductor moves, we also change the direction of the current. Moving a straight wire up and down so that it cuts magnetic lines of force produces surges of current that *alternate* in direction. The practicable way of generating continuous alternating currents of electricity is the use of a rectangular loop of wire (armature) mounted on an axis so that it can be rotated in a magnetic field.

The method of introducing current into the outside circuit consists of connecting the ends of the wire in the armature to two *slip rings* upon which two *brushes* (metal or carbon) rest. Since each brush makes constant contact with the same slip ring, the current in the outside circuit alternates in step with the alternations in armature. (See diagram on page 292.)

The DC Generator. The simple DC generator is identical in construction with the AC machine, except that the slip rings are replaced by a split-ring commutator (the same type as used in the DC motor). The action of the commutator may be understood from the diagram on page 292. Brush 1 always makes contact with the side of the loop moving downward, and brush 2 with the side moving upward. In this way, the current is kept flowing to the outside circuit in one direction, even though the current in the armature is alternating.

By using more coils set at angles to each other in the armature so that some coil is always cutting lines of force at the maximum rate, a more even flow of current results. Each coil contributes its share of current (through its own pair of segments) at regular intervals.

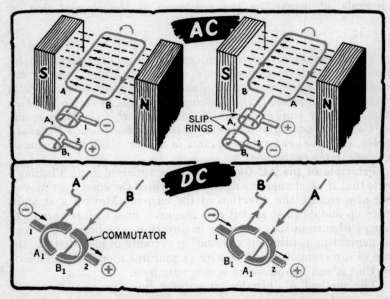

In the top diagram (left) illustrating the action of the AC generator, coil side *B* moves up through the magnetic field. According to Fleming's rule, an emf is induced in the direction shown; brush 2 is therefore +. Conversely, brush 1 is —. As the coil rotates in the counterclockwise direction shown in the right-hand side of the drawing, coil side B moves downward through the magnetic field, thus reversing the direction of the emf induced. Since side *B* is connected with slip ring B_1, which is in turn connected with brush 2, brush 2 is now —, while brush 1 becomes +.

In the DC generator, the direction of the emf alternates in the rotating coil just as it did in the AC generator. However, the polarity of the brushes in the DC generator does not alternate. This is accomplished by substituting a split commutator for the slip rings. Thus, when coil side *B* is moving up, its commutator segment (B_1) makes contact with brush 2, which becomes +. When coil side B moves down (thus reversing the direction of the emf), its commutator segment rotates and now makes contact with brush 1, which remains —.

The current needed to energize the field poles of the DC generator is taken from the generator itself. It is only a small per cent of the output of the machine. The field and the armature may be connected in series (series-wound), in parallel (shunt-wound), or in a combination of series and parallel (compound-wound).

Lenz's Law. An important characteristic of induced currents is demonstrated by the experiment illustrated on page 294.

The facts illustrated in the diagram are summarized in Lenz's law, stated as follows: *an induced current always flows in such a direction that its magnetism opposes the motion or the change that induced it.* There are many applications of Lenz's law, especially in connection with alternating currents.

Back EMF of a Motor. Comparison of the DC generator (page 291) and the DC motor (page 288) reveals that they are identical in construction. In fact, either is a reversible machine; that is, when mechanical energy forces the armature to rotate against the resistance of the magnetic field, mechanical energy is transformed into electrical energy. When an electric current is sent through the windings of the armature, the armature rotates by

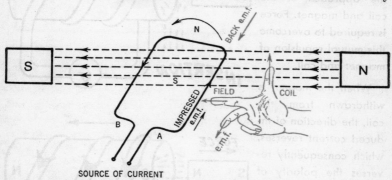

As the current flows through the coil in the direction of the impressed emf, a magnetic field is set up, the north pole of which is above the coil and the south pole below the coil. Magnetic attraction and repulsion turn the coil in the direction shown. However, as one side of the coil (A) moves up, it cuts the lines of force and an emf is induced in it. As can be seen from Fleming's rule, this induced or back emf is opposite to the impressed emf.

As the magnetic lines of force of the bar magnet cut the coil, a current is induced in the coil in the direction shown by the arrows. This induced current sets up its own magnetic field. Applying the right-hand rule, we find that this field has a north pole on the left.

Since like poles repel each other, the two magnetic fields oppose the approach of the coil and magnet. Force is required to overcome this mutual repulsion of magnet and coil.

When the magnet is withdrawn from the coil, the direction of induced current reverses, which consequently reverses the polarity of the coil. Since unlike poles attract each other, the two magnetic fields oppose the separation of the magnet and coil.

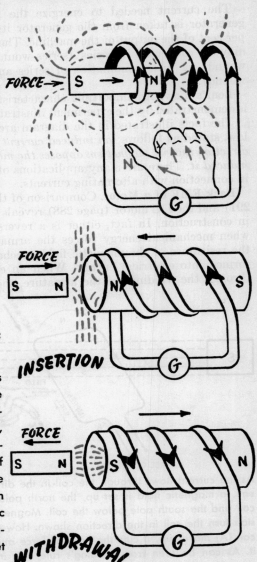

INSERTION

WITHDRAWAL

reaction against the magnetic field and thus transforms electrical energy into mechanical energy, or work.

When the machine operates as a motor, its rotating armature still cuts the magnetic lines of force, and will therefore act as a generator and have an emf induced in it. By Lenz's law, this induced emf will tend to oppose the rotation producing it. In other words, the induced emf should oppose the applied emf (which is actually responsible for the rotation). The diagram on page 293 shows that this is actually what occurs. The induced emf is called a *back* or *counter* emf, and it acts to reduce the effective emf driving current through the armature. For example, if a motor is operating on a 120-volt line, and is developing a back emf of 110 volts, the net emf is $120 - 110 = 10$ volts. If the armature resistance is 2 ohms, only 5 amperes will flow through the armature instead of 60 amperes as might at first be expected.

Because a slow-running motor does not build up a large back emf, it draws more current than when running at full speed. To prevent damage from excess current, "starting boxes" are frequently employed. These are resistances which keep the current small to protect the armature windings as the motor starts; they "cut out" (perhaps automatically) as the motor speeds up and develops a larger back emf.

CURRENTS INDUCE CURRENTS

Changing the Magnetic Field Electrically. We have seen that (1) when a current flows through a conductor a magnetic field is produced about the conductor in proportion to the intensity of the current; (2) when a coil is moved through a magnetic field or the field is moved through a coil an emf is induced. Up to this point we have concerned ourselves with moving the magnetic field by *mechanical* means. Faraday discovered that the magnetic field can also be moved *electrically*. He wound two independent coils of wire on the same iron core. One coil (the *primary*) was connected to a battery and the other coil (the *secondary*) was connected to a galvanometer. An emf was induced and current flowed in the secondary whenever a current was *started or stopped in the primary*. The *changing* magnetic field produced electrically by the starting or stopping of current in the primary acted exactly like the changing magnetic field produced mechanically by moving a coil and a magnetic field with respect to each other. Thus an emf was induced in the secondary coil. This induced emf is produced whenever the current in the primary is *changing in magnitude or direction*.

Inductance. It will readily be seen from Faraday's experiment above that if only one coil is considered, a changing current in the coil will induce an emf in turns of wire of *the same coil*. According to Lenz's law, this induced emf opposes the change in current producing it. The property of a circuit which opposes any

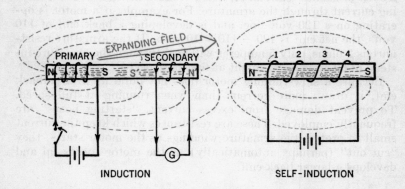

In the diagram at the left, as the switch is closed, current builds up in the primary. This increasing current produces an expanding magnetic field which "sweeps" across the turns of the secondary, inducing a current in the secondary. Note that the magnetic field of the induced current is opposite in polarity to that of the primary.

The diagram at the right illustrates how induction takes place within a single coil. Let us assume the diagram shows the current and magnetic field at maximum strength. If the circuit is now broken, the field will collapse. As the collapsing field sweeps across the individual turns of the coil, an emf is induced which opposes the change in current producing it. Thus the induced emf tends to keep the current flowing even after the circuit is broken. This induced emf is often sufficient to cause a spark to jump the gap in the circuit.

change in the amount of current flowing is called *inductance*. A *coil* of wire in an electrical circuit gives that circuit the property of inductance. Inductance in a circuit is analogous to inertia in in mechanics; in fact, inductance is sometimes called *electromagnetic inertia.*

When current begins to flow in a coil, the resulting magnetic field builds up and sweeps through the coil, inducing a back emf in the coil which tends to prevent the rise in current. Hence, the current builds up slowly to maximum strength. When the current flow is steady and there is no relative motion of magnetic field and conductor, no inductance effect is produced. When the current is stopped, the magnetic field collapses or withdraws, and the induced emf is in the opposite direction; that is, it tends to oppose the stopping of the current and to keep it flowing. With alternating current, these effects of inductance are produced with every alternation of the current and have a very important influence over the current which flows.

Mutual inductance is the term used when the effect of induction is such that a current change in one circuit produces an induced emf in another circuit. The term "magnetic coupling" is often used to indicate that there is a mutual inductance between two coils. A common application of mutual inductance is in the transformer.

The magnitude of inductance depends upon the physical characteristics of the coils, such as size, number of turns, spacing between turns, etc.

The *henry* is the unit of inductance. It may be defined as *the inductance present when a current change of one ampere per second produces an induced emf of one volt.* The symbol for inductance is *L.* Practical units of inductance, except for large iron-cored coils, are the *millihenry* and the *microhenry* (for radio coils, for example).

The Transformer. The transformer is used to control the voltage of an alternating current. This electrical device consists essentially of a primary coil and a secondary coil insulated from each other, but wound on the same iron core and thus coupled together by mutual inductance. When alternating current flows in the primary, an alternating magnetic field is established through the iron core. The lines of force in the core cut the windings of the secondary coil and induce an alternating emf in this circuit. The voltage of the primary bears the same ratio to the voltage induced in the secondary that the number of turns in the primary coil bears to the number of turns in the secondary coil.

$$\frac{\text{Primary Voltage}}{\text{Secondary Voltage}} = \frac{\text{Primary Turns}}{\text{Secondary Turns}}$$

$$\frac{E_1}{E_2} = \frac{N_1}{N_2}$$

A *step-up* transformer is one in which the output voltage is greater than the input voltage; that is, the secondary has more turns than the primary. Transformers of this type are used in the commercial transmission of electric power over long distances and in the operation of X-ray tubes, neon signs, fluorescent lights, and numerous electrical devices; small step-up transformers are frequently employed in certain radio circuits.

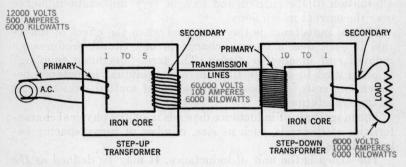

A *step-down* transformer is one in which the output voltage is less than the input voltage; hence, the secondary has fewer turns than the primary. Bell-ringing transformers are of this type; step-down transformers are also used in electric welding and to reduce the voltage of commercial electric power to suitable and safe values for use in homes and for other applications.

Power Transmission in the Transformer. The transformer does not create electrical energy; it merely changes the voltage-amperage ratio in the same way that a mechanical machine changes the force-distance ratio. As with machines, if the transformer were 100% efficient, the power output (secondary volts × secondary amperes) would equal the power input (primary volts × primary amperes).

$$E_1 I_1 = E_2 I_2, \text{ or } \frac{E_1}{E_2} = \frac{I_2}{I_1}$$

However, there are some energy losses in the transformer, but they are small compared to the losses in mechanical machines. Transformers having efficiencies from 95% to more than 99% are not unusual. Again, as in the case of machines,

$$\text{Efficiency} = \frac{\text{Power Output}}{\text{Power Input}}$$

One reason for the more widespread use of AC power than of DC power is the ease with which the voltage can be increased for long-distance transmission and then reduced for local consumption. Stepping up the voltage reduces the current and enables a given amount of power to be transmitted through smaller wires and with smaller heat losses. Why this is so becomes clear when it is recalled that (1) the flow of current through a conductor always produces heat; (2) the amount of heat produced is proportional to I^2R. Hence, the energy loss along the line is only ¼ as much when 1 ampere flows as when 2 amperes flow, or ⅑ as much as when 3 amperes flow, etc.

Alternating current is just as well suited for lighting and heating purposes as direct current and motors have been devised which operate well on AC. However, AC cannot be used for electroplating, electrolysis, charging storage batteries, and similar purposes, but this disadvantage can be overcome by changing the AC to DC by the use of rectifiers (p. 317), or by using an AC motor to drive a DC generator.

TYPICAL PROBLEMS

A transformer has 600 turns of wire in the primary coil and 20 turns in the secondary coil. The input voltage is 3600 volts. What is the output voltage?

$$\frac{E_1}{E_2} = \frac{N_1}{N_2}$$

$$\frac{3600}{E_2} = \frac{600}{20}$$

$$E_2 = \frac{3600 \times 20}{600} = 120 \text{ volts}$$

If a current of 3 amperes is drawn from the secondary of the above transformer, and 98% efficiency is assumed, (a) what is the

power output; (*b*) what is the power input; (*c*) what current flows
in the primary?

(*a*) Power Output = Secondary Volts × Amperes

$$W_2 = E_2 \times I_2; W_2 = 120 \times 3 = \textbf{360 watts}$$

(*b*) Power Input × Efficiency = Power Output

$$W_1 \times 0.98 = W_2; W_1 = \frac{W_2}{0.98}; = \frac{360}{0.98} = \textbf{367 watts}$$

(*c*) Power Input = Primary Volts × Amperes

$$W_1 = E_1 \times I_1; I_1 = \frac{W_1}{E_1}; I_1 = \frac{367}{3600} = \textbf{0.102 amp}$$

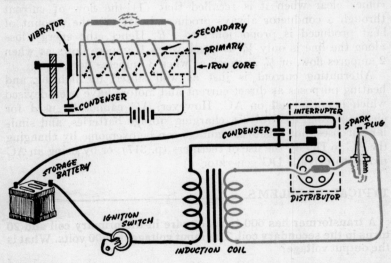

The Induction Coil. The lower diagram shows the application of the
induction coil to the ignition system of an automobile. In both diagrams the secondary circuit is shown in red.

The Induction Coil. The induction coil is substantially a transformer that operates on direct current. The essential parts of the
induction coil are: (1) a *primary coil* of fairly heavy wire wound
upon (2) a soft iron *core;* (3) an *automatic make and break*
device (vibrator) as in the electric bell; (4) a *secondary coil* of

very many turns of fine wire wound around the primary and completely insulated from it, the open ends of the secondary coil forming a spark gap; (5) a *condenser* connected in parallel with the vibrator to absorb current surges and thus prevent excessive sparking at the contact points of the primary circuit.

With each "make" and "break" of the primary circuit, a magnetic field builds up about the primary and then collapses, cutting the many more turns of the secondary. Since the "break" occurs much more quickly than the "make" and the magnitude of the induced emf depends on the rate of change of current, a spark is produced between the terminals of the secondary only on the "break." Hence the output of the induction coil is a rapidly pulsating DC. Although the secondary voltage is very high, the current in the secondary is very small, since the power output (secondary volts × amperes) cannot be larger than the power input (primary volts × amperes).

Induction coils provide the high voltage needed to produce sparks at the spark plugs of automotive and aircraft engines.

Principle of the Telephone. The essential parts of a telephone system are transmitters, receivers, transformers, a source of electric current, and a line to carry the current from one station to another. (See diagram on page 302.)

The transmitter is really a box filled with carbon granules and a movable diaphragm as one side of the box. The receiver consists of a permanent magnet around each pole of which is wound a coil of wire. The receiver also contains a thin iron diaphragm.

Sound waves enter the transmitter and cause its diaphragm to vibrate. This motion of the diaphragm compresses and releases the carbon granules, changing their electrical resistance. When the carbon granules are compressed, they are in good contact and offer less resistance to the flow of current than when they are released and make poor contacts with each other. The current through the transmitter circuit, therefore, fluctuates in step with the sound waves that set the diaphragm in motion.

By transformer action, this fluctuating current induces a much higher emf with corresponding fluctuations in the receiver circuit. The fluctuating current which flows to the receiver varies the strength of the magnet which attracts the thin iron diaphragm. This causes it to vibrate at the same rate and in the same manner as the diaphragm of the transmitter, and thus to reproduce the sounds impressed upon the transmitter.

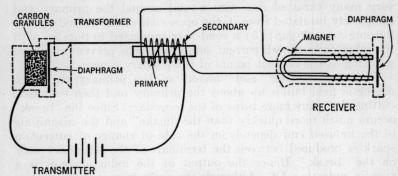

CARBON GRANULES
TRANSFORMER
SECONDARY
DIAPHRAGM
MAGNET
DIAPHRAGM
PRIMARY
RECEIVER
TRANSMITTER

One-way Telephone Circuit

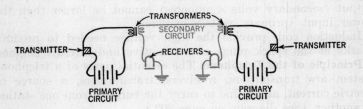

TRANSFORMERS
SECONDARY CIRCUIT
RECEIVERS
TRANSMITTER
TRANSMITTER
PRIMARY CIRCUIT
PRIMARY CIRCUIT

Two-Way Telephone Circuit. The secondary circuit is shown in red.

BEST ANSWER TEST

1. A current will be induced in a conductor whenever it is made to (1) move parallel to lines of force; (2) cut lines of force; (3) come in contact with a magnet.

2. The shape of the lines of force around a current-carrying conductor is (1) oval; (2) horseshoe; (3) circular; (4) parabolic.

3. The man who first observed the magnetic effect of a current was (1) Edison; (2) Faraday; (3) Fleming; (4) Oersted; (5) Henry.

4. In a step-down transformer the current in the secondary is (1) the same as; (2) smaller than; (3) larger than—that in the primary.

5. The diaphragm of the receiver of a telephone must be made of (1) copper; (2) hard rubber; (3) iron; (4) tin.

6. A telephone transmitter contains (1) an electromagnet; (2) the transformer; (3) a permanent magnet; (4) carbon granules.

7. Electrical energy is transformed into mechanical energy by means of (1) the dynamo; (2) the motor; (3) the transformer; (4) the magnet.

8. The armature of an electric motor draws less current when running than when held stationary. This is an example of (1) the right-hand rule; (2) the law of attraction and repulsion; (3) Lenz's law; (4) transformer action.

9. Increasing the current in an electromagnet makes it (1) have more magnetism; (2) have less magnetism; (3) have neither more nor less magnetism; (4) have more resistance.

10. The purpose of the commutator in the electric motor is to (1) cause a magnetic field; (2) reduce the resistance of the armature; (3) reverse the current in the armature; (4) increase the resistance of the armature.

QUESTIONS

1. (a) Describe an experiment to show how an electric current may be produced by induction. (b) What did the experiment show about the direction of the induced currents?

2. Give two reasons why it is more economical for electric companies to furnish their patrons with alternating current rather than with direct current.

3. (a) Explain how an electric current may cause the coil of a galvanometer to move. (b) What force brings the indicator back to zero when the circuit is broken? (c) How may a galvanometer be converted into a voltmeter?

4. A toy electric motor is made to operate on a 10-volt alternating current. Houses are usually supplied with a 110-volt alternating current. (a) Given a supply of insulated wire and an iron rod about 1 inch in diameter and 8 inches long, explain how to obtain a suitable current to operate the toy motor. Make use of a diagram to show the proper electric connections and indicate, wherever coils are used, the approximate number of turns of wire in each coil. (b) Explain why a commercial device made for this purpose would probably be more efficient.

5. Describe an experiment in which (a) an electric current may be used to make a magnet, (b) a magnet may be used to produce an electric current.

6. The voltage of alternating current is often raised to 22,000 volts or more, in order that the current may be transmitted long distances economically. Describe how this change in voltage is accomplished, and explain why economy results.

7. What determines the strength of an electromagnet?

8. How do the relay and the sounder of a telegraph system differ?

9. What may be done to reverse the direction of rotation of an electric motor? Will reversing the plug in the socket reverse the direction of rotation? Why?

10. Explain how an increased amount of current taken from a generator will automatically cause the driver of the generator to work harder.

11. State whether each of the following statements is true or false, and give a reason for your answer. (a) A freely-swinging electromagnet will set itself in an east-west direction. (b) A transformer will operate either on AC or pulsating DC. (c) The man who first discovered induced currents was Oersted. (d) A bell-ringing transformer is a step-down transformer. (e) 1000 microhenries equal 1 millihenry.

PROBLEMS

1. What is the strength in ampere-turns of an electromagnet (*a*) of 500 turns and 0.5 amp, (*b*) of 800 turns and 2.5 amp?

Ans. (a) 250 amp-turns (b) 2000 amp-turns

2. An electromagnet contains 1500 turns of wire in the coil and draws a current of 3 amp from a 120-volt line. (*a*) What is the resistance of coil? (*b*) If the current decreases to 2 amp (due to a voltage reduction), how many turns of wire must be added to maintain the same strength? (Neglect the additional resistance added.) Ans. (a) 40 ohms (b) 750 turns

3. A certain model Weston voltmeter draws 0.016 amp for a full-scale deflection of 50 volts. (*a*) What is the resistance of the meter? (*b*) What is the resistance per volt? (*c*) What resistance would be needed to permit the measurement of 125 volts?

Ans. (a) 3125 ohms (b) 62.5 ohms/volt (c) 4680 ohms additional

4. The coil of an ammeter will burn out if more than 30 mils flow through it. If the resistance of the coil is 0.5 ohm, what value shunt is needed to permit the measurement of 3 amp? Ans. 0.005 ohms

5. An electric motor is connected to a 120-volt line. It develops a back emf of 110 volts. The current through the motor when running is 8 amperes. (*a*) What is the net emf driving current through the motor? (*b*) What is the resistance of the motor? Ans. (a) 10 v (b) 1.25 ohms

6. What current will flow through the armature of a motor having a resistance of 7.5 ohms when the impressed emf is 115 volts and the counter emf is 112 volts? Ans. 0.4 amp

7. When the armature of a motor is held stationary and is connected to a 6-volt source, a current of 3 amp flows. When connected to a 120-volt source and running, the current is 2 amp. Calculate: (*a*) the resistance of the motor; (*b*) the back emf when running.

Ans. (a) 2 ohms (b) 116 v

8. A transformer delivers 6 volts output when the input is 120 volts. If the primary has 1000 turns, how many turns has the secondary?

Ans. 50

9. The primary of a transformer has 300 turns and carries a current of 2 amperes when connected to a 110-volt line. The secondary has 1500 turns. Assuming 100% efficiency, calculate (*a*) the output voltage; (*b*) the current in the secondary. Ans. (a) 550 v (b) 0.4 amp

10. A transformer has 1600 turns in the primary and 200 turns in the secondary. It is connected to a 120-volt line and 0.4 amp is drawn from the secondary. Assuming 96% efficiency, calculate: (*a*) output voltage; (*b*) output power; (*c*) input power; (*d*) input current.

Ans. (a) 15 v (b) 6 watts (c) 6.25 watts (d) 0.052 amp

TWENTY-TWO— ALTERNATING CURRENT

General. *A direct current is one that always flows in the same direction.* However, even a direct current must start from zero and build up to a steady value when a switch is closed. Ordinarily, these momentary variations may be neglected.

An alternating current is one which continually changes in magnitude and periodically reverses in direction. That is, the current builds up from zero to a peak value in one direction through the conductor, then dies down to zero; builds up to a peak value in the opposite direction, then dies down to zero— and so on, repeatedly. Thus the momentary variations produced in DC circuits by opening and closing a switch are ever-present in AC circuits.

Since the flow of current produces a magnetic field, an alternating current produces a field which repeatedly expands and collapses, reversing polarity with each reversal of direction of the current. If this field cuts a conductor, a voltage is induced in it. The induced voltage may act on the circuit itself (self induction), or on any other circuit with which it is coupled (mutual induction).

In order to take into account the induced voltages which are nearly always present in AC circuits, in addition to the impressed voltage, special AC formulas for Ohm's law have been developed.

Generation of AC Voltage. The nature of alternating current can readily be understood by the study of a model AC generator and its action plotted in graph form. Connect the generator to a galvanometer and rotate the coil slowly at uniform speed in a counter-clockwise direction. (See diagram, page 306.)

When the coil moves through the horizontal position (0°) shown in the illustration, the initial induced emf will be zero because the sides of the loop, AA' and BB', move parallel to the lines of force in the field, and therefore do not cut any (A on the central diagram). The fact that all of the lines of force pass through the coil when it is at this position does not mean that there is an induced emf. The magnitude of the induced emf is proportional to the *rate* at which lines of force are cut.

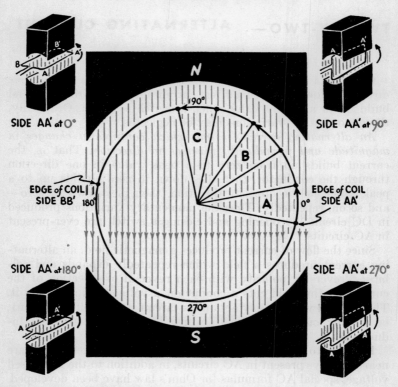

Generation of AC Voltage. The four small diagrams show the coil in four positions.

As the coil rotates away from the horizontal position, very little emf is induced at first because, during a small angular movement, comparatively few lines of force cut the coil. As rotation continues (B and C), the coil cuts the lines of force at an increasing rate and the induced emf increases accordingly. In B, for example, the coil cuts 5 lines of force. In C it cuts 7 lines. Maximum emf is induced when the coil reaches the vertical position (90°), because then AA′ and BB′ move at right angles to the field and, during a small angular movement, the maximum number of lines of force are cut.

As rotation of the coil continues, the induced emf has the same direction (Fleming's right-hand rule, page 290), but gradually diminishes until it again becomes zero when the coil reaches the horizontal position (180°). Beyond this point the direction of the induced emf reverses. AA′ is now moving down and BB′ is moving up. The magnitude of the voltage again increases to a maximum when the coil has rotated 270°, and then gradually decreases to zero as the coil once more reaches the horizontal position from which it started.

One complete rotation of the coil takes 360° and is called a *cycle*. There are two *alternations* or reversals in every cycle. The number of cycles per second is the *frequency*. The voltage being generated at any instant is called the *instantaneous* voltage, and is represented by the small letter, *e*.

Graphic Representation of AC Voltage or Current. If the magnitude of the induced voltage at any instant is plotted against the number of degrees through which the coil has rotated from the initial position, the graph obtained is a *sine curve;* that is, it has the same form as the curve

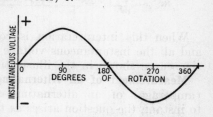

Sine Curve of AC Voltage

obtained by plotting the sine of an angle against its measurement in degrees. The current produced by an alternating emf also has a sine wave form.

Interpretation of a Rotating Vector in Graph Form. A *voltage vector* is a straight line drawn to scale to represent the *maximum voltage* (E_{max}) produced by the generator. By imagining that the vector rotates counter-clockwise about a point, the *instantaneous voltage* at any angular position of the coil is equal to *the vertical component* of the rotating vector at that position, or *phase*.

In the illustration (page 308), the arrow shown at position 1 represents the voltage vector at its 0° position. At this position, the vector has no vertical component; hence, the emf is zero. 30° of rotation brings the vector to position 2, and the instantaneous emf (e_2) at this point is represented by the scale value of the vertical component. At 60° of rotation, component e_3 is the instantaneous voltage. When the rotating vector reaches the 90° position, the vector and its vertical component are equal; this means that the instantaneous voltage is maximum (E_{max}).

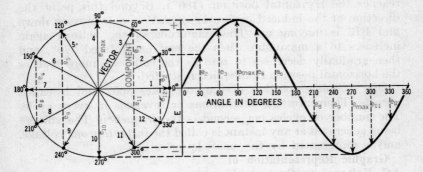

When this interpretation is continued for 360° of rotation and all the instantaneous voltage values are plotted, the simple sine curve shown in the illustration is obtained.

Measurement of an Alternating Current. Since the strength (amperage) of an alternating current changes from instant to instant, the question arises as to how to measure the effective strength of the current in amperes. The best method is to find the DC current value which produces the *same heating effect* (that is develops the *same power*) as the AC current in question. This current value is called the *effective* value (I_{eff}) of the AC current and is found to be 0.707 times the maximum current:

$$I_{eff} = 0.707\,I_{max}$$

By using the effective value, AC and DC currents can be compared, and voltage, current, and power relationships on AC can be determined as readily as on DC. AC meters read effective values of current and voltage. The effective value of AC voltages is defined in the same way as that of AC currents, and bears the same ratio to the maximum value:

$$E_{eff} = 0.707\,E_{max}$$

Phase Relations of AC Voltage and Current. In AC, voltage and current do not always reach their zero and maximum values at the same instant. If the zero and maximum points on the sine curves of voltage and current in an AC circuit coincide, the voltage and current are said to be *in phase*. This means that they vary in step with each other; both pass through zero and reach their peak values at exactly the same time. If they do not vary in step with each other, that is, if one passes through zero or reaches its peak value at a different time from the other, they are said to be *out of phase*. Whichever passes through zero or reaches its maximum value first along the time axis is said to *lead* the other.

The graphic representation of a rotating vector will illustrate phase relationships between alternating current and voltage. In the top diagram, voltage and current are in phase, as shown by the sine curve representation of the rotating vectors. (The horizontal axis is marked off in degrees corresponding to the positions of the voltage vector and represents the time interval for one cycle.) The outer circle represents the circumference described by the rotating voltage vector. In the position shown, the voltage vector is at 90°; therefore its vertical component or instantaneous voltage is maximum. The inner circle represents the circumference described by the rotating current vector, which is also at maximum. Since both voltage and current are at maximum value (90°) *at the same instant*, they are said to be in phase.

In the diagram (p. 310), the voltage and current vectors are shown at the instant that the voltage vector reaches 90°. At this instant the current vector is, let us say, at 60°. In other words, the voltage and current are out of phase. The angle between the two vectors indicates the extent to which they are out of phase. This angle is called the *phase angle*. The phase angle in this case is 30°. Since the current vector is 30° behind the voltage vector, the current is said to *lag* the voltage by 30° (or voltage *leads* current by 30°). This phase angle remains constant as these two vectors rotate. The phase angle between voltage and current may be anything between 0° and 180°, lead or lag.

Phase relationships may exist between voltage and current, as above. As will be seen when we consider alternating current circuits containing coils and condensers, phase relationships may also exist between a voltage in one part of a circuit and a voltage in another part, or between a current in one part of a circuit and a current in another part of a circuit.

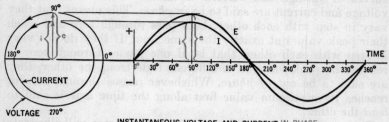

INSTANTANEOUS VOLTAGE AND CURRENT IN PHASE

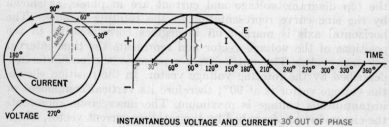

INSTANTANEOUS VOLTAGE AND CURRENT 30° OUT OF PHASE

Impedance in AC Circuits. If a DC voltage of 120 volts is applied to a straight conductor whose resistance is 8 ohms, a DC current of 15 amperes will flow (120 ÷ 8). If an AC voltage of 120 volts (effective) is applied to this straight conductor, the AC current produced will also be 15 amperes. Imagine now that this conductor is wound into a coil around an iron core. When the DC voltage of 120 volts is again applied, the current will still be the same—15 amperes—since the resistance of the wire has not changed. However, when 120 volts of AC are applied, the back emf of self-induction (see p. 293), produced by the ever-varying magnetic field of the AC current, opposes the applied voltage, and the current is consequently less than 15 amperes.

This opposition to the flow of AC currents through an inductance, apart from its DC resistance, is called *inductive reactance.* Inductive reactance is measured in ohms, and is represented by X_L.

The total opposition of the coil to the AC current (that is, the combination of its reactance and its resistance) is called impedance, also measured in ohms, and represented by Z. For AC circuits, Z is substituted for R in Ohm's law:

$$Z = \frac{E}{I}; \; I = \frac{E}{Z}; \; E = IZ$$

Calculation of Inductive Reactance. The amount of reactance offered by a given coil depends on two quantities:

1. The *frequency* of the AC current—as the frequency increases, the rate at which the current is changing also increases, thus increasing the strength of the back emf and hence increasing the reactance. Inductive reactance is proportional to frequency.

2. The *inductance* in henries—the greater the inductance the greater is the back emf produced, and hence the greater is the reactance.

Mathematically, inductive reactance in ohms is given by the following formula:

$$X_L = 2\pi fL$$

where f is the frequency in cycles per second, and L is the inductance in henries.

Calculation of Impedance. The impedance of a coil is, as we have just stated, the combination of resistance and reactance. However, it is not the arithmetical sum of the two. We shall now see how the actual impedance can be determined by using our knowledge of vectors. The vector representation of currents and voltages is an extremely powerful tool—in fact, without it it would be almost impossible to analyze alternating current circuits.

Consider first a pure inductance (one with no resistance) in series with a pure resistance, connected to an AC voltage source. There will be an AC current flowing in this circuit and, since the inductance and resistance are in series, the currents in both must be identical in magnitude and in phase.

When the current is passing through its zero value, it is changing most rapidly. Hence the emf of self-induction across the coil is maximum at this instant. When the current is at its maximum value, it is not changing at all; hence the induced emf must be

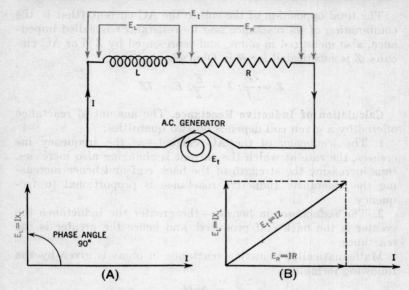

Inductance and Resistance in Series

zero at that instant. Thus we see that the back emf of an inductance is 90° out of phase with the current—the voltage is maximum when the current is zero and vice versa. In other words the voltage E_L across the coil (which is equal to the back emf) is 90° out of phase with the current. Actually it *leads* the current by 90°. This can be represented by the vector diagram (A) showing E_L as a vector leading I by 90°.

Since the coil is assumed to have no resistance, its impedance is just its reactance, X_L. Therefore we have written $E_L = IX_L$ on the vector (applying Ohm's law for AC).

In the resistance, however, current and voltage are in phase: at the instant of zero current, there is zero voltage drop; at the instant of maximum current, there is maximum voltage drop across the resistance. Thus E_R is shown as a vector in phase with the current I, and equal to IR (vector diagram B).

What, then, is E_t, the total voltage across this circuit? It is the sum of E_L and E_R, but not their arithmetical sum—it is their *vector* sum as found by the method explained on page 95. Thus we show E_t as the vector sum of E_L and E_R (diagram B). By Ohm's law, $E_t = IZ$, Z being the actual impedance of the entire circuit.

Applying the Pythagorean theorem,

$$E_t{}^2 = E_L{}^2 + E_R{}^2$$

or, substituting their equivalent values,

$$(IZ)^2 = (IX_L)^2 + (IR)^2$$

From the second equation, we can cancel I, giving the following general formula for the impedance of an inductance and resistance in series:

$$Z^2 = X_L{}^2 + R^2$$

$$Z = \sqrt{X_L{}^2 + R^2}$$

All practical inductances also have resistance. They act, however, as though they were pure inductances in series with pure resistances, so that the impedance of any coil is given by the same formula.

Condensers and Capacitive Reactance. When a DC voltage is impressed across a condenser in a circuit, there is a small momentary current as the plates of the condenser become charged, after which the current drops to zero. But when an AC voltage is impressed across a condenser, current repeatedly flows into and out of the plates charging them first one way and then the other. Thus, condensers stop or block the flow of DC, but permit the flow of AC.

The voltage across a condenser is maximum and the charging current is zero when the condenser is fully charged. The voltage is zero and the current maximum when the condenser is discharged and about to charge in the opposite direction. Thus, we find that the voltage across a condenser in an AC circuit is out of phase with the current by 90°, as in

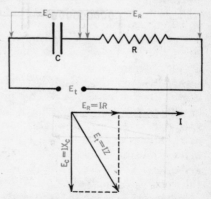

Capacitance and Resistance in Series

the case of inductances. However, the condenser voltage *lags* the current by 90°, whereas in the inductance it *leads* by 90°.

Using the same method as for inductances, we can find the impedance of a condenser and resistance in series. The vector diagram is shown in the illustration, with $E_C = IX_C$ lagging $E_R = IR$. The formula for the impedance is:

$$Z = \sqrt{X_C^2 + R^2}$$

The reactance of a condenser (*capacitive reactance*) varies inversely as the frequency and inversely as its capacitance, C:

$$X_C = \frac{1}{2\pi f C}$$

Series Circuits Containing Inductance, Capacitance, and Resistance. If the vector diagram of a series circuit containing L, C, and R elements is constructed (see diagram), we find that the total impedance is given by the formula:

$$Z = \sqrt{R^2 + (X_L - X_C)^2}$$

In other words, capacitive reactance and inductive reactance tend to neutralize each other in a series circuit, because their vectors are in opposite directions. Since X_L increases with an

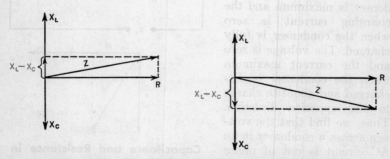

Inductance, Capacitance and Resistance in Series

increase in frequency, while X_C decreases, there is always a particular frequency at which $X_L = X_C$, and the term $(X_L - X_C)^2$ cancels out of the impedance formula. The frequency at which this happens is called the *resonant frequency* of the circuit. At *resonance*, the total impedance consists only of the pure resistance of the circuit. The current is therefore a maximum (for a given voltage), and in phase with the voltage.

We can find the resonant frequency by setting X_L, which is $2\pi f L$, equal to X_C, which is $\dfrac{1}{2\pi f C}$, and solving for f in terms of L and C. We find that:

$$f_{\text{resonance}} = \frac{1}{2\pi\sqrt{LC}}$$

TYPICAL PROBLEM

A coil of 150 millihenries inductance is in series with a condenser of 2 microfarads capacitance. The coil has a DC resistance of 50 ohms, and the resistance of the condenser is negligible. An AC voltage of 100 volts, 120 cycles per second, is applied to the circuit. (a) What is the total impedance of the circuit? (b) What current will flow? (c) What is the resonant frequency of the circuit? (d) What current will flow when the frequency of the applied voltage is the same as the resonant frequency?

(a) $Z = \sqrt{R^2 + (X_L - X_C)^2}$; $X_L = 2\pi f L$; $X_C = \dfrac{1}{2\pi f C}$

$X_L = 2\pi \times 120 \times 0.15 = $ **113 ohms**

$X_C = \dfrac{1}{2\pi \times 120 \times 2 \times 10^{-6}} = $ **663 ohms**

$Z = \sqrt{(50)^2 + (113 - 663)^2} = \sqrt{2500 + 302,500} = $ **552 ohms**

(b) $I = \dfrac{E}{Z} = \dfrac{100}{552} = $ **0.181 amperes**

(c) $f_{\text{res}} = \dfrac{1}{2\pi\sqrt{LC}} = \dfrac{1}{2\pi\sqrt{0.15 \times 2 \times 10^{-6}}} = $ **291 cycles per second**

(d) $I = \dfrac{E}{Z} = \dfrac{E}{R} = \dfrac{100}{50} = $ **2 amperes**

Parallel Circuits and Resonance. When a coil (pure inductance) and a condenser (pure capacitance) are connected in parallel across the same AC voltage (A), an interesting situation occurs. As the vector diagram (B) shows, the current in the inductance (I_L) lags the voltage by 90°, while the current in the condenser (I_C) leads the voltage by 90°. The two currents are therefore 180° out of phase. The total current in the main line, I_t, is the vector sum of the branch currents, I_L and I_C. Since at resonance the inductive reactance equals the capacitive reactance, the two curents I_L and I_C are equal, and their vector sum is zero (D)! In other words, at the resonant frequency (C), no current flows in the main line, $(I_t = 0)$. Large currents may, however, be flowing inside the parallel circuit. The use of such parallel resonant circuits in radio is described on pages 336–337.

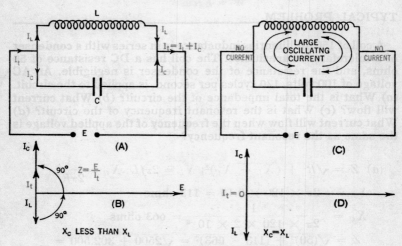

Resonance in a Parallel Circuit

Actually parallel circuits always contain some resistance. This resistance acts to make the phase angle between the current vectors less than 180°. As a result, even at resonance some current will flow in the main line, but this current is usually very small. Therefore, the impedance of a parallel circuit is always maximum at the resonant frequency. (Compare with a series circuit, in which the impedance is a *minimum* at the resonant frequency.)

Power in AC Circuits. In DC circuits, the product of volts and amperes is the power in watts. In AC circuits this product, called *volt-amperes,* is not always equal to power because voltage and current are often out of phase. If the voltage and current are *in phase* in an AC circuit, the power in watts *is* equal to the product of volts (effective) and amperes (effective):

$$W = E_{eff}I_{eff} \text{ (zero phase angle)}$$

If current and voltage are not in phase (which is usually the case because all circuits contain some inductance or capacitance), the power in watts is given by the following formula:

$$W = EI\cos\phi$$

where ϕ is the phase angle between current and voltage, and E and I are the effective values. Thus if $\phi = 90°$, $\cos \phi = 0$, and there is no power in the circuit. The quantity, $\cos \phi$, is called the *power factor* of the circuit, since it is the factor by which the volt-amperes must be multiplied to obtain true power. The power factor varies from 0 for $\phi = 90°$ to 1 for $\phi = 0°$. For a phase angle of 30°, for example, the power factor ($\cos 30°$) is 0.866.

Regardless of phase, power in an AC circuit can always be found by using the formula:

$$W = I^2R$$

Rectification of AC Current. By the use of various devices, some mechanical and some electrical, AC can be changed to DC. The process is called *rectification* and the devices are called *rectifiers.*

The motor-generator set. This device consists of an AC motor which drives a DC generator. There is no electrical connection between the two machines, but they are mounted on the s me shaft. A similar combination may be used to convert DC to AC. The motor and generator are sometimes combined to form one machine called a *rotary converter.*

The copper oxide rectifier. A copper disc coated on one side with red copper oxide offers much less resistance to the flow of current from the copper oxide to the copper than from the copper to the copper oxide. Consequently, an AC voltage gives pulses

HALF WAVE RECTIFICATION   FULL WAVE RECTIFICATION

During the half of the AC voltage cycle when the upper terminal is positive, current flows through the rectifier in the direction shown. During the other half of the cycle, no current flows. This is shown in graph form above the circuit diagram.

The red arrows show the path of the current when the upper terminal is positive. The black arrows show the current flow when the upper terminal is negative. Note that current, in each case, flows through the load in the same direction.

of current in the direction from copper oxide to copper, but there is practically no flow from copper to copper oxide.

A single copper oxide rectifier gives *half-wave* rectification, as shown in the left half of the diagram. Current flows through the circuit only during one half of the voltage cycle. In the diagram at the right, four rectifiers have been connected in a *bridge circuit*, which gives *full-wave* rectification. As the caption explains, current flows through the load resistance during the entire AC cycle, and always in the same direction. Note that the copper oxide rectifier produces a pulsating DC current, not a steady one such as is obtained from DC generators and motor-generator converters.

Copper oxide rectifiers are used in some radios and small battery chargers.

The vacuum tube rectifier. The use of vacuum tubes to rectify AC is explained on page 342.

QUESTIONS

1. (a) What is meant by a *sine curve?* (b) Explain why it is possible to represent AC voltages and currents by sine curves.

2. How would the wave form of the voltage generated by an alternator be affected if the magnetic field were not uniform?

3. (a) What is meant by the *effective value* of an AC voltage or current? (b) Why is it desired to use such a value?

4. What is meant by *half-wave* and *full-wave* rectification of AC?

5. Diagram and explain a single diode rectifier.

6. What are some uses for rectifiers of various kinds?

PROBLEMS

1. The maximum voltage generated by an alternator is 160 volts. Calculate: (a) the instantaneous voltage at 30° of rotation, (b) the instantaneous voltage at 45° of rotation.   Ans. (a) 80 v (b) 113 v

2. If the peak value of an AC current is 8 amp, and the voltage peak is 141 volts, what would be the reading of a properly-connected (a) ammeter; (b) voltmeter?   Ans. (a) 5.65 amp (b) 100 v

3. (a) What would be the true power in the circuit of problem 2 if E and I are in phase? (b) What would be the true power if the phase angle were 60°?   Ans. (a) 565 watts (b) 282 watts

4. (a) What is the impedance of a circuit containing 300 ohms of resistance and 500 ohms of inductive reactance in series? (b) Draw a vector diagram to represent these values.   Ans. (a) 583 ohms

5. (a) What is the impedance of a circuit containing 500 ohms of resistance in series with 1200 ohms of capacitive reactance? (b) Draw a vector diagram to represent these values.   Ans. (a) 1300 ohms

6. An AC circuit contains 300 ohms of resistance, 500 ohms of inductive reactance, and 1200 ohms of capacitive reactance in series. (a) Calculate the impedance of the circuit. (b) Draw a vector diagram to represent these values.   Ans. (a) 762 ohms

7. If the line voltage is 120 volts, calculate the current in problem 6.   Ans. 0.157 amp

8. With the current flowing as calculated in problem 7, calculate the voltage across each circuit element in problem 6.   Ans. R—47.3 v; L—78.8 v; C—189 v

9. A pure inductive reactance of 40 ohms is in parallel with a pure capacitive reactance of 36 ohms, across a voltage of 144 volts. Find (a) the current in each branch; (b) the line current; (c) the impedance of the combination.   Ans. (a) $I_L = 3.6$ amp; $I_c = 4.0$ amp (b) 0.4 amp (c) 360 ohms

TWENTY-THREE

SOUND

What Is Sound? To be exact, sound is the sensation produced in the brain when the eardrum is caused to vibrate. According to this strict definition, a phonograph playing in a soundproof room produces no sound if there is no ear and brain present to hear it. However, the phonograph does produce sound *waves* in the air of the room, and these waves would produce the sensation of sound in the ears of anyone present. Therefore in practice the sound wave itself is referred to as a sound.

Sources of Sound. All sound originates in matter that is vibrating. A vibrating body forces the particles of air, water, bone, or other medium which surrounds it to vibrate at the same rate and in the same manner as its own particles are vibrating. The surrounding particles set their neighbors into similar vibration, until particles at some distance from the original source are vibrating. It is in this manner that sound vibrations eventually reach the eardrum from a vibrating source.

The fact that bodies producing sound are vibrating rapidly can easily be demonstrated. A tuning fork which is emitting sound will dash the surface of water into a spray if touched to the water; it will also cause a ping pong ball, suspended from a string, to jump violently away when touched with one prong.

Sound Waves. There are several important facts about the transmission of sound vibrations which should be recognized. In the first place, sound vibrations are different from the random vibrations of molecules due to heat; in a body emitting sound, relatively large portions of the body are moving back and forth in unison, and in a regular manner; the same is true of a medium transmitting a sound vibration.

Secondly, the vibrations are propagated as waves of pressure variations in the medium. The particles of the medium move over short distances, but the total effect is that of a wave moving rapidly through the medium.

Thirdly, sound waves are *longitudinal* waves; the particles of the medium move to and fro, but unlike the situation in the rope wave (page **179**), the particles move *in the direction* of motion of the wave rather than at right angles to it (*transverse* waves).

Fourthly, like all waves, a sound wave is a fluctuating force, and as such carries energy with it; this sound energy can be made to do work and can be transformed into other forms of energy (such as electrical energy in a microphone).

Finally, sound waves travel only in material media; they cannot traverse an empty space, but are transferred from one material to another only when the two materials are in contact. Thus a bell operating under a bell jar can be heard if air is present in the jar; but if the jar is evacuated by a pump, the sound of the bell disappears, although the bell is still visibly operating.

Production of a Sound Wave. A tuning fork producing a sound wave is shown in the following diagram. Consider one prong which is vibrating so that it moves now to the right, now to the left. As it swings to the right, it pushes the molecules of air

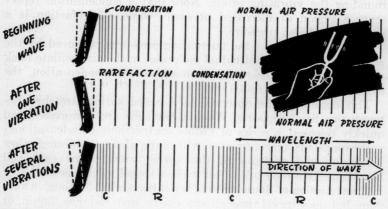

Production of Sound Waves in Air. Condensations are indicated by red lines.

alongside it toward the right, and closer to their neighbors; the first row of molecules therefore transmits the push they receive to the next row; this second row then moves to the right giving the third row a push, etc. Any region in which the air molecules are more closely spaced than normal is called a *condensation*.

By the action just described, a condensation starts moving away from the tuning fork prong after its first half-vibration to the right.

The prong now completes one vibration by swinging back to the left, leaving a partial vacuum or region of reduced pressure behind it. The first row of molecules, which by this time has transmitted its original push to its neighbors, now flows back into this region of reduced pressure, or *rarefaction*, produced by the motion of the prong. The neighboring rows, finding the pressure on their left relieved, follow into the rarefaction, but not before they, too, have sent the condensation on its way. In this manner, a rarefaction moves through the air, following on the heels of the advancing condensation.

The prong now swings once more to the right, sending another condensation after the rarefaction, and then back to the left, sending another rarefaction after the condensation. Thus a series of condensations and rarefactions move out through the air surrounding the vibrating prong. Note that a condensation represents a region of increased pressure, while a rarefaction is a region of reduced pressure.

Under the action of the fluctuating pressures produced by the passage of the wave, individual molecules in the air oscillate back and forth, contributing at one moment to a condensation, the next moment to a rarefaction.

This action can be observed in a coiled spring stretched between two fixed supports. When a few coils are compressed and quickly released, a series of visible contractions (condensations) and expansions (rarefactions) will move along the spring. Slow motion moving pictures of this spring would show each coil behaving like a molecule of air when a sound wave passes.

Transmission of Sound. Sound is not transmitted through a vacuum, but does travel through any elastic material, gas, liquid, or solid. The destructive effect of a depth bomb is the result of the transmission of an enormous pressure wave (sound wave) sent out by the exploding bomb; this wave can crush a submarine even at a considerable distance from the actual explosion.

As sound waves in air radiate from a source, in ever-widening spheres, they become weaker because the area over which the original energy is spread becomes greater. The effect is similar to the decrease in illumination as the distance from a light source increases (page 187). By confining the sound energy to a taut string, its dissipation can be lessened and the sound can be transmitted relatively undiminished over considerable distances, just as a parallel beam of light will illuminate objects at a great distance. Sound waves, like light waves, can also be reflected and focussed.

Velocity of Sound in Air. The velocity of a sound wave in a medium depends on only two things: (1) the elastic constants of the medium, and (2) the temperature of the medium. The velocity is independent of the frequency of the sound and independent of its *amplitude* (strength). The velocity of sound is least in gases, somewhat greater in liquids, and greatest in solids. In steel, for example, the velocity of sound is eleven to fifteen times as great as in air.

The velocity of sound in air is **1090 ft per sec** at 0°C. The speed increases by 2 ft per sec for each degree Centigrade rise in temperature. Thus at 20°C the speed of sound in air is 1090 + (2 × 20) = 1130 ft per sec. Using this information, the distance of a lightning flash, or a firing gun can be determined by measuring the time between seeing the flash and hearing the resulting thunder or explosion. (The time of transmission of the light is negligible in comparison with the time of travel of the sound and can be ignored in the calculations.)

TYPICAL PROBLEM

The report of a gun is heard 9.2 seconds after its flash is seen. How far is the gun from the observation point? Air temperature is 15°C.

velocity of sound = 1090 + (2 × 15) = 1120 ft per sec
distance = velocity × time; $D = 1120 \times 9.2 = $ **10,300 ft**

Frequency and Wavelength. Since the velocity of sound in a given medium (such as air) is constant except for temperature variations, the higher the frequency of a sound wave the shorter its wavelength. Thus the wavelength of a sound whose frequency is 280 cycles (vibrations) per second, in air at 15°C ($v = 1120$ ft per sec), would be:

$$l = v/f = 1120/280 = \textbf{4 ft.}$$

The condensations of such a wave would be 4 ft apart. A sound of frequency twice as great (560 cycles per second) would have half the wavelength—2 ft; the wavelength for 140 cycles would be 8 ft.

Pitch of a Sound. Every musical sound has a pitch; the sound of a piccolo is said to be *high-pitched;* that of a tuba is *low-pitched.* The pitch or "height" of a tone depends on its frequency. The greater the frequency, the higher the pitch. The human ear responds to tones ranging from a low pitch of about 16 cycles per second to a high pitch of about 20,000 cycles per second; our sensitivity to high tones decreases with age, so that older persons usually cannot hear tones above 12,000 or 15,000 cycles per second. The tone "A" above "middle C" on the piano has a frequency of 440 cycles per second. The frequency of a tone doubles with each *octave;* the "A" an octave higher is 880 cycles; an octave lower it is 220 cycles.

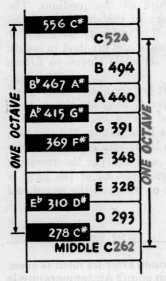

The frequency of a note doubles for each octave of pitch.

Graphic Representation of a Wave. A sound wave can be represented by a graph as can an alternating current (page 307). In the graph of the sound wave, the air pressure is plotted against time, just as the current value is plotted against time for an alternating current. For a tone of a single frequency, a sine curve is obtained (see page 325). (In this graph, zero pressure is taken as the average atmospheric pressure. Positive pressures (condensations) are above atmospheric, negative pressures (rarefactions) are below.)

The maximum change in pressure (*AB* on the diagram) is called the *amplitude* of the wave. The amplitude is also the maximum distance which a molecule in a sound wave moves from its normal position. The strength or loudness of a sound is proportional to its amplitude.

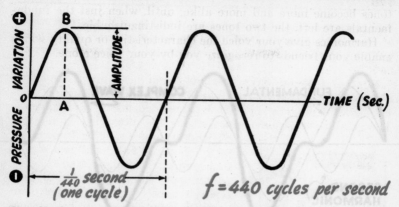

Graph of a Sound Wave. The graph shows how the pressure varies at a point as the sound wave goes by. This is not a picture of the wave in space—sound waves are longitudinal waves, not transverse.

Harmonics or Overtones. No musical instrument ever produces a pure tone, that is, a tone of a single frequency. It actually produces a mixture of tones. The lowest frequency in this mixture is usually the strongest, and is called the *fundamental*. The other tones produced have frequencies which are multiples of the fundamental frequency. These tones are called *overtones* or *harmonics*. A tone whose frequency is twice the fundamental is called the second harmonic; a tone of five times the fundamental frequency is called the fifth harmonic; etc.

Quality of a Tone. With a little practice anyone can learn to distinguish and recognize the instrument producing a given note, because the same note played on different instruments has a different *quality* in each case. For example, nobody would confuse middle C played on the piano with middle C played on a clarinet even though both have the same fundamental frequency. The reason for this is that the tone produced by each instrument varies as to the *number* and *relative strengths* of the harmonics it contains, and therefore varies as to its effect on the ear. There is an interesting experiment in which the higher harmonics of the tones from two different instruments are removed one by one by special electrical filters; as these harmonics are removed, the tones become more and more alike, until, when just the fundamentals are left, the two tones are indistinguishable.

Harmonics give your voice the characteristics or quality which enable your friends to recognize you by your voice alone.

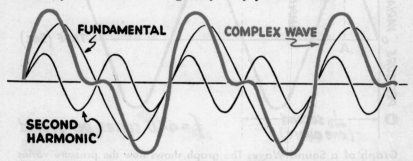

FUNDAMENTAL   COMPLEX WAVE

SECOND
HARMONIC

The complex wave shown in red is actually the sum of two simple sine waves, one with twice the frequency of the other.

Graph of a Mixed Tone. The graph of a mixed tone can be found simply by adding the graphs of all its component frequencies. The result is a distorted wave-form as shown above. A musical instrument can be recognized by its wave-form alone, since the wave-form depends on the number and strength of harmonics present. In fact, any wave-form, even of unknown origin, can be broken down into a series of harmonics by a process called *harmonic analysis.* Harmonic analysis plays an important role in determining the causes and corrective measures for vibrations in airplane engines, propellers, and other machines, where the vibration usually has a highly distorted wave-form.

Summary. Every musical sound has three important characteristics:

1. *Fundamental frequency,* which determines the pitch of the sound;

2. *Amplitude,* which determines the loudness of the sound;

3. *Harmonics,* which determine the quality of the sound.

Noises. Sounds in which the frequencies have whole-number ratios to each other are pleasant to the ear, and are called *musical.* Many sounds consist of a mixture of frequencies which have no definite relation to one another. Such a sound has no fundamental frequency, and is called a *noise.*

Laws of Strings. When a violinist wishes to produce a higher note he shortens the effective part of the string by pressing his finger down upon it. A long string vibrates more slowly and gives a lower note than a short string, provided other conditions are held constant. Doubling the length of a string cuts its frequency of vibration in half and lowers the pitch of the note produced by one octave. The *first law of strings* states that the frequency varies inversely as the length of the string.

The pitch of a string can also be raised by tightening the string, or lowered by loosening it. Thus the pitch of a tone can

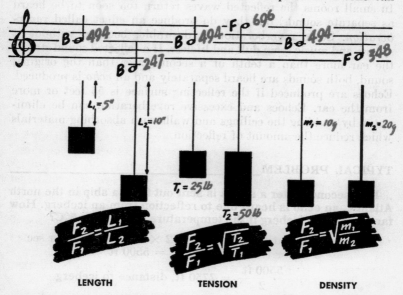

LENGTH   TENSION   DENSITY

Factors Determining the Pitch of a String. The weights attached to the lower ends of the strings represent tension. The numbers in red (opposite the notes) are frequencies of vibration. In the first pair of strings, all factors are the same except length. Notice that the string which is twice as long has half the frequency—which checks with the formula given. In the second pair of strings, the tension is varied. The numbers in red again satisfy the formula given. In the third pair of strings, the unit weight (m) of the string is changed. Check the values in red against the formula.

be controlled by varying the tension upon the string which produces it. When the tension of the string is made four times as great the pitch is doubled; if it is made nine times as great the pitch is tripled, etc. The *second law of strings* states that the frequency varies directly as the square root of the tension.

Heavy strings give low notes; light strings give high notes. The *third law of strings* states that the frequency of a string varies inversely as the square root of its weight per unit length.

Reflection of Sound. The intensity of sound in a room is partially maintained by the back and forth reflection of sound waves. In small rooms the reflected waves return too soon to be heard as separate sounds, but they do produce an effect called *reverberation.* Some reverberation is desirable, because without it speech and music seem dull and lifeless. If a reflected sound strikes the ear more than a tenth of a second later than the original sound, both sounds are heard separately and an *echo* is produced. Echoes are produced if the reflecting surface is 55 feet or more from the ear. Echoes and excessive reverberation can be eliminated by padding the ceilings and walls with absorbing materials which reduce the amount of reflection.

TYPICAL PROBLEM

Five seconds after a sound is sent out from a ship in the north Atlantic, an echo is heard due to reflection from an iceberg. How far away is the iceberg if the temperature of the air is 5°C?

Speed of sound at 5°C = 1090 + (2 × 5) = 1100 ft per sec
$$d = vt; d = 1100 \times 5 = 5500 \text{ ft}$$

$$\frac{5500 \text{ ft}}{2} = 2750 \text{ ft, distance to iceberg}$$

Sonic Sounding. The reflection of sound waves is used in many determinations of depth and distance. For example, the depth of the ocean floor is measured by sending a sound pulse down through the water, and noting the time interval when the echo is returned. It has recently been shown that bats (which are blind) guide their flight around obstacles by means of echoes of high-pitched sounds which the bats produce while in flight. These sounds emitted by bats are beyond the human audible range, having frequencies of about 50,000 cycles per second. Sounds which are too high-pitched for human ears to hear are called *supersonic*.

Forced Vibrations. If the handle of a vibrating tuning fork is pressed against the table, the volume or amplitude of the sound will increase. The table has been forced to vibrate at the frequency of the tuning fork, thereby increasing the amount of surface radiating sound. The sounding board of the piano and the thin wood box of the violin are used to increase the strength of all the tones produced by the strings, by means of these *forced vibrations*.

Sympathetic Vibrations and Resonance. Every body, freely suspended so that friction will not "damp out" its vibrations, will vibrate at a particular frequency when it is struck. This is called its *natural frequency of vibration*. When two vibrating bodies have the same natural frequency, they are said to be in *resonance*. If one vibrating body is touched to or brought near another with the same natural frequency, the second will begin to vibrate at that frequency; the amplitude of the induced vibration will generally be greater than that in ordinary forced vibrations because each condensation from the "exciting" body arrives in time to reinforce the condensation of the responding body, thus building up a strong vibration. The total volume of sound is also increased because condensations and rarefactions from both bodies are in step and strengthen each other.

Vibrations induced in a body because of resonance are called *sympathetic vibrations*. A picture wire or windowpane may be excited to sympathetic vibration when certain notes are played on a piano or come over the radio. If one of the keys of a piano is held down, and the corresponding key an octave lower is struck sharply and released, the string being held open will be heard sounding at its own frequency. The second harmonic of the lower tone, being in resonance with this string, has set the string vibrating by sympathetic vibration. By holding each of the piano keys down in turn, and striking the same note each time, all the harmonics of that note can be discovered by this method of sympathetic vibrations.

Resonance of Air Columns. Solid bodies are not the only ones with natural frequencies. The air in a bottle, or in a long tube, has a definite natural frequency, and such a body of air will

vibrate sympathetically when excited by a sound of its frequency.
The "sound of the sea" in a sea-shell is produced by resonance
of the air in the shell with some frequency in the many sounds
around us at all times.

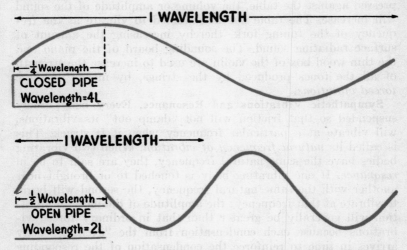

I WAVELENGTH

¼ Wavelength

CLOSED PIPE
Wavelength=4L

I WAVELENGTH

½ Wavelength

OPEN PIPE
Wavelength=2L

The Laws of Pipes. A closed pipe emits or resonates with a sound
whose wavelength is four times the length of the pipe. The wavelength
for an open pipe is only twice the length of the pipe. The longitudinal
sound wave has been represented as a transverse wave, in order to
show the distance between successive condensations.

Laws of Pipes. Pipes such as those of the pipe organ are described as either open or closed pipes. *Open pipes* are open at
both ends and *closed pipes* are open at only one end. Various
wind instruments are really pipes in which the sound is due to
the fact that the air column within the pipe acts as a resonator.
In wind instruments, this resonator is set in vibration by a reed
(as in the saxophone) or by blowing air across a sharp edge or
opening (as in the flute or organ pipe), or by forcing air through
a narrow opening (as that formed by the lips of the cornet
player). In speech the air enclosed by the nasal passages, mouth,
and head cavities acts as the resonator for the vibrations caused
by air forced between the vocal cords.

A closed pipe gives reinforcement to a sound when the length of the pipe is one-fourth the wave length of the sound. An open pipe gives reinforcement to a sound when the length of the pipe is one half the wave length of the sound. Thus an open pipe produces a note whose frequency is double (an octave higher than) that produced by a closed pipe of the same length.

When a hole is bored in a pipe, the effect is the same as if the pipe were cut off at that point. This explains the use of holes or "stops" in wind instruments. These holes are opened or closed by means of the fingers or valves in order to change the resonant length of the pipe, and hence alter the pitch of the tone produced.

TYPICAL PROBLEMS

The frequency of a tuning fork is 256 vps, and the temperature is 19°C. Find the length of the closed pipe necessary to give resonance.

velocity of sound at 19°C = 1090 + (2 × 19) = 1128 ft/sec
$v = n \times l$; 1128 = 256 × l; hence, l = 4.4 ft, wavelength

$\frac{1}{4}l$ = 1.1 ft, length of closed pipe giving resonance

What is the frequency of a tuning fork if a closed pipe 18 inches long reinforces the sound emitted by the fork? (The temperature is 22°C.)

wavelength = 4 × 18 inches = 72 in = 6 ft
$v = n \times l$; 1134 = 6 × n; hence, **n = 189 vps**

Beats. If two notes of somewhat different frequencies are sounded together, their waves periodically get in step and reinforce each other, then get out of step and interfere with each other. The result is a pulsating or throbbing sound. These pulsations are called *beats*. For example, if two tunings forks, one with a frequency of 200 and the other with a frequency of 210, are sounded together, they are in step and out of step 10 times each second, and the ear hears 10 throbs each second. The number of beats is always equal to the difference in the frequencies of the two notes.

If the number of beats per second is about 5 or 6, the sound is not very disagreeable. If this number is increased to about 30, the discord is very unpleasant; when the number of beats is increased still further to about 60, the sound again becomes agreeable. Harmonies and discords in music depend upon the beats produced by combinations of various tones.

QUESTIONS

1. What are the three characteristics that identify a sound?
2. How do you account for some objects in a room vibrating when certain notes are sounded on a piano or over a radio?
3. Explain the action of (a) a megaphone; (b) an ear trumpet.
4. How does the violinist produce (a) a higher note, (b) a louder sound when playing on a given string?
5. State whether each of the following statements is true or false, and give a reason for your answer. (a) High-pitched tones and low-pitched tones have the same velocity in air. (b) A stretched wire and a tuning fork, when sounded together, produce 8 beats per sec. If the frequency of the fork is 320 vps, the frequency of the wire must be 328 vps. (c) The speed of sound in air at 40°C is 1130 ft per sec. (d) Echoes are caused by the interference of sound waves.

PROBLEMS

1. A boat whistle is heard 3.5 seconds after it is seen to blow. How far away is the boat? (Temperature, 10°C.)   Ans. 3885 ft
2. How long after a whistle is blown, will an echo be heard from a cliff 2 miles away, on a day when the temperature is 25°C?   Ans. 18.5 sec
3. How long after a stone is dropped from the top of a building 576 ft tall will the sound of its striking the ground be heard if the air temperature is 31°C? (The time for the stone to fall to the ground is obtained from the relation $d = \frac{1}{2}gt^2$.)   Ans. 6.5 sec
4. (a) When the temperature is 15°C what is the wave length of middle C whose frequency is 256? (b) What would the wave length of this note be at 30°C?   Ans. (a) 4.38 ft (b) 4.50 ft
5. What is the frequency of a tuning fork whose sound is reinforced by a closed tube 12 inches long when the temperature is 20°C?
                                        Ans. 282.5 vps
6. (a) What is the length of a closed pipe that resonates to a note whose frequency is 565 vibrations per second (temperature 20°C)? (b) What should the length of a closed organ pipe be to give this note? (c) What should the length of an open organ pipe be to give this note?   Ans. (a) 6 in (b) 6 in (c) 12 in
7. A stretched string has a frequency of 256 vps when the tension is 16 lb. What will be the frequency if (a) the length is reduced to one-half? (b) The tension is increased to 64 lb? (c) Both (a) and (b) are done together?   Ans. (a) 512 vps (b) 512 vps (c) 1024 vps

The Basic Idea in Radio Communication. The principle of radio communication is illustrated by the simple transformer shown in the diagram. By closing the switch in the primary circuit, the lamp in the secondary circuit is illuminated; opening the switch puts out the light. There is no direct wire connection between the switch and the lamp; the energy is transmitted to the lamp by an alternating electromagnetic field in the core of the transformer. This is a simple form of wireless control of one circuit (the secondary) by another circuit (the primary).

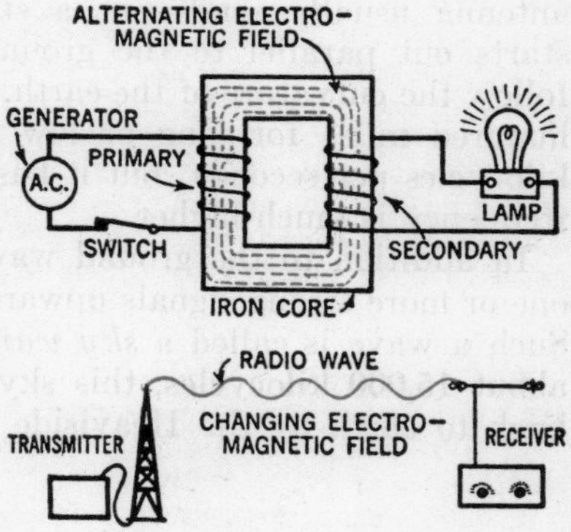

In wireless communication over large distances, the principle remains the same. An alternating current generator (the transmitter) sets up an alternating electromagnetic field everywhere in space, thus acting like the primary of a transformer. A secondary, the receiver, absorbs energy from this field and uses it to operate or control some signalling device such as a loud speaker.

The electromagnetic field of a radio transmitter does not come into existence instantaneously everywhere in space; it is propagated through space as a wave traveling with the speed of light. As pointed out previously radio waves and light waves are identical in nature, differing only in wavelength.

Frequency and Wavelength. As in other waves, *frequency* × *wavelength* = *velocity*. In radio waves,

frequency in kc × wavelength in meters = 300,000.

Properties of Radio Waves. As radio waves radiate away from the transmitter, their strength decreases, just as the intensity of light diminishes as you recede from the source. For communication over long distances, large amounts of energy must be put into the radio wave. The *transmitting antenna* is a device, usually in the form of a long wire or tall metal tower, which is designed to radiate radio waves efficiently. The *receiving antenna* is likewise designed to *absorb* a maximum amount of energy from the radio wave as it passes.

Most antennas radiate waves in all directions, but emit the strongest waves in just a few definite directions. For example, an antenna usually sends out a strong *ground wave*—one which starts out parallel to the ground. This ground wave tends to follow the curvature of the earth. It can be received up to several hundred miles for long or low frequency waves (100 to 1600 kilocycles per second), but it has a very limited range when the frequency is much higher.

In addition to the ground wave, an antenna usually radiates one or more strong signals upwards at an angle to the horizontal. Such a wave is called a *sky wave*. If the frequency is less than about 15,000 kilocycles, this sky wave will usually be reflected back to earth by the Heaviside and other ionized layers of the

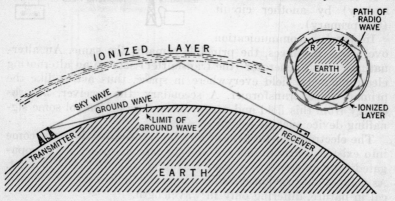

The red lines show some of the possible paths of a radio wave.

upper atmosphere. In fact, by repeated reflection between the earth and these ionized layers, a single wave may circle the globe before being received. It is the reflection of sky waves that makes long-distance radio communication possible.

If the frequency is above 15,000 kc, the waves (called *ultra-high frequency* waves) act very much like light waves. The ground wave does not follow the earth's curvature and hence cannot be received beyond the horizon. The sky wave, on the other hand, is not reflected by the ionized layers, and continues on into space. While not suitable for long-distance communication, ultra-high frequency waves are ideal for plane-to-ground communication, "walkie-talkie" sets, and *radar* (**RA**dio **D**etection **A**nd **R**anging). In radar, an ultra-high frequency radio beam is used like a searchlight to detect enemy aircraft or ships by reflection. Unlike searchlights, the radar beam penetrates fog and clouds, and also gives the distance of the reflecting object.

RESONANCE AND TUNING

The Tuned Circuit. The problem at the transmitter is to generate an alternating current of a definite high frequency. At the receiver, one particular radio signal must be selected from the thousands which fill the air at all times. In accomplishing both purposes, the same circuit plays an important part. As the diagram shows, this circuit is simply a condenser and coil in parallel. It is called a *tuned circuit* because electric currents will oscillate in it at a definite frequency.

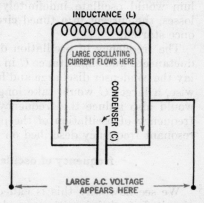

INDUCTANCE (L)

LARGE OSCILLATING CURRENT FLOWS HERE

CONDENSER (C)

LARGE A.C. VOLTAGE APPEARS HERE

The Parallel-Tuned Circuit. A current tends to oscillate at a definite frequency inside the parallel circuit, while a large AC voltage appears between the terminals of the circuit.

On page 316, the current and voltage relationships in such a circuit were derived mathematically by means of vectors. In this paragraph we will try to see what is taking place physically inside the circuit. Imagine first that the condenser and coil are disconnected, and the condenser then charged by a battery or DC generator. Then suppose the charged condenser is connected to the coil. Immediately electrons (current) will begin to flow from one condenser plate to the other through the coil. But the inductance of the coil tends to prevent the building-up of this current, thereby delaying the discharge. Nevertheless, the current continues to increase in strength as long as there is an unbalance of charge on the condenser. Eventually the condenser will be discharged completely, but a large current will be flowing through the coil at that time. The inductance now tends to prevent the slowing down of this current, so that by the time the current is brought to zero, the condenser is fully charged in the opposite direction. As soon as the current reaches zero, the condenser begins to discharge in the other direction, and the whole cycle is repeated. This is exactly analogous to the action of the balance wheel of a clock, or a swinging pendulum. The force tending to produce motion reaches zero just as the velocity reaches a maximum, and inertia keeps the body going until a strong force builds up in the opposite direction and reverses the swing. If it were not for frictional losses, a pendulum would oscillate indefinitely; if it were not for resistance losses, the current in a tuned circuit would oscillate indefinitely, once started.

The frequency of oscillation depends on the values of the inductance L and capacitance C in the circuit. A larger L would delay the condenser discharge and hence reduce the frequency; likewise, a larger C would take longer to charge and discharge and would also reduce the frequency. It turns out that the natural frequency of oscillation of the parallel circuit is the same as its resonant frequency described on page 315:

$$\text{frequency of oscillation} = \frac{1}{2\pi\sqrt{LC}}$$

We see now why this is called the resonant frequency of the circuit. It is the circuit's natural frequency of oscillation, just as the resonant frequency of a tuning fork is its natural frequency of vibration.

Electrical Resonance. The typical antenna circuit of a radio receiver is shown in the diagram. Each radio wave passing the antenna induces an alternating current in the antenna at the frequency of the radio wave. This high-frequency (radio-frequency or rf) current flows between antenna and ground through the coil L_1. This current in turn induces another current, by transformer action, in coil L_2 of the tuned circuit L_2C. The antenna current is very weak, so that ordinarily it would induce a small voltage in L_2. If, however, the frequency of the antenna current is the same as the resonant frequency of the tuned circuit, a very large oscillating current will be set up in the tuned circuit. The effect is exactly similar to sympathetic vibration or resonance in sound (p. 329), or resonance in any vibrating system. Under these conditions the tuned circuit is said to be *in resonance* with the antenna current and with the radio wave producing it. At any other frequency of the

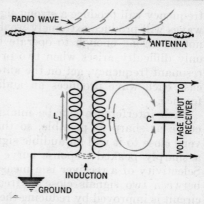

The tuned circuit of a receiver tends to resonate with the AC currents produced in the antenna circuit by a radio wave of the proper frequency.

antenna current, a current of that frequency will still be induced in the tuned circuit, but its magnitude will be much less than it was at resonance; the result is now similar to forced vibration rather than sympathetic or resonant vibration.

Selectivity of a Tuned Circuit. If a graph of the current in the tuned circuit is plotted against frequency of antenna current (the latter assumed to be constant in amplitude), a curve similar to that shown will be obtained, with a pronounced "peak" at the resonant frequency. It is seen that frequencies much removed from the resonant frequency produce only small currents in the tuned circuit. Thus a radio wave of the resonant

Response Curve of the Tuned Circuit L_2C. The AC generator (f) represents a radio wave inducing a current in L_1. The curve shows the strength of the current induced in L_2 as the frequency, f, varies.

frequency will produce a strong signal in the receiver; other radio waves will produce extremely weak signals, which ordinarily will not be strong enough to operate the earphones or speaker. The only difficulty arises when two or more signals, all close to the resonant frequency, act on the antenna at the same time. In that case each wave produces an audible signal, resulting in interference.

Such interference can be minimized by making the response curve as sharp as possible, so that only at exact resonance or very close to it will an audible signal result. A tuned circuit with a sharply peaked response curve is said to be highly *selective*. Selectivity of a receiver is a measure of its ability to distinguish between two signals close in frequency. Selectivity of a tuned circuit is improved by reducing the resistance of its elements.

Tuning. If either the condenser or coil of the tuned circuit is made variable, the circuit can be tuned at will to any desired frequency—thus bringing it into resonance with any radio wave. This is exactly what we do when we turn the tuning knob of a broadcast receiver. Look behind the panel of a radio while tuning it from one station to another and you will see the movable plates of a variable condenser rotating and thereby changing the capacitance of the condenser.

Note that currents are being produced in the antenna by all radio waves. The tuned circuit simply selects the desired one for

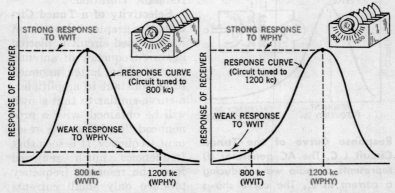

How a Radio Receiver Is Tuned. At the left, the set is tuned to Station WVIT (800 kc). At the right, it is tuned to Station WPHY (1200 kc).

amplification in the receiver by moving the resonance "peak" until it coincides with the frequency of the desired wave.

VACUUM TUBES

Thermionic Emission. Before proceeding further with the discussion of generation and detection of radio waves, a second fundamental device in modern radio circuits, the vacuum tube, must be explained. The vacuum tube makes use of the emission of electrons from hot bodies. When any substance is heated sufficiently, some of its electrons acquire enough energy to leave the surface. This emission of electrons as a result of increased temperature is called *thermionic emission.*

As electrons leave the body, the body acquires a positive charge and attracts the emitted electrons back to the surface. Thus electrons are continuously rising from and falling back into the surface of the emitting body. While no individual electron remains in the space around the body very long, there is always a cloud of electrons surrounding the body. This cloud of electrons is called the space charge. Electrons are always dropping out of the space charge, but are at the same time replaced by others being emitted. Thus the number of electrons in the space charge remains constant as long as the temperature remains the same. An increase in temperature increases the number of electrons present in the space charge.

The Diode (Two-Element Vacuum Tube). The simplest vacuum tube consists of a glass or metal shell, evacuated of almost all gases, and containing two elements—a *filament* or *cathode*, and a *plate*. The filament is a resistance wire, like the filament of an electric light bulb, but treated so that it is capable of a high thermionic emission. The two ends of the filament are brought out to terminals in the base of the tube, so that an electric current can be passed through the filament, thus heating it and causing it to emit electrons. The plate is simply a metal cylinder or disc supported at a distance from the filament, and connected to a third terminal in the base of the tube.

When the filament is connected to a battery or other power supply (usually between 2 and 6 volts), the filament is heated, emits electrons, and produces a space charge around it. If the plate is now connected to the positive terminal of a DC power source (such as a battery), and the negative terminal of the

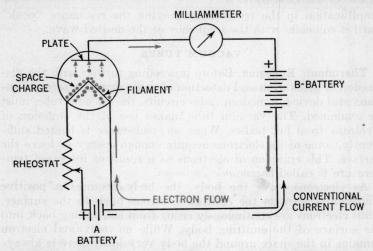

A Diode in Operation. The rheostat controls the temperature of the filament.

power source connected to one end of the filament, a difference of potential will be set up between the plate and the filament. The positive plate will then attract to it some of the electrons in the space charge, and electrons will flow from the plate through the battery, into the filament, and back into the space charge. This electron flow is of course an electric current. (By the convention of current flow, the current is said to flow from the battery toward the plate in the external circuit; the vacuum tube gives proof, however, that the flow of electrons which really constitutes an electric current is in the opposite direction.)

Characteristic Curves of the Diode. It is customary to represent the plate potential by the symbol E_p, the current in the plate circuit by I_p, and the filament heating current by I_f. As E_p increases positively from zero, I_p also increases, as the plate draws more and more of the electrons from the space charge. At some value of E_p, the attraction of the positive plate will be so great that *all* the electrons emitted by the filament will be flowing to the plate. The reservoir of electrons which the space charge represents will be supplying its maximum flow. If E_p is increased further, no change will take place in I_p. This maximum value of

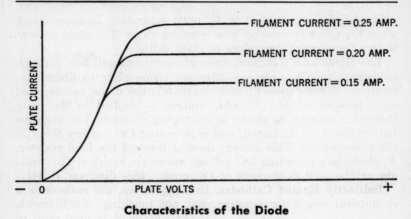

Characteristics of the Diode

I_p is called the *saturation current*. If, however, the filament temperature is raised by increasing I_f, more electrons will be made available, the saturation current will increase, and will be obtained at a higher value of E_p. These facts about a vacuum tube can be presented most clearly and most compactly by a set of graphs called the *characteristic curves* (or simply, the characteristics) of the tube. In the case of the diode, we usually plot I_p against E_p for various values of I_f. As can be seen from these

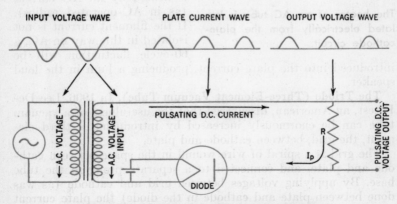

Changing AC to DC with a Diode Rectifier

curves, I_p is proportional to E_p until saturation is approached, when the curve flattens off to a constant value. The plate current is zero for all negative values of plate voltage.

The Diode as a Rectifier. Since plate current will flow through a vacuum tube in only one direction (from plate to filament—electrons flowing from filament to plate), the diode can be used as a rectifier of AC. The AC voltage is applied to the plate through a resistor, as shown in the wiring diagram. The negative half-cycles are eliminated, and a pulsating DC current flows in the plate circuit. This current flowing through the load resistor, R, produces a pulsating DC voltage across the resistor. This voltage can be used as a source of DC power. (See diagram, p. 341.)

Indirectly Heated Cathodes. In many tubes, the cathode is a cylindrical sleeve surrounding, but not touching, the filament.

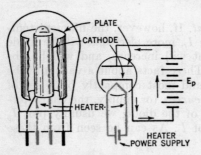

The heater of an AC tube is isolated electrically from the plate-cathode circuit.

The filament is used only to heat the cathode, and plate current flows between cathode and plate through a separate cathode connection in the base of the tube. This construction completely isolates the filament heating current from the plate circuit, a desirable result when the filament is heated by an AC current (as in AC-operated radios). If the filament current is not isolated in this way on AC, a 60-cycle fluctuation will be introduced into the plate current, producing a hum in the loud speaker.

The Triode (Three-Element Vacuum Tube). In 1906, Lee De-Forest, an American, discovered that the usefulness of a vacuum tube can be enormously increased by introducing a third element, the grid, between cathode and plate.

The grid is a spiral of wire wound in the space between cathode and plate, and connected to a separate prong in the tube base. By applying voltages between grid and cathode (as was done between plate and cathode in the diode) the plate current can be controlled, without changing the plate voltage. When the grid is made more positive, it helps the plate attract electrons, thereby increasing the plate current; when the grid is made more negative, it repels electrons, making it more difficult for electrons to reach the plate and thereby reducing the plate current. Because of the wide spacing of the grid wires, these wires do not physically impede the flow of electrons to the plate—they simply control the flow through the action of an electrostatic field.

Because the grid is nearer the space charge, it has a greater influence over the electrons than has the plate. Consequently a small change in grid voltage produces a much larger change in plate current than the same change in plate voltage would produce. For example, a

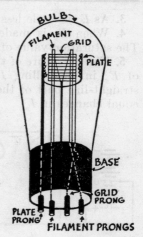

Construction of the Triode

change of 1 volt in grid voltage may produce the same change in plate current as a 10-volt change in plate voltage. Such a tube has an *amplification factor* of 10.

Very little current flows in the grid circuit. This means that very little energy or power is required by the grid. Thus with small amounts of power relatively large currents and powers can be controlled in the plate circuit. The triode can therefore be used as a *power* amplifier as well as a *voltage* amplifier.

Triode Characteristics. The graphs (p. 344) show how the plate current of a typical triode varies as the grid voltage varies, for various fixed values of plate voltage. These curves were obtained by applying a fixed voltage to the plate and reading the plate current on a milliammeter as various grid voltages were applied to the grid. The data was collected for each value of plate voltage shown. These characteristics reveal the following points.

1. For each value of E_p, there is a definite grid potential which will reduce I_p to zero; this point is called *cutoff*, and the value of E_g that produces it is called *cutoff bias*.

2. The larger E_p is, the more negative E_g must be to produce cutoff.

3. As E_g is made less negative, I_p increases.

4. When E_g is made sufficiently positive, saturation occurs. The saturation value of I_p is the same for all values of E_p.

5. The curvature of the characteristics indicates that the effect of E_g in controlling I_p is not uniform; only in the central, straight-line part of the curves do equal changes in E_g produce equal changes in I_p.

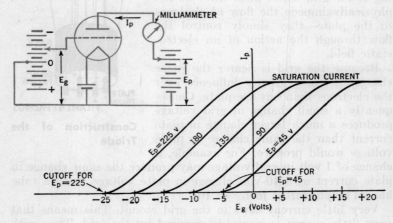

Triode Characteristics

Effect of Signal Voltage on Plate Current of Triode. A triode is frequently used to reproduce E_g (grid voltage) variations in amplified form across a resistance or impedance in the plate circuit. This is illustrated in the diagram on page 345. The input voltage is called the *signal* or *excitation* and is represented by e_g.

Assume that the fixed grid voltage or *bias* (E_c) is — 10 volts and that the signal voltage (e_g) is a sine wave emf of 4 volts peak value. When E_g varies from point A to B, the effect is to increase I_p from the value at A' to the value at B'. As E_g swings through point C and back to point D, I_p increases to C' and decreases to D'; when E_g is at point E, I_p reaches its average value of E'; etc. The output plate current variations are plotted and show a corresponding sine wave form. Similarity of input and output waves represent good fidelity, that is, faithful reproduction. Only when the tube is operated along the straight-line part of the characteristic is this obtained. If operation extends to saturation at one end or cutoff at the other, the output wave will not match the input wave; *distortion* is thus introduced.

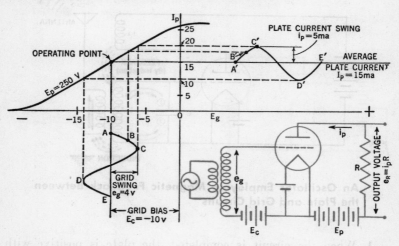

The varying plate current flowing through the resistance in the plate circuit produces a voltage drop that varies similarly. This voltage variation is much larger than the variation of the signal applied to the grid. Hence, amplification has been obtained. The voltage amplification or *gain* of the tube and circuit (called a *stage*) is expressed by the formula:

$$\text{voltage gain} = \frac{\text{output voltage}}{\text{signal voltage}}$$

The output voltage is introduced into the next stage for further amplification (or perhaps into headphones or a loudspeaker) by a suitable *coupling* device.

OSCILLATORS

The Triode as a High-Frequency Generator (Oscillator). We shall now see how a triode in combination with a tuned circuit can be made to generate a high-frequency alternating current.

One typical circuit for accomplishing this purpose is shown in the diagram. Its operation is as follows:

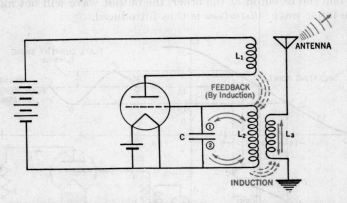

An Oscillator Employing Magnetic Feedback Between the Plate and Grid Circuits

1. When the circuit is completed, the plate is positive with respect to the filament. Plate current begins to flow.

2. As plate current flows through coil L_1, a magnetic field builds up and cuts the turns of wire in coil L_2, thus inducing a current in L_2.

3. The current through L_2 is in such a direction as to draw electrons away from the grid and plate 1 of the condenser C and store them on plate 2 of the condenser. Thus the condenser becomes charged and the grid becomes more positive.

4. The positive grid increases the plate current, which in turn strengthens the field around L_1, which induces a stronger current in L_2, which charges the condenser still more and makes the grid more positive, which further increases the plate current—and so on.

5. As a result, the plate current quickly rises to saturation and become steady; therefore the magnetic field around L_1 becomes steady, and the inductive effect on L_2 disappears.

6. The condenser now begins to discharge through L_2, making the grid less positive. This causes the plate current to decrease.

The resulting decrease in the magnetic field around L_1 induces an emf in L_2 which aids the discharge of the condenser, thus making the grid even less positive. This continues until the grid is so negative that plate current is cut off altogether.

7. The condenser has in the meantime become charged in the opposite direction—plate 1 is negative and plate 2 positive. It now begins to discharge once more, causing the grid to become more positive, and the entire cycle repeats.

Thus an oscillating current of high frequency is set up in the L_2C circuit. This LC circuit is called a *tank* circuit. The rate at which the sequence of steps 1 to 7 occurs—in other words, the frequency of oscillation—is the same as the resonant frequency of the tank circuit.

The oscillating current in L_2 induces an rf voltage in L_3, and this voltage causes electrons to surge back and forth between the antenna and ground, thereby causing the emission of a radio wave at the same frequency as the frequency of oscillation in L_2C.

Feedback. The magnetic coupling between L_1 in the plate circuit and L_2 in the grid circuit is called *feedback*, because some of the energy in the plate circuit is "fed back" into the grid circuit. In *positive* feedback, any change in plate current result in a change in grid voltage which acts to *increase* that change; in *negative* feedback, any change in plate current is *opposed* by the corresponding action induced in the grid circuit. Positive feedback is always necessary to produce oscillation.

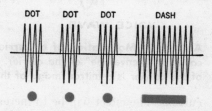

Radio Telegraphy. The radio wave emitted by the oscillator is called a *carrier wave*. The carrier wave can be turned on and off by

The carrier wave is interrupted to send "dots" and "dashes" in Morse code.

means of a key inserted in the plate or grid circuit of the oscillator. Thus a series of dots and dashes can be sent out in the form of "pieces" of the carrier, and messages can be sent in code (such as International Morse code). To transmit speech and music, however, the carrier wave must be *modulated*, as described in the next paragraph.

MODULATION

Amplitude Modulation. If the output of a microphone, phonograph pick-up, or similar device is properly connected or coupled to the plate circuit of an oscillator, the sound fluctuations will be superimposed on the radio frequency fluctuations of the plate

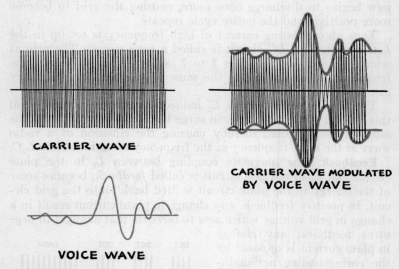

CARRIER WAVE

CARRIER WAVE MODULATED
BY VOICE WAVE

VOICE WAVE

Amplitude Modulation of a Carrier. Note how the voice wave becomes the "envelope" of the carrier. The envelope of the bottom half of the carrier is a mirror image of the envelope of the top half.

current. The effect will be to increase and decrease the amplitude of the rf carrier wave in accordance with the variations of the sound or *audio frequency* wave. Thus the carrier wave will have an *envelope* with the same shape as the audio frequency (af) wave, as shown in the diagram. This process is called *amplitude modulation.*

Frequency Modulation. The rf carrier wave has two distinguishing features—its amplitude and its frequency. We have seen how the *amplitude* can be modulated to carry audio frequency signals. Practical methods have now been developed for modulating the *frequency* of the carrier, keeping its amplitude constant. This development is largely the work of Major E. H. Armstrong, an outstanding pioneer in radio history.

In frequency modulation (FM) the frequency of the carrier increases and decreases around its average value in step with the audio frequency fluctuations. Since the amplitude of the wave is constant, an ordinary receiver designed to respond to AM will give no response to FM—special receivers are necessary to hear FM programs.

FM has certain distinct advantages, chief of which is the virtual elimination of static and other electrical disturbances. The reason for this is that static is an amplitude modulation of the carrier wave produced by radiation from lightning discharges, motor sparks, etc. Since the FM receiver does not respond to amplitude fluctuations, the static noises never reach the loud speaker.

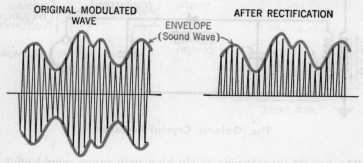

ORIGINAL MODULATED WAVE

AFTER RECTIFICATION

ENVELOPE (Sound Wave)

A loud speaker or earphone will respond to the audio frequency envelope of the carrier after rectification.

DETECTION

Detection. Detection is essentially the process of separating the audio frequencies or modulation envelope from the rf carrier in the receiver in order to make headphone or loudspeaker response possible. First, the modulated wave must be rectified; that is, one half must be eliminated so that the wave pulses are all in one direction. Then provision must be made to send the af component through the headphones or speaker and to by-pass the rf component. This discussion will be limited to detectors for AM only; FM detectors operate on entirely different principles.

The crystal detector. A simple crystal detector circuit is shown in the diagram. The incoming modulated signal induces an rf voltage (and electron surge) in the antenna. The antenna current induces an oscillating current in the tuned circuit. The voltage across the tuned circuit tends to drive an oscillating current through the earphones and crystal. But the crystal, usually galena (lead sulfide), acts as a one-way valve for electrons, allowing current to flow through it in only one direction. Thus the crystal rectifies the modulated signal, eliminating the negative half. The output current through the crystal is unidirectional, but varies at an rf rate; the amplitude has the same shape as the modulation envelope and varies at an af rate.

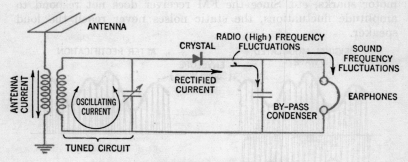

The (Galena) Crystal Receiver

The headphones, having fairly high inductance, would offer a very high impedance to rf currents; therefore the entire current output of the crystal cannot be sent through the headphones without seriously reducing the current strength. This problem is solved by "short-circuiting" the headphones for rf with a "by-pass" condenser of fairly low capacitance. This condenser offers a low impedance path for the rf component of the crystal current, but a high impedance path for the lower frequency af component. As a result, the af component takes the "easier" (lower impedance) path through the headphones, while the rf component takes the path through the condenser (the easier path for it).

The use of fixed condensers to provide separate paths for currents of different frequencies is fundamental to all radio circuits. The most important application of this kind is separating DC (zero frequency) currents from AC currents. Whenever you see a fixed condenser in a circuit diagram, you can be sure it is either separating DC from AC or af from rf currents.

The diode detector. As shown by the diagram, the simple diode detector circuit closely resembles that of the crystal detector. Likewise, the operation is basically the same. Since plate current flows only when the plate is positive, the negative loops of the modulated input are eliminated. The rectified plate current contains rf and af components. The af goes through the headphones and the rf goes through the by-pass condenser. The diode detector is employed in nearly all receivers today because it can rectify larger currents than any other detector with very little distortion.

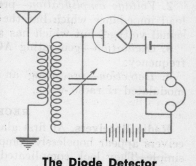

The Diode Detector

If the grid bias of a triode detector is set for plate current cut-off, plate current flows only on the positive half-cycles of the grid signal voltage. If the bias is set for plate current saturation, the plate current dips during the negative half-cycles of grid signal voltage. In either case, the AC voltage applied to the grid is rectified in the plate circuit.

Triode detectors. Triodes can be used as detectors by operating them biased almost to cutoff. On each positive swing of the signal, a pulse of plate current flows; but the negative swing has practically no effect on plate current because the grid voltage swings below the cutoff bias. The same result can be obtained by operating the tube biased almost to the saturation point, in which case the positive swing of the signal has little effect on the plate current. Triodes used as detectors have the advantage of amplifying the rectified signal, but they do not give as good fidelity as diodes.

Functions of Vacuum Tubes Summarized. The various functions of vacuum tubes have now been described. They are:

1. *Rectification*—changing AC to DC.

2. *Voltage amplification*—producing an AC voltage across a load impedance which has the same frequency as the input or signal voltage, but which has a greater amplitude.

3. *Oscillation*—generating AC currents and voltages of high frequency.

4. *Detection*—producing an audio frequency signal from a modulated rf radio -wave.

RECEIVERS

Radio Receivers. At first glance, circuit diagrams of radio receivers appear hopelessly complicated. Actually, they are fairly simple. They look complicated because many successive operations must be performed on an incoming radio signal, and the whole set of operations is presented in one diagram. If, however, the circuit is broken down into small sections, each performing a single function, the circuit becomes easy to understand. This is what we do when we draw a block diagram of a receiver. Within each block you imagine one of the special circuits which have been described in this chapter. A line connecting one block with another means that the output of the first block becomes the input of the next. A few examples will serve to explain block diagrams.

Tuned Radio Frequency Receivers. The block diagram of a 5-tube "trf" receiver follows.

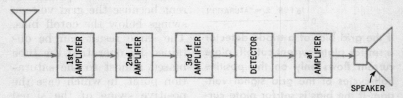

The incoming signal picked up by the antenna is selected by the tuned circuit of the first radio frequency amplifier. The amplified output of this stage is introduced into the tuned circuit of the next stage for further amplification. This is repeated in the third stage. The highly-amplified modulated signal next enters the detector circuit, where the rf and af components are separated. The af is then sufficiently amplified in the next stage to operate the loudspeaker. Note that there are no rf currents anywhere in the last stage.

The three rf amplifiers and the detector must all tune accurately to the same frequency. This is accomplished with one tuning dial by mounting the rotating plates of all four identical variable condensers on the same shaft. Trf receivers have good fidelity, but only moderate selectivity and sensitivity.

Superheterodyne Receivers. This type of receiver circuit was designed by Major Armstrong during World War I; it has today replaced nearly all other types of general purpose receivers. The block diagram of a 6-tube superheterodyne receiver follows.

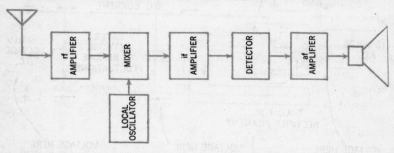

The desired signal frequency is selected by the tuned rf amplifier, and the amplified output is introduced into the *mixer* stage. The mixer combines this rf signal with a radio frequency generated by the *local oscillator*. The oscillator frequency is controlled by a tuning condenser which is varied at the same time the rf amplifier is tuned, and by the same dial. Provision is made so that the frequency of the oscillator is always higher than that of the selected signal by a constant value, usually 465 kilocycles. When these two frequencies are combined in the mixer, a new *intermediate frequency* (if), the difference between them, is produced in accordance with the principle of beats (p. 331). For example, if a signal frequency of 1200 kc is selected, the frequency of the local oscillator will be 1665 kc; hence the intermediate frequency will be 1665 − 1200 kc = 465 kc. The production of a beat frequency in this manner is called *heterodyning*, and is the unique feature of superhet receivers. The 465 kc if output of the mixer (which is still modulated) is amplified in the if

stage (a *fixed frequency* amplifier), the output of which goes
through the detector and af amplifier to the speaker.

Chief advantages of superheterodyne circuits are high amplification in the if stage, increased selectivity and sensitivity, and
good fidelity. In some circuits, the rf amplifier is omitted; the
functions of mixer and oscillator may also be performed by a
single tube known as a *converter*. The superheterodyne principle
is used in FM and television, as well as in AM broadcasting.

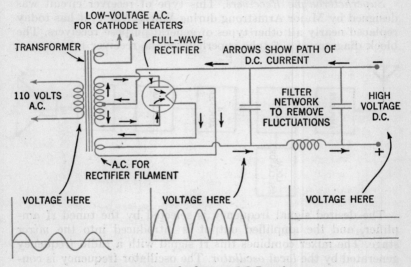

Power Supply for an AC Receiver

Power Supplies for AC Receivers. Since the majority of power
circuits in the home supply 110 volts of AC, it is desirable to
design radio receivers so that they can be operated directly from
such power lines, instead of using batteries. In order to do this, a
power supply must be incorporated within the receiver which will
provide low voltage for the vacuum tube cathode heaters and a
high DC voltage for the vacuum tube plates. This is accomplished by means of a transformer with several secondary windings, and a rectifier vacuum tube, connected as shown in the diagram. One winding of the transformer steps up the house voltage
to the desired plate voltage. The rectifier tube (a double diode)

then changes this AC voltage to DC; since the diode has two plates, and the plates are connected to the transformer in such a way that they are positive alternately, both halves of the AC cycle are rectified. One plate operates during one half, the other plate during the other half of the cycle. The fluctuations in the DC produced are smoothed out by a *filter network* of condensers and inductances.

OTHER APPLICATIONS OF THE VACUUM TUBE

Photoelectric Effect. The *photoelectric cell,* or "electric eye," operates on the fact that certain metals, notably cesium, rubidium, potassium, and selenium, emit electrons when light is directed on their surfaces. This is known as the *photoelectric effect,* and has many applications, especially when used in conjunction with vacuum tube circuits.

One type of photoelectric cell is a vacuum tube with a loop of wire at its center maintained at a positive potential. The cell has an inside coating of the sensitive metal at negative potential. When light strikes the cell, the sensitive metal gives off electrons

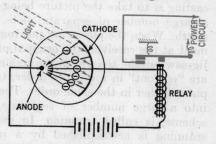

When light strikes the cathode, the relay is energized, thus closing a circuit which operates some electrical device.

which are attracted to the positive electrode; thus current flows in the circuit. The intensity of this current varies directly with the intensity of the light falling on the sensitive surface.

The feeble current produced by the cell can be made to operate electromagnetic relays which control larger currents that may, in turn, open or close doors, turn on drinking fountains, operate burglar alarms, etc. Photoelectric cells are vital elements in modern sound motion pictures and in television.

Sound Motion Pictures. Modern sound pictures are projected from films upon which the sound as well as the action have been recorded. During production, the sound accompaniment enters a microphone. The weak pulsating current is amplified and made to operate a *light valve,* a slit opening between two metal strips that alternately move closer together and farther apart according to the pulsations of the current. The light valve regulates the amount of light from a lamp that passes through to affect the edge of the film alongside the recording of the action. When the film is developed, the *sound track* shows up as a series of light and dark bands of varying width. The reproduction of the sound portion of such film consists of concentrating light on the sound track and allowing that which gets through to fall upon a photoelectric cell. The resulting pulsating current is introduced into an amplifier which operates a loudspeaker. Here the original sound accompaniment is reproduced.

Television. *Transmission.* The basic idea in television broadcasting is to take the picture being telecast and break it up into a large number of separate spots, like the pieces of a jig-saw puzzle. When the pieces are put together in their proper arrangement at the receiver, the original picture is reconstructed. In the jig-saw puzzle, the pieces are scrambled; in television, the pieces are "cut out" in a definite order, transmitted in that order, and put together in the same order. The process of dividing a picture into a large number of segments, according to some definite scheme, is called *scanning*. In modern television transmitters, scanning is accomplished by a moving electronic beam in a special tube called an *iconoscope*.

In the iconoscope is a screen for receiving the image to be transmitted. This screen is made of mica with a metal plate on one side and perhaps 200,000 tiny light-sensitive globules on the other—really 200,000 tiny photoelectric cells. A cathode emits electrons, and a high-voltage electrode drives them in a beam toward the screen. One pair of electromagnetic coils above and below the electron beam and another pair on either side deflect the beam horizontally and vertically so that it will strike any desired point on the screen.

The image of the scene being televised is focused on the light-sensitive screen by an ordinary lens system. The pattern of light "kicks out" electrons from the globules in proportion to the light intensity at various points. The globules thus become charged positively forming a "charge" image of the scene. By condenser action, the metal plate on the other side of the mica screen becomes charged negatively.

By means of the deflecting coils, the electron beam is now

made to move at high speed from one side of the screen to the other in parallel, slanting lines, thus scanning this "charge" image. This beam replaces the electrons lost by the globules; each time it does so, the metal plate on the other side of the screen also discharges. The electrons leaving the charged plate constitute a varying current whose intensity corresponds to the intensity of the light pattern at the various points of the image. This current is amplified and used to modulate an rf carrier. This modulating signal consists of many frequencies, varying from low af to high frequencies of about 4000 kc. This complex signal is called the *video* signal, and corresponds to the audio signal in sound broadcasting.

Reception. The television receiver contains another special vacuum tube, called the *kinescope,* which reproduces the "sight" portion of the broadcast. On the inside of the large end is a flourescent coating to serve as a screen. A beam of electrons bombards this screen and causes it to glow with an intensity proportional to the intensity of the electron stream, which in turn depends on the video-frequency currents being received. Deflecting coils or plates make the electron beam move across the screen in the same manner as in the iconoscope, and the rate and manner of deflection is synchronized with the transmitter. Thus the image reproduced on the kinescope screen is made to correspond with the image on the screen of the iconoscope.

The reality of television, as with moving pictures, depends on persistence of vision. In television we see a succession of pictures drawn by the lightning strokes of an "electronic pencil." Each part of the screen fluoresces for a short interval after the passage of the beam, so that the image at any one point persists until the next passage of the beam across that point. The electron beam travels across the screen at a rate of about 2 miles per second, constructing as many as 30 complete pictures per second. Thus there is no appreciable flicker on the screen.

BEST ANSWER TEST

1. Almost all radio receivers in use today employ (1) storage batteries; (2) diode detectors; (3) crystal detectors; (4) no detectors.

2. Nowadays, most receivers are tuned by means of (1) fixed inductors; (2) fixed condensers; (3) variable condensers; (4) triodes.

3. In a triode, the electron stream flows mostly from (1) plate to grid; (2) grid to cathode; (3) cathode to grid; (4) cathode to tetrode; (5) cathode to plate.

4. The amplifying properties of a triode are due entirely to the effect of (1) the grid on plate current; (2) the plate on grid current; (3) the cathode on plate current; (4) the cathode on grid current; (5) the tuned circuit.

5. Of the following, the one least associated with radio development is (1) Armstrong; (2) Hertz; (3) DeForest; (4) Maxwell; (5) Ohm.

6. A triode could be converted for use as a diode by connecting (1) grid to cathode; (2) grid to plate; (3) cathode to plate; (4) to an AC power supply.

QUESTIONS

1. Turn on a radio receiver and then charge and discharge a Leyden jar, or operate a static machine, while the set is on. Explain the "static" heard on a radio during an electrical storm.

2. Explain by an analogy with resonance in sound what is accomplished by the "tuning" of a radio receiver.

3. How do you account for the fact that a comparatively small change in grid voltage will cause a much larger change in the plate current of an amplifier tube?

4. Explain what happens in the antenna when radio waves fall upon it.

5. Explain how an LC circuit produces a high-frequency oscillating current.

6. What determines the strength of the current that flows in the plate circuit of a photoelectric cell.

7. A radio program is broadcast from an open-air platform in Portland, Maine. Who hears the words and music first, (a) a listener 200 feet from the platform in Portland, Maine, or (b) a listener at his radio receiver in Portland, Oregon, 3000 miles distant? (Air temperature is 30°C.)

8. An amateur radio transmitter is operated from a 120-volt, 60-cycle house circuit. (a) The heater of one vacuum tube operates at 10 volts. Draw a fully-labeled diagram of a transformer that will provide this voltage. (b) The plate of another tube operates at 480 volts. Draw a fully-labeled diagram of a transformer that will provide this voltage. (c) Could one transformer provide both of the required voltages? Explain. (d) The plates of most vacuum tubes require DC voltage. Name one device that will furnish this DC from the AC source. (e) The filament of the vacuum tube in (a) has a resistance of 2 ohms. Calculate its power consumption. (f) If the filament transformer is 80% efficient, what current does the operating filament draw from the house circuit?

TWENTY-FIVE— PHYSICS OF THE
AIRPLANE

INTRODUCTION

Man's first recorded flight into the atmosphere occurred more
than a century ago in France when De Rozier soared aloft in a
lighter-than-air balloon developed by the Montgolfier brothers.
Successful balloon flights spurred attempts to build heavier-than-
air flying machines. In 1810, Cayley, an Englishman, built such
an aircraft, the design of which was basically sound. Cayley
failed, however, because an adequate engine was not available
(the gasoline engine had not been invented and the steam engine

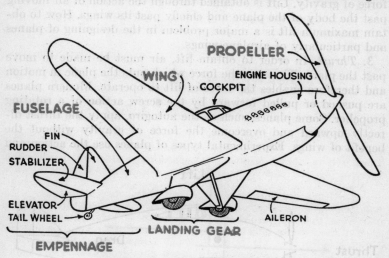

The Principal Parts of the Airplane

was too heavy). In 1840, Stringfellow equipped a small glider with
a miniature steam engine and, by successfully flying it, demonstrated that flight in a power-driven, heavier-than-air machine
was certainly a possibility. Not until 1903 did this possibility be-

come a reality when the Wright brothers built a plane and successfully flew it a Kitty Hawk, North Carolina.

The modern airplane is one of the most remarkable products of applied science. The facts and principles of physics account for its existence, determine its construction, and control its operation. The purpose of this section is to survey these facts and principles as they are seen at work in the airplane.

The Forces Acting on an Airplane. Four main forces act upon the airplane in flight. The relationships among these forces determine the action and efficiency of the airplane.

1. *Weight.* The weight of the plane and its occupants or cargo must be lifted against the force of gravity. Therefore, when designing a plane, the lightest materials possible are chosen. Duralumin, a light alloy metal, plastics and plywood are some materials used.

2. *Lift.* This is the force that counterbalances or overcomes the force of gravity. Lift is obtained through the action of air moving past the body of the plane and chiefly past its wings. How to obtain maximum lift is a major problem in the designing of planes and particularly of airplane wings.

3. *Thrust.* In order to obtain lift, air must be made to move past the plane. Thrust is the force which puts the plane in motion and therefore enables the force of lift to operate. Modern planes are pushed or pulled forward by the screw action of a rotating propeller. Some planes, such as the autogiro, apply the thrust directly upward and overcome the force of gravity without the benefit of wings. Experimental types of planes use the action and

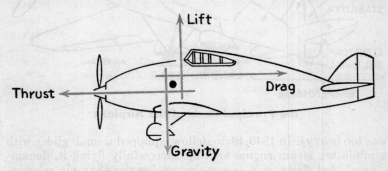

Forces Acting on an Airplane in Flight

reaction of exploding gases (rocket-type planes) to move the plane forward and thus obtain lift.

4. *Drag.* This is the resistance offered by the parts of the plane to motion through the air. Airplane designers try to reduce drag to a minimum by streamlining all parts of the plane and by preparing the surfaces of the materials so that minimum resistance is offered to the flow of air.

LIFT

Lift results from the action of air on a moving airfoil (wing or similar surface). A small fraction of the lift results from the increased pressure caused by the dynamic action of the air against the lower surface of the wing. This action is similar to that operating on a kite. When a kite is drawn against the wind the increased pressure on the kite's lower surface forces the kite higher. However, the greater part of the lift imparted to an airfoil results from the *decreased* pressure on the upper surface of the wing and the consequent difference in pressure or unbalanced force operating on the wing. This difference in pressure is explained by Bernoulli's principle.

Bernoulli's Principle and the Venturi Tube. If an object is placed in air, and both the object and the air are motionless, air pressure on all sides of the object is identical. If either the air or the object is made to move, differences in pressure on the object result. This is readily seen from a few simple experiments.

If a piece of paper is held in the fingers and air is blown across the top surface, the paper will rise. A difference in pressure resulted which forced the paper to rise against the force of gravity. This difference in pressure was brought about by the increased velocity of the air flowing past the top surface of the paper as compared with the relatively stationary air on the bottom surface.

When the bulb on a common atomizer is squeezed, air is made to move with increased velocity across the open end of a tube. The air pressure at the open end is decreased. The unchanged air pressure in the bottom of the atomizer forces the liquid up and out of the open end of the tube.

These and other similar observations led to the statement of Bernoulli's principle. *The pressure of a fluid (liquid or gas) decreases at points where the speed of the fluid increases.* In other words, within the same fluid, high speed of flow is associated with

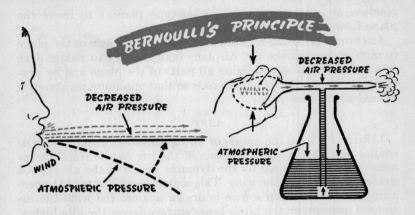

BERNOULLI'S PRINCIPLE

DECREASED AIR PRESSURE

DECREASED AIR PRESSURE

WIND

ATMOSPHERIC PRESSURE

WIND

ATMOSPHERIC PRESSURE

low pressure, and low speed with high pressure. This principle was first stated to explain pressure changes of a liquid flowing within a pipe whose cross-sectional area varied. A pipe in which the cross-sectional area gradually decreases and then increases again is called a *venturi*. The diagram shows a simple venturi. The pipe is largest at point *A*, smallest at point *B* and intermediate at point *C*. As fluid is forced through the pipe, the speed of flow is least at point *A*, greatest at point *B* and intermediate at point *C*. The pres-

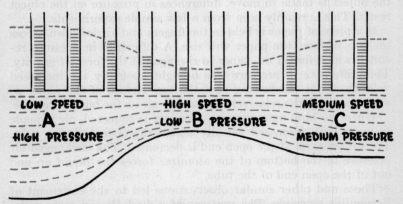

LOW SPEED
A
HIGH PRESSURE

HIGH SPEED
LOW **B** PRESSURE

MEDIUM SPEED
C
MEDIUM PRESSURE

Bernoulli's Principle Applied to the Venturi. The height of the liquid in each vertical tube measures the pressure at that point.

sure at point A is greatest; the pressure at point B is least, and that at point C is intermediate.

Streamlines. A line drawn to represent the path of a fluid particle as it streams or flows past a point is called a streamline. While streamlines are ordinarily invisible, the pattern formed by them can be observed visually in several ways, much in the same manner that we were able to note the pattern of magnetic lines of force by the use of iron filings. Thus, if smoke is introduced into

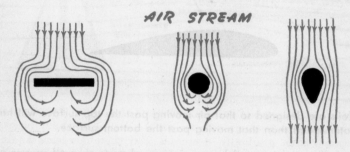

AIR STREAM

The shape of a body in a moving airstream determines the pattern of the streamlines. The body on the right offers the least resistance to the airflow.

a stream of air, the visible particles of smoke will trace the streamlines of the flowing air.

The shape of an object determines the pattern of streamlines formed when a fluid flows past the object. The diagram shows some of these patterns for several differently shaped objects.

Application of Bernoulli's Principle and Streamlines to an Airfoil. A difference in pressure (as a result of Bernoulli's principle) is produced on an airfoil by streamlining it in such a way that the air moving past the top of the airfoil has a greater velocity than that flowing past the lower surface. The cross-section of the wing of an airplane, as shown in the diagram, is designed so that the air which rushes past it when the airplane flies is divided at the leading edge of the wing, some of the streamlines taking the longer path along the curved surface of the wing and some taking the shorter path along the straight surface. Portions of air taking either path reach the trailing edge of the wing at the same time, provided they hit the leading edge at the same time. This, of course, means that the air moving over the curved or longer path is travelling faster than the air moving along the shorter, straight surface. Thus, according to Bernoulli's principle, there is lower pressure over the curved surface of the wing.

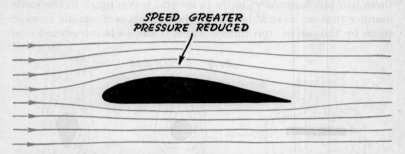

SPEED GREATER
PRESSURE REDUCED

Airfoils are designed so that air moving past the top surface will have greater speed than that moving past the bottom surface.

It is of course a well known fact in physics that whenever opposing forces become unbalanced, acceleration will take place in the direction of the resultant of these forces. The difference in forces exerted upon the two surfaces of the airfoil produces a resultant lift which causes the airfoil to rise. In the case of the airplane, this difference must be enough to overcome the pull of gravity on the plane before upward acceleration becomes possible. Since atmospheric pressure is about 15 lb per square inch (or a little more than a ton per square foot) a difference of only one per cent in the pressure on the top surface as compared with the pressure on the bottom surface of an airfoil produces a lifting force of 21.6 lb per square foot. It is obvious that nothing comparable to a vacuum is developed above the top surface, as is sometimes implied. The difference of one per cent is close to actual conditions and is sufficient to produce very large lift forces.

How the Total Lift Varies. The amount of lift that a wing produces depends upon five factors: (1) We have just seen how pressure difference per unit area produces lift. All other things being equal, therefore, it is obvious that an *increase in wing area produces a proportional increase in total lift*. (2) Furthermore, since air pressure is dependent upon the density of the air, it is readily seen that the *total lift varies with air density.* (3) The *total lift also varies directly as the square of the velocity.* Thus, if the velocity of the air flowing past the wing is doubled, the lift is four times as great. The lift of a wing also depends upon (4) its *angle of attack* and (5) the *shape of its cross section.*

Angle of Attack. The angle of attack is measured in terms of the relative wind. *Relative wind* is the direction of the air moving past the wing of an airplane in flight, and is always opposite to the direction in which the airplane is travelling. The velocity of

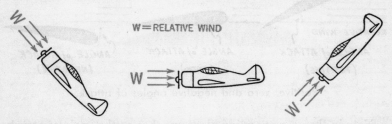

W = RELATIVE WIND

The relative wind is always opposite to the direction of travel of the plane.

the relative wind is called airspeed, which is the speed of the air in terms of the airplane. Airspeed has nothing to do with ground speed, which is the speed of the airplane in terms of the ground over which it passes. For example, the airspeed indicator of an airplane in flight shows 200 miles per hour. This means only that the air is moving past the airplane (or the airplane through the air) at a speed of 200 miles per hour. If the pilot were flying "blind" and wanted to know his ground speed he would have to obtain the direction and velocity of the wind from a weather station. If he found that he was bucking a head wind of 200 miles per hour, his ground speed would be zero. If he found that the head wind was 100 miles per hour, his ground speed would be 100 miles per hour. If he found that there was a tail wind of 100 miles per hour, his ground speed would be 300 miles per hour. If the wind were blowing at an angle to the plane's heading, the airspeed and wind velocity would have to be added vectorially to find the ground speed.

The angle of attack is the angle between the relative wind and the wing chord (a straight line between the leading and trailing edges of a wing). The wing has a *positive angle* of attack if its leading edge is higher than its trailing edge in relation to the relative wind. If the leading edge is lower than the trailing edge, the angle of attack is *negative*. If the wing chord and the relative wind are parallel, the wing has a *zero* angle of attack.

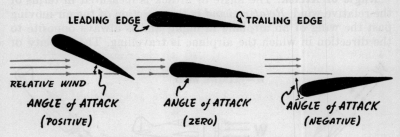

Positive, zero and negative angles of attack.

Note in the accompanying diagrams that as the angle of attack increases, the air, because of its inertia, begins to break away from the upper surface of the wing. Instead of the streamlines following the curvature of the wing, eddies are formed near the trailing edge. The angle of attack just before this *burbling* or breakdown of the streamline flow is called the *stalling angle*. (A plane stalls when the lift developed by the wings is insufficient to support the plane.) Beyond the stalling angle, the lift decreases rapidly as burbling destroys the effectiveness of the airfoil. This decrease in lift is partly due to the creation of dead air space

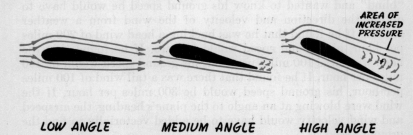

Too high an angle of attack for an airfoil of given cross section results in a decrease in lift.

which, according to Bernoulli's principle, means increased pressure. The stalling angle is also the angle of maximum *lift coefficient*. The maximum lift coefficient varies with different wing shapes.

The equation for calculating the lift of a wing has been found to be:

$$\text{lift} = \frac{C_L \, d \, SV^2}{2}$$

where C_L = the *coefficient of lift*, which is obtained experimentally in wind tunnel tests for each angle of attack of the type of airfoil being considered;

d = the *density* of the air in *slugs* (a slug is equivalent to a weight of 32.2 pounds);

S = *area* of the wing in square feet; and

V = the *airspeed* in feet per second.

TYPICAL PROBLEM

A wing has an area of 200 sq ft, a coefficient of lift of 0.9 when the angle of attack is 7°, and the airspeed is 150 miles per hour. Find the lift when the density of the air is .002343 slugs per cubic foot. (Change miles per hour to feet per second.)

$$\begin{aligned}
\text{lift} &= \frac{C_L \, d \, S \, V^2}{2} \\
&= \frac{0.9 \times .002343 \times 200 \times (220)^2}{2} \\
&= 10,200 \text{ pounds}
\end{aligned}$$

Drag. As was stated at the beginning of this section, drag is the resistance offered by parts of the airplane to motion through the air. This drag is made up of two parts—the drag of the wings and the drag of all other parts of the plane.

The *wing drag* itself can be considered in two parts: (1) the *profile drag* produced simply by the fluid friction of the air flowing over the wing surfaces (skin friction), and by any eddies and burbles behind the wing; (2) the *induced drag* which is present only when lift is being developed. Air "spilling" around the edge of the wing from the high pressure region below the wing to the

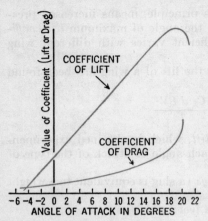

Graph showing how the lift and drag of an airfoil vary as the angle of attack varies.

low pressure region above it produces *wing-tip vortices* which also results in drag.

The drag of the rest of the plane (all parts which do not contribute to lift) is called *parasite drag.*

Lift-Drag Ratio. For convenience, the sum of all the lift forces on a wing can be combined mathematically into one force which is equivalent to all the smaller lift forces. A similar resultant can be found for all the drag forces acting on a wing. As with lift, too, different angles of attack result in different amounts of retarding forces or drag. The amount of drag is computed by a formula similar to that for computing lift:

$$\text{Drag} = \frac{C_D \, d \, S \, V^2}{2}$$

The resultant of the lift and drag forces acting on a wing is determined vectorially.

The only difference between the lift and drag formulas is that C_D, the experimentally determined coefficient of drag, is substituted for the coefficient of lift.

The sum of all of the lift forces and the sum of all of the drag forces can be combined mathematically and then treated as a single force, the *resultant*. The lift and drag components are combined by the usual method of treating them as sides of a parallelogram and then using the diagonal of the parallelogram as the resultant. In order to construct this parallelogram you must remember that the lift is always perpendicular to the relative wind while the drag is always parallel to and in the opposite direction of the relative wind.

Thrust and Power Factors. Airspeed is produced by *thrust*, the forward-acting force on an airplane. Without airspeed no airplane could remain aloft. A pilot makes use of the acceleration due to gravity to develop sufficient airspeed to pull out of a spin or a stall. He points the nose of the plane downward and dives the plane. As gravitational pull accelerates the plane, airspeed picks up until sufficient lift is produced on the wings to maintain the plane in level, controlled flight.

Powered planes develop thrust by means of a propeller that is rotated by an engine. As the engine turns the propeller, airspeed with reference to the propeller blades is produced. The propeller then acts as an airfoil. The unbalanced pressures produced in rotation move the propeller forward and thus move the plane.

The force which the thrust acts against and in opposite direction to is the *total drag*. Since total drag as well as lift vary roughly as the square of the velocity, it is readily seen that the engine output must increase markedly to obtain an increase in velocity.

When thrust is just equal to drag, the plane continues at the same velocity. The plane accelerates (increases its velocity) when thrust is greater than drag. When drag exceeds thrust, the plane slows down. Angle of attack, velocity, density of the air, nature of the airplane surface (waxed or unwaxed, fabric or metal, etc.) all affect drag and hence the power output needed from the engine.

Drag during level flight does not change with altitude. Since it becomes necessary to fly faster in less dense air in order to maintain the plane at the higher altitude, the drag is automatically increased to the same value that it had in level flight at the lower altitude. Since power is proportional to thrust (or drag) times speed, and the velocity must be increased in the less dense air at higher altitudes, it follows that the engine must provide more horsepower for level flight at the higher altitude even though the drag remains constant.

An airplane uses less power to maintain level flight when a higher angle of attack is maintained than when the angle of attack is smaller. At lower angles of attack greater speed is necessary in order to prevent loss of altitude. With a higher angle of attack the velocity, as well as the gas consumption, is less for level flight. Addition of weight, such as by taking on freight or passengers, makes it necessary to fly the plane faster and hence use more power in order to maintain level flight for a given angle of attack. Of two planes in which all considerations are the same except the wing area, the one with larger wing area will require less power for level flight. It will also have the smaller velocity during level flight.

The extent to which the power output of the engine ("brake" horsepower) is actually delivered as power output by the propeller depends upon the efficiency of the propeller.

High pitch propellers are efficient for fast, level flight whereas low pitch propellers are efficient for climbing. This explains the use of variable pitch propellers. Some variable pitch propellers are controllable-pitch propellers in the sense that the pitch can be adjusted during flight; adjustable-pitch propellers are those which must be set by hand before taking off. Fixed-pitch propellers may have a pitch designed for some special purpose such as rapid climbing. Frequently they have a medium pitch since this is best for cruising.

CONTROL OF THE AIRPLANE

General. The airplane moves in a fluid medium in which is it free to rotate in any plane. Rotation of the plane takes place about its center gravity (CG). The diagram on page 371 shows the longitudinal, vertical, and lateral axes of the airplane. All three axes pass through the center of gravity. Airplanes are designed to be stable except in a few cases, such as certain fighting planes, in which slight instability gives greater maneuverability. A plane is stable when forces tend to bring it back to its original position whenever its equilibrium is disturbed. Disturbance of the equilibrium may take place about any one of the three axes of the plane. Thus we find it necessary to consider longitudinal, lateral, and directional stability.

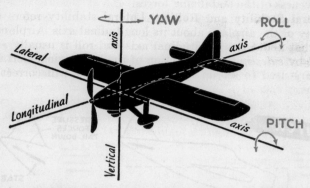

Longitudinal, vertical (normal), and lateral axes of the airplane. The point at which the three axes intersect is called the center of gravity.

Longitudinal Stability and Pitching. Longitudinal stability refers to the stability about the lateral axis. Rotation of the airplane about the lateral axis causing the nose of the plane to move up or down is called *pitching*. The position of the center of gravity along the longitudinal axis of the plane is of prime importance in determining the longitudinal stability of the plane. Other important considerations are the vertical position of the center of gravity, the position of the thrust line of the propeller, and the design of the empennage.

When the clockwise and counterclockwise moments are balanced about the center of gravity, the plane does not pitch. You can, however, see how this balance could be suddenly upset by a shifting of cargo which had not been properly fastened. The balance is somewhat upset, of course, even by the consumption of fuel.

The device for controlling longitudinal stability is the *tailplane* which consists of the *stabilizer* and *elevator*. When a stable airplane pitches, the relative wind then hits the tailplane at angles which automatically set up restorative forces. For example, if a gust of wind forces the tail up, air pressure on the upper surface of the stabilizer forces the tail down again. Long fuselages give these tail forces longer distances to act through and thus increase the effectiveness of the stabilizing forces.

Lateral Stability and Rolling. Lateral stability refers to the stability of the airplane about its longitudinal axis. Airplanes *roll* somewhat about the longitudinal axis and roll is usually accompanied by *sideslip* in the direction of the lower wing. Certain devices are used to set up restoring forces that will correct these motions.

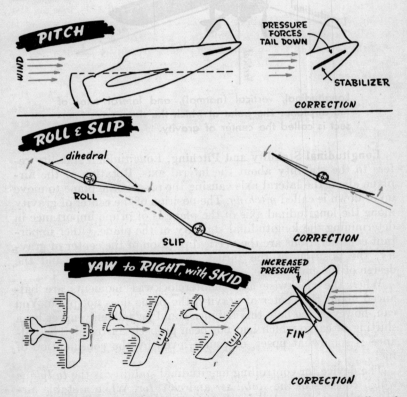

The stable airplane is designed to correct undesirable pitch, roll and and skid.

Dihedral is employed in most planes to counteract side slip in a roll. Wings with dihedral are tilted upward. The angle between the tilted wing and a horizontal line is called the *dihedral angle*. If, during a gust, one wing loses lift and drops, the air strikes it at a higher angle of attack than it does the upper wing. This increase of the angle of attack for the lower wing increases the lift on this wing and tends to push it back up again. At the same time the angle of attack decreases for the upper wing and the decrease of lift upon this wing further helps the restoring process.

Directional Stability and Yawing. Directional stability refers to stability about the vertical axis. Rotation of the nose of the plane to right or left about this axis is called *yawing*. Yawing is usually accompanied by skidding. An airplane has directional stability or stability in yaw if moments are automatically set up as soon as the rotation takes place that tend to return the plane to its original position.

When forces cause the plane to rotate momentarily in yaw, the side force due to the relative wind acting against the exposed side area (particularly against the fin or vertical stabilizer) moves the tail back to its former position.

Controlling the Motions of the Airplane. Any surface which is designed to obtain reaction from the air through which it moves is called an airfoil. The wings are designed to obtain lift, but other airfoils, such as the rudder, elevator, ailerons, and tabs are used to steer and balance the plane during flight. The rudder is attached to the fin or vertical stabilizer which, as we have just seen corrects the yawing of a plane. When the rudder is manipulated by the pilot in order to turn the plane, the forces acting on the rudder are brought into play and the plane is made to yaw deliberately. Similarly, the elevator, which is attached to the horizontal stabilizer, enables the plane to dive or to climb. The action of the elevator, therefore, is similar to the stabilizer which controls involuntary upward and downward pitching. The ailerons, which are essentially movable sections of the trailing edge of the wings, prevent slipping and skidding during a turn, as described in the next paragraph. While diving and climbing involve chiefly the use of the elevator, turns or banks involve all or almost all of the control surfaces of the plane.

Banking the Plane. The ailerons and elevator on the airplane are moved by means of the stick. The stick is a steel rod which extends up through the floor in front of the pilot. A linkage system connects the stick with the elevator and ailerons. The universal-joint mounting of the stick makes it possible to move the stick in any direction throughout a complete circle. When the stick is moved sideways, one aileron rotates upward and the other down-

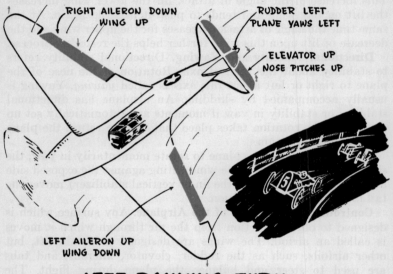

**RIGHT AILERON DOWN
WING UP**

**RUDDER LEFT
PLANE YAWS LEFT**

**ELEVATOR UP
NOSE PITCHES UP**

**LEFT AILERON UP
WING DOWN**

·LEFT·BANKING·TURN·

ward. For example, when the pilot moves the stick to the left, the left aileron is raised and the right one is lowered. The lifting force of the left wing is decreased when the left aileron is raised, while the lift of the right wing is increased when its aileron is lowered. As a result, the airplane flies with the left wing lower than the right wing since the former has less lift than the right wing. Flying an airplane with one wing higher than the other is termed *banking*. A plane should be banked toward the left as described above when the airplane is making a turn to the left. This is done to prevent the airplane from skidding. The effect is the same as that obtained when a curve on a roadway is banked to counterbalance the tendency of the vehicles to run off the outside of the curve.

The stick also controls the movement of the elevator. When the pilot pulls the stick backward, the elevator is raised and vice versa. When the elevator is raised, the air striking against it forces the tail of the plane down and the nose up. This, of course, is the position when the airplane is ascending. If the stick is moved forward and to the left, the airplane would be descending in a left bank.

During banking, the rudder must also be operated in order to point the nose of the plane in the direction in which the turn is to be made. The rudder is operated by means of a rudder bar or two foot-pedals. When the left pedal is pushed down, the rudder is pulled toward the left side of the plane. In this position of the rudder, the air rushing backward along the fuselage exerts the greater force on the left side of the rudder and hence pushes the tail horizontally toward the right. The nose of the plane turns toward the left as required for a left bank. The student pilot learns through experience how to combine aileron and rudder action so as to obtain smoothness and safety in flying.

Flaps. Reducing the wing area of planes increases their speed. Thus racing planes sometimes have "clipped wings." This practice increases the *wing loading* (total weight of the plane divided by the wing area). Faster velocities are then necessary in order to obtain the required lift. This also increases the landing speed and hence the danger at the time of landing. In order to make landings possible at relatively low speed, most airplanes are equipped with *flaps.* Experimental planes equipped with elaborate flaps systems have been able to approximate the autogiro's ability to hover over one spot. The flaps on most planes consist of hinged sections on the trailing edge of the wings. They are somewhat like the ailerons except that they are closer to the fuselage. Their operation is unlike that of the ailerons in that both flaps are lowered or raised simultaneously. A single control operates both of them.

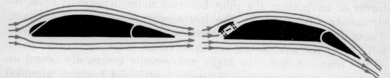

Left: Slot and flap in neutral position. *Right:* Slot raised and flap lowered, producing increased lift.

When the flaps are lowered, they serve two functions: (1) they increase the lift; (2) they increase drag, and thus act as a brake. The pilot must be experienced in their use since he can easily stall the plane by lowering the flaps when his speed has been reduced too greatly. Some types of flaps do not reduce the landing speed but are used to make a steeper glide possible when landing.

Slots. If the angle of attack is increased beyond the angle of maximum lift, burbling sets in and the airplane eventually stalls because of loss of lift. When the airplane stalls it is momentarily out of control. The wings of many airplanes are equipped with *slots* in order to reduce the abruptness of a stall and to make it possible for the wings to assume a greater angle of attack without stalling. The slot accomplishes this by reducing burbling. It consists of an auxiliary airfoil usually near the leading edge of the wing. At low angles of attack it lies in place at the leading edge but at high angles of attack the auxiliary airfoil automatically moves out to form a slot through which air then flows. The effect of the slot upon the airstream is to make it follow along the wing without breaking away even at angles of attack which may be twice as great as that which would cause stalling if the slot were not used. Slots and flaps when used together prove to be very effective in increasing the lift coefficient, in lowering the landing speed, and in improving the control of the plane during flight.

Instruments Used in Controlling Flight. When the weather is fair and well-mapped landmarks are visible, the pilot can navigate his plane simply by observing the landscape. This method of navigation is called *contact flight*. However, when flying over water or when the visibility is zero, or when all familiarity with the landscape is lacking, the pilot must resort to (1) *dead reckoning,* (2) *radio navigation* using radio aids, or (3) *celestial navigation* (provided the heavenly bodies are visible). In the latter forms of navigation the pilot becomes more dependent upon instruments with dials on the instrument panel of the airplane. These instruments are in addition to the usual instruments which tell him of the mechanical condition of his engine and other parts of the plane. Among the flight instruments commonly found on airplanes are the compass, altimeter, artificial horizon, airspeed indicator, turn and bank indicator, rate of climb indicator, and, of course, a clock.

BEST ANSWER TEST

1. When a pilot tries to turn the plane without sufficient banking, the plane is likely to undergo (1) stalling; (2) slipping; (3) skidding; (4) burbling; (5) spinning.

2. For a plane in level flight, lift equals (1) thrust; (2) drag; (3) coefficient of drag; (4) the weight of the plane.

3. Drag produced by parts of the plane other than the wings is termed (1) parasitic drag; (2) coefficient of drag; (3) downwash; (4) turbulance.

4. A plane flying 280 mph ground speed and heading into a head wind of 60 mph has an air speed of (1) 280; (2) 60; (3) 340; (4) 220—mph.

5. Doubling the air speed of a plane (1) doubles; (2) quadruples; (3) reduces to ½; (4) reduces to ¼—the original lift exerted by the wings.

6. The angle of attack which produces maximum lift is termed (1) the stalling angle; (2) the dihedral angle; (3) the cathedral angle; (4) the angle of incidence.

7. An increase in altitude, other factors remaining constant results in (1) increased lift; (2) decreased lift; (3) no change in lift.

8. When a plane is in steady, level flight, all of the forces acting on the plane (1) are in equilibrium; (2) have disappeared; (3) act only forward and upward; (4) act only backward and downward.

9. The lift-drag ratio of a wing at a given angle of attack is (1) lift divided by drag; (2) drag divided by lift; (3) drag multiplied by lift; (4) the same as for any other angle of attack.

QUESTIONS

1. What is the advantage to a plane taking off to head into the wind?

2. Distinguish between: (a) *air speed* and *ground speed;* (b) *angle of attack* and *dihedral angle*.

3. Why is it necessary for a plane to fly at higher air speeds at higher altitudes?

4. (a) What are the three axes of a plane? (b) How is stability along each axis obtained?

5. What are the factors which determine (a) lift, (b) drag?

6. Distinguish between: (a) *coefficient of lift* and *coefficient of drag*. (b) What factors determine each?

7. State Bernoulli's principle, and point out its relation to the physics of flight.

8. Explain how the dihedral angle tends to keep a plane right side up.

9. Distinguish between: (a) pitching; (b) rolling; (c) yawing.

10. How would the control surfaces of a plane be set to produce (a) pitching upward; (b) yawing to the left; (c) banking during a right turn?

11. What is the relation between angle of attack and burbling?

12. Compare the landing speed of a plane at high- and low-level airfields. Explain.

13. Discuss the meaning and importance of streamlining.

Ampere, André (1775–1836). *French*. Relations between electricity and magnetism.

Archimedes (287–212 B.C.). *Greek*. Laws of buoyancy and levers.

Becquerel, Antoine (1852–1908). *French*. Discovered radioactivity.

Bell, Alexander Graham (1847–1922). *American*. Invented telephone.

Bohr, Niels (1885–   ). *Danish*. Theory of atomic structure.

Boyle, Robert (1626–1691). *Irish*. Pressure-volume relation in a gas.

Bunsen, Robert (1811–1899). *German*. Spectroscope and photometer.

Charles, Jacques (1746–1823). *French*. Pressure-temperature relation in a gas.

Coulomb, Charles (1736–1806). *French*. Laws of magnetic and electrical attraction.

Curie, Marie (1867–1934). *French*. Isolated radium; radioactivity.

Edison, Thomas A. (1847–1931). *American*. Phonograph, incandescent lamp, motion pictures.

Einstein, Albert (1879–   ). *German*. Photoelectric effect; relativity.

Faraday, Michael (1791–1867). *English*. Electromagnetism; laws of electrolysis.

Franklin, Benjamin (1706–1790). *American*. Static electricity.

Galileo (1564–1642). *Italian*. Laws of falling bodies and pendulum.

von Guericke, Otto (1602–1686). *German*. Air pump; atmospheric pressure.

Henry, Joseph (1799–1878). *American*. Electromagnet; self-induction.

Hertz, Heinrich (1857–1894). *German*. Discovered wireless waves.

Hooke, Robert (1635–1702). *English*. Law of elasticity.

Huygens, Christian (1625–1695). *Dutch*. Wave theory of light.

Joule, James (1818–1889). *English*. Mechanical equivalent of heat.

Lord Kelvin (1824–1907). *English*. Absolute temperature scale.

Marconi, Guglielmo (1874–1937). *Italian*. Invented wireless telegraphy.

Maxwell, James Clerk (1831–1879). *Scotch*. Electromagnetic theory.

Michelson, Albert (1852–1931). *American*. Measurements of speed of light.

Millikan, Robert A. (1868–   ). *American*. Charge on the electron; cosmic rays.

Newton, Isaac (1642–1727). *English*. Laws of gravitation and motion.

Oersted, Hans (1777–1851). *Danish*. Discovered magnetic field around a current.

Ohm, George (1787–1854). *German*. Laws of electrical resistance.

Pascal, Blaise (1623–1662). *French*. Transmission of pressure in fluids.

Planck, Max (1858–   ). *German*. Quantum theory of light.

Roemer, Olaus (1644–1710). *Danish*. First measurement of speed of light.

Roentgen, William (1845–1923). *German*. Discovered X-rays.

Count Rumford (Benjamin Thompson) (1753–1814). Production of heat from mechanical energy.

Thomson, Sir Joseph (1856–1940). *English*. Nature of cathode rays.

Torricelli, Evangelista (1608–1647). *Italian*. Invented mercury barometer.

Volta, Alessandro (1745–1827). *Italian*. Electroscope, condenser, voltaic cell.

Watt, James (1736–1819). *Scotch*. Developed steam engine.

INDEX